Water and Water Pollution Handbook

VOLUME 2

(in four volumes)

Water and Water Pollution Handbook

VOLUME 2

(*in four volumes*)

Edited by **LEONARD L. CIACCIO**

GTE LABORATORIES INCORPORATED
BAYSIDE, NEW YORK

MARCEL DEKKER, INC., New York   1971

CHEMISTRY

MARCEL DEKKER, INC.
95 Madison Avenue, New York, New York 10016

LIBRARY OF CONGRESS CATALOG CARD NUMBER 78-134780
ISBN 0-8247-1116-5

PRINTED IN THE UNITED STATES OF AMERICA

Contributors to Volume 2

Julian B. Andelman, *Graduate School of Public Health, University of Pittsburgh, Pittsburgh, Pennsylvania*

S. Charles Caruso, *Mellon Institute, Carnegie-Mellon University, Pittsburgh, Pennsylvania*

Max Katz, *College of Fisheries, University of Washington, Seattle, Washington*

Darrell L. King, *Department of Civil Engineering, University of Missouri, Columbia, Missouri*

William Tuthill Lammers, *Department of Biology, Davidson College, Davidson, North Carolina*

Pasquale V. Scarpino, *Environmental Health Engineering, Department of Civil Engineering, University of Cincinnati, Cincinnati, Ohio*

Contents

Part II Chemical, Physical, Bacterial, Viral Instrumental, and Bioassay Techniques

Contents of Volume 1

*Present address: Environomics, Houston, Texas.

Contents of Volume 3

Contents of Volume 4

Part **II**

Chemical, Physical, Bacterial, Viral, Instrumental, and Bioassay Techniques

Chapter 10 Sampling in Natural Waters and Waste Effluents

Darrell L. King
DEPARTMENT OF CIVIL ENGINEERING
UNIVERSITY OF MISSOURI
COLUMBIA, MISSOURI

I. Introduction

Samples are collected from aquatic ecosystems for many different reasons, but in all cases the ultimate aim is to accumulate data which are used to delineate selected properties of specific bodies of water. The reasons for sampling may vary from measurement of a single parameter for waste treatment process control to a need for a complete ecological study of an entire lake or stream. Most of the current interest

451

in sampling natural waters and waste effluents is associated with measuring and documenting alterations in water quality caused by human activity. At times such changes are obvious, but most often degradation of water quality is a slow, continuous series of subtle alterations. Although many methods are available for evaluating such changes, knowledge of the physical, chemical, and biological variations associated with the addition of different types of waste is fundamental to any sampling program. Works by Hynes(1), Klein(2), Mackenthun and Ingram(3), Sawyer and McCarty(4), and the recent compilation of older papers by Keup et al.(5) are especially valuable to anyone involved with sampling polluted waters. The more general works of Welch(6), Hutchinson (7, 8), Ruttner(9), and Reid(10) cover the broad range of aquatic ecology, and *Standard Methods*(11) and Welch's book on sampling(12) are invaluable to anyone planning an aquatic sampling program.

There are many different approaches to evaluating water quality; the chemist uses chemical methods and techniques in his assessment, the biologist most often uses species composition and diversity as his yardstick, the microbiologist records number and type of bacteria, and the engineer relies primarily on measurements of oxygen availability and demand (see Chaps. 13–15, 19 and 23). All of these methods are useful, but none of them serves as the universal measure of water quality. In most successful studies several different methods are employed. The objective of the study will dictate the appropriate analytical scheme, but the first requirement of any method is the collection of a representative sample from the aquatic ecosystem under study. The number and kind of samples required as well as the method of collection will vary with the objectives of the study, but many considerations are common to all sampling schemes.

The purpose of this chapter is to discuss these common relationships as well as some of the many techniques used to collect samples from natural waters and waste effluents.

II. General Considerations

In planning any investigation of either natural waters or waste water, the two most important considerations are the measurement of significant parameters and the collection of representative samples. For most studies of aquatic systems it is impossible to measure all variables, and usually it is necessary to limit analysis to just a few selected parameters. The time required for collecting and analyzing water samples is the factor most often limiting the number of variables which can be considered. Since time is limited, the number of parameters measured must be optimized so that the data recorded are those which are most helpful in solving the problem under investigation.

Many different, but interrelated, factors must be considered in planning any field study of an aquatic system. Obviously, the field measurement program cannot be formulated intelligently until a specific reason for the study has been defined. Selection of measurement parameters is dictated by both the objective of the study and the time available for sample collection and analysis. The analytical scheme chosen influences the sampling program, but the availability of sampling gear and the ability to collect representative samples also limit the testing program. Thus, the problem must be well defined and all facets of the investigation must be considered prior to sample collection.

One of the best methods of meshing all these considerations into a workable sampling plan is to list all pertinent environmental variables and their interrelationships in crude equation form. Algebraic rearrangement of the various equations yields a systems model from which the most important parameters can be isolated and considered for the testing program. If the system under investigation is poorly understood, it may not be possible to use this approach. In this case, a simple sketch of the expected interactions between the environmental parameters aids in the selection of the more important variables for measurement.

After the testing program has been optimized to fit within the limits imposed by all of the different factors, the specific collection methods and sampling schedule can be selected. Sample size, number, frequency, and pattern required to obtain an adequate level of precision should at least be estimated prior to the establishment of the sampling schedule. The precision required depends largely on the objective of the study. One or two grab samples may give all the precision necessary in one case, while a much more sophisticated sampling program may be a prerequisite to meeting the objectives of another study.

A. Sample Size

The size of sample required for any given determination is related directly to the concentration of the measurement parameter in the sample and to the amount of material required for an accurate analysis. Where the same analytical technique is used in many different types of water, the concentration of the substance being measured is the factor dictating sample size. For example, determination of phytoplankton biomass in an oligotrophic lake will require much larger sample volumes than will the same measurement in a sewage lagoon.

Because of the collection, transportation, and handling problems, it is always desirable to restrict the sample volume to the minimum amount necessary for accurate analysis. The ultimate restraint is the lower limit of precision and accuracy of the analytical method; but better results can be obtained if the sample volume is large enough to allow measurement well above this lower limit.

B. Sample Number and Frequency

The number of samples which may be obtained depends on the time required to collect and process each sample. Generally, it is desirable to collect samples from as many different points within a body of water as time permits, but it is equally important to obtain accurate measures of each variable at each point. In fact, well-defined measures of concentration and variability of one or two of the more important parameters at a few carefully selected sampling stations are of more value than single determinations of many different parameters taken from a large number of sampling sites.

The number of samples and the frequency of sample collection required for a representative value at each sampling station are related directly to the variability of the parameter being studied and to the level of statistical significance specified. The 0.05 level of significance is the generally accepted statistical standard by which data are judged, but this level often is unobtainable in ecological investigations and lesser levels of significance may prove useful in comparisons of many inconstant biological populations. Needham and Usinger(13) suggest that while a prohibitive number of samples may be required to gain statistically significant measures of stream benthic invertebrate biomass and numbers, the results of only two samples allow a reasonably accurate measure of the principal groups. A similar observation has been made by Gaufin et al.(14).

When testing environmental data for statistical significance, the biological significance of the data also must be considered. An extremely accurate, statistically well-defined, long-term, average measure of dissolved oxygen concentration at noon in a body of water is not as valuable as a single curve of diurnal change in dissolved oxygen concentration where samples are collected at 2-hr intervals for both light and dark periods. High daytime dissolved oxygen concentration may be offset by very low night values which result in fish kills(15, 16). Accurate measures of diurnal or seasonal variability of environmental parameters are usually of greater importance than average values, for, as has been noted by Tarzwell and Gaufin(17), it is not the average but the extreme conditions that are hazardous to aquatic ecosystems.

The frequency of sample collection depends on the variability of both the measurement parameter and the environment but is limited by the number of samples which may be collected and processed. However, provisions for evaluating environmental variability should be included in all sampling programs.

C. Sample Pattern

The variability of the environment also is an important factor which must be considered in formulating the sampling pattern and selecting individual sampling sites. The specificity of the biota for narrow environmental niches and incomplete mixing of waste effluents with the receiving waters also must be considered.

The dependence of both plants and animals on the physical and chemical features of the aquatic milieu has been discussed by Hawkes(18), Hynes(1), and many others. It is the interaction of these physical and chemical factors with the biotic community that is the subject of most investigations of both natural waters and waste effluents. This is true regardless of whether the measurement parameter is change in dissolved oxygen for an oxygen sag curve, change in biochemical oxygen demand with time or distance, or a direct measurement of alteration in the biotic community.

An example of the importance of this consideration is seen in the selection of sampling sites for the measurement of plant life in different types of aquatic systems. The flora of streams is composed largely of attached forms, and the most important factors, in addition to light energy and nutrients for photosynthesis, appear to be current velocity and type of benthic substrate. In fact, Butcher(19) was able to distinguish five different stream bed types, each with a characteristic plant community. Phytoplankton, while rarely important in streams, is usually the dominant form of plant life in lakes. The most important factors limiting phytoplankton growth in such systems are the availability of light energy and nutrients, current being of lesser importance. Measurements of lake flora can be made from water samples, but such samples from most streams include only those algae which have been scoured from benthic substrates. Investigation of plant life in streams, then, must include samples of the benthic community.

Aquatic animals also are limited by water movement, and many of the benthic invertebrates have specialized body structures which allow them to live in extremely rapid currents. However, for most of the aquatic invertebrates the main factors limiting population development are the

type of substrate, the availability of food, and the ability of the organism
to withstand low dissolved oxygen tensions.

When selecting individual sampling sites, the dependence of aquatic
organisms on specific environmental niches must be considered. To
ensure biological significance in the results of field collections, consideration of the specificity of aquatic organisms should have priority over the
statistical considerations required for a statistically valid sampling
scheme.

The amount of mixing of waste streams within the receiving water
and the degree of dilution are factors that often are overlooked in field
sampling. Entering waste streams may be channeled down one side of
a receiving stream or reservoir for a considerable distance before becoming mixed with the bulk of the receiving water. However, most waste
effluents contain at least one inorganic salt in concentration greatly
exceeding that in the receiving water. Such salts — provided they are not
rapidly utilized by the biota, sorbed, or precipitated — can be used to
evaluate the degree of mixing. The waste material is thoroughly mixed
with the receiving water when the salt concentration is constant throughout the entire body of water. For municipal wastes discharging to fresh
water, the chloride ion can be used for this purpose.

If the discharge rate of the waste effluent is known or can be measured,
the salt dilution technique(20) can be modified to gain good estimates
of both the amount of dilution and the flow rate of a receiving stream. In
addition to the discharge rate of the waste stream, this method also requires measurement of the salt concentration in the waste stream, in the
receiving stream above the point of influent, and at a point downstream
from the influent where the waste is thoroughly mixed with the receiving
stream. If Q_a is the rate of discharge of the waste stream in liters per
second and Cl_a, Cl_b, and Cl_c are the chloride concentrations in milligrams
per liter of the waste stream, the receiving stream above, and the receiving
stream below the point of influent, respectively, the discharge rate of the
receiving stream upstream (Q_b) and downstream (Q_c) can be determined
as follows:

$$(Q_c)(Cl_c) = (Q_a)(Cl_a) + (Q_b)(Cl_b)$$

or

$$(Q_c)(Cl_c) = (Q_a)(Cl_a) + (Q_c - Q_a)(Cl_b)$$

Rearranging and solving for Q_c yields

$$Q_c = Q_a \frac{Cl_a - Cl_b}{Cl_c - Cl_b}$$

and

$$Q_b = Q_c - Q_a$$

This method is especially useful in small streams where it is often difficult to find adequate cross sections for the conventional flow-measuring devices. Since only a few measurements are required, this technique can be used to estimate both discharge and dilution prior to establishment of the sampling sites.

Knowledge of the amount of waste water and the degree of mixing with the receiving water is useful in positioning individual sampling sites. In streams this information can be used to determine the distance between sampling stations. In lakes knowledge of the concentration of the salt tracer can be used to delimit plumes of waste which may extend for a considerable distance from the waste source.

The simplest sampling pattern is to make all collections at points of easy access, such as collecting stream samples at bridges and lake samples from boat docks. However, a more complete coverage of the area is required to meet the objectives of most studies of aquatic ecosystems.

Lakes or reservoirs are particularly difficult to evaluate from a single sampling site. The inshore or littoral zone usually supports a different biotic community and sustains a different level of production than does the deeper, open water area. Mackenthun and Ingram(3) suggest that a transection sampling grid be used for lakes, with all transects intersecting at the deepest point in the lake. The primary advantage of this method is that if samples are taken at various depths at fairly close intervals along each transect, a three-dimensional picture of the lake can be constructed. Contour maps of benthic physical, chemical, and biotic conditions can be constructed and correlated with vertical changes in these parameters in the overlying water to give a complete picture of the lake ecosystem. In reservoirs, through which there may be considerable water movement, cross sections at various points along the length of the impoundment can be used to monitor changing conditions.

The number of transections used depends on the purpose of the study and on the time available for sampling. The results from a single cross section can be used to gain considerable insight into the condition of a particular lake environment, but a more complete understanding of the ecology of such an ecosystem can be obtained if time permits sample collection along several such transects.

An alternate method of sampling in lakes is to collect samples at randomly selected points throughout the lake. If the lake is divided into two or more discrete ecological sections, a stratified random method may be used in which the number of samples collected at random points within each section is directly related to the fraction of the total lake area made up by that section. However, for most investigations sampling along carefully selected transects gives more information per hour of sampling time.

Constant water movement poses special problems to sampling in streams, and in all but the larger rivers it generally is more fruitful to devote most of the effort to collection of samples from the stream bottom. The benthic environment reflects the quality of the water which passes over it and yet is not subject to as much diurnal and day-to-day variation as is the moving water of the stream.

Streams are composed of three different zones, differentiated primarily by physical factors such as current velocity, water depth, and type of benthic substrate. Riffles and pools usually are well defined, but there are other areas in most streams — often referred to as runs or flats — which are intermediate between riffles and pools. Each of these three zones represents a different environment inhabited by different biota and should be treated separately during any stream sampling program.

There is little deposition of sediments in riffles, and the firm benthic substrate serves as a good attachment site for periphytic organisms. The turbulent movement of the water allows a good exchange of nutrients and metabolic end products between the water and the attached biota, and light penetration into the relatively shallow riffle areas supports active photosynthetic growth. It is this combination of factors that enables riffles to support the highest level of production in streams. In polluted streams, the turbulent nature of the riffles increases reaeration, leading to higher dissolved oxygen concentrations; and below points of waste influent, clean water organisms appear in the riffles long before they can be found in pools or runs. Even in heavily polluted streams this increased oxygenation allows development of extensive growths of *Sphaerotilus* and other aerobic, heterotrophic forms in the riffles. These attached growths are stimulated by waste materials, and both the autotrophic and heterotrophic forms are subject to periodic sloughing and deposition into the more quiescent pool areas. It is this scoured material that comprises much of the stream plankton, even in the larger rivers (21).

In pools, the greater depth and lower current velocity limit both light intensity and nutrient exchange, and production is limited. Pools are areas of deposition for particulate matter suspended in the water and for those organisms scoured from the riffles. Reaeration is reduced in pools, and the benthic community in the often flocculant substrate reflects the lower dissolved oxygen concentration and organic enrichment of the pool bottom.

The benthic environment within the runs or flats is intermediate between that of riffles and pools. The biotic community in these areas also is intermediate and is composed of a mixture of organisms characteristic of both riffles and pools.

The selection of specific sample collection sites on a stream depends primarily on the type of stream and on the objective of the study, but riffles, pools, and runs are sufficiently different to require special consideration. Benthic samples from riffles reflect the best condition in the section of stream under study, while such samples from adjoining pools generally represent the poorest condition within the area. For most stream studies, especially where time is limited, it is more profitable to take all benthic samples from a common type of environment, i.e., riffles, or pools, or runs, Such samples should never be taken indiscriminately without regard to benthic and hydraulic conditions. In those streams where it is possible, collection of all benthic samples from riffles with similar hydraulic characteristics usually yields the best results.

Sample collection sites in streams should be located both above and below the point of influent of each waste stream and tributary to allow evaluation of the effects of these inflowing waters. In many instances, particularly below points of waste inflow, it is desirable to measure the degree of alteration or recovery within the stream following a marked change in water quality. This can be accomplished by collecting samples at several points downstream from the waste influent. Analysis of these samples allows measurement of the change in the stream system with both time and distance. The distance between these downstream sampling sites may be 100 m, 1 mile, or any other appropriate distance, but all samples should be collected from similar benthic environments.

It is more difficult to show the effects of waste discharge on lakes than it is in streams. There may be a measurable change in both benthic and planktonic biota in the immediate vicinity of the waste inlet, but wastes often are dispersed throughout the entire lake, leading to gradual degradation of the whole system. Samples in such cases are collected to record subtle changes in both the biotic and chemical nature of the lake. Slight alteration in composition of the algal community may be the only change noticed, and it may be difficult to correlate such a change with any characteristic of the waste influent. For this reason, monitoring of lake ecosystems for alterations associated with waste inflow often must be extended over a period of years before a positive correlation can be made.

In lakes the concentration of extrinsic material usually increases slowly throughout the entire lake and the sampling problem is one of time, with space or distance playing a small role. In streams the concentration of waste material depends on dilution but is greatest at the point below waste inflow where mixing is completed. If the waste is subject to natural physical or chemical removal or biotic utilization, the concentration will decrease in a downstream direction. Depending on the amount of waste discharged, this downstream change in both time and space allows separation and identification of definite polluted and recovery zones in streams.

In general, there is less dilution capacity in streams than there is in lakes, and the resulting higher concentrations of waste materials below points of inflow cause more obvious alterations of biotic communities in streams. For this reason it is easier to document waste-caused changes in stream ecosystems than it is in lakes. Thus, a greater degree of expertise is required to interpret the subtle waste-induced changes in lakes than is required for the more obvious response of stream communities to waste materials.

The two most important parameters in the sampling of waste streams are measures of the strength and volume of the waste material. If the character of the waste stream is relatively constant, infrequent sampling may be all that is required. However, if there is a marked day-to-day or diurnal variation in either volume or strength, the sampling program used should include provisions for measuring this variability.

Knowledge of concentrations of various pollutants in waste effluents is useful, but such values alone do not yield much information about the interaction of the waste stream with the receiving water. Estimates of flow rates should be obtained from both the waste stream and the receiving stream whenever samples are collected for the measurement of waste concentration. Such data allow calculation of the total amount of waste discharged and the degree of dilution of the waste material in the receiving water. Many natural streams are subject to wide seasonal variation in flow, and discharge measurements are of special importance in those cases where relatively constant waste streams discharge to highly variable receiving streams.

Evaluation and analysis of the quality of both natural waters and waste waters are limited to two types of samples. These are: (a) samples of water taken directly from the lake or stream and (b) samples collected from those portions of benthic substrate in constant contact with the water. Whenever possible, both types of samples should be collected from the same sites.

III. Water Samples

Water samples from lakes and streams are collected to allow measurement of a wide variety of physical, chemical, and biological parameters. While only a few of the possible measurements are required in most studies, all of the various environmental parameters can be grouped into three broad categories: They are either dissolved gases, dissolved solids, or particulate solids.

A. Dissolved Gases

Water may be analyzed for several different dissolved gases, but oxygen is the one most commonly measured in all aquatic environments. Oxygen is required constantly by all aerobic organisms and is thus the most critical dissolved gas in all bodies of water. Photosynthetic activity of the plant community produces oxygen during the daylight hours, and if oxygen production exceeds the respiration rate, the dissolved oxygen content will increase during the day. The entire biotic community requires oxygen during the night hours and the minimum dissolved oxygen concentration usually is reached just before dawn. The amount of diurnal variation is greater in organically enriched or polluted waters where daytime supersaturation may be offset by oxygen concentrations approaching zero in the hours just before sunrise.

Water movement can have a significant effect on oxygen concentration by accelerating both the rate of loss during periods of supersaturation and the rate of reaeration at low oxygen tensions. Diurnal variability of dissolved oxygen is greatest in quiescent lakes and ponds and usually is least noticeable in rapidly flowing streams. In slow-flowing streams there may be considerable diurnal variation, and oxygen sag curves constructed from samples collected only during the daylight hours often underestimate the stress on the aquatic biota. Because of the constant demand for oxygen by the biotic community, the minimum concentration and the duration of the minimum are much more important than measures of the average or maximum concentration.

The diurnal change in dissolved oxygen concentration should be considered and measured in all studies of aquatic ecosystems. Good measures of this diurnal change can be used to evaluate the overall metabolism within a body of water, including both photosynthetic activity and respiration(22,23). Periodic determinations of these metabolic rates are useful in evaluating the well-being of the water under investigation and often are more informative than comprehensive measurement of other environmental variables. If time does not permit routine measurement of this variability, the concentration of dissolved oxygen should be determined at least twice each sampling day, once at midafternoon and once just before dawn.

Samples for the determination of dissolved oxygen should be collected in narrow-mouthed, ground-glass-stoppered bottles holding 200–300 ml. Special samplers such as the Nansen water bottle and the Kemmerer water sampler should be used to collect all water samples for dissolved oxygen determination to avoid exchange of oxygen between the sample and the atmosphere. Other precautions involved in sampling for dissolved oxygen are outlined by Welch(12) and in Standard Methods(11).

Carbon dioxide, the physiological complement of oxygen, is another dissolved gas that is often included as a study parameter in investigations of aquatic systems. The intimate relationship of carbon dioxide with the bicarbonate buffer system and the difficulty in analyzing for free carbon dioxide limit the usefulness of this parameter.

B. Dissolved Solids

Most of the material present in both natural waters and waste waters is comprised of both inorganic and organic dissolved solids. Substances which pass through the pores in a 0.45-μ filter are generally considered to be in the dissolved phase.

Inorganic dissolved solids are composed of ionic substances which include nutrients such as nitrogen and phosphorous, salts such as chloride, sulfate, and carbonate, and toxic materials such as heavy metals and cyanide. With the exception of bicarbonate and carbonate, the inorganic solids are not subject to much diurnal variation; seasonal variation also may be limited. Exceptions are those waters which receive effluents from waste-producing industries which discharge large amounts of dissolved material on an intermittent or seasonal basis.

Although it is necessary to evaluate the variability of each inorganic substance used as a study parameter, sample frequency required for these dissolved materials is much less than that required for most other parameters. In lakes there may be a seasonal variation of dissolved nutrients, with the maximums associated with the spring and fall overturns. In streams which receive waste materials the concentration of dissolved inorganics is usually greatest during periods of low flow.

There may be considerable diurnal variation in bicarbonate and carbonate concentration in those waters supporting active photosynthetic activity. The bicarbonate–carbonate buffer system serves as a reserve carbon source for photosynthesis, and in enriched systems the limited availability of carbon dioxide from this source may be the factor limiting photosynthesis (24). In such waters diel measurements of pH or bicarbonate or carbonate concentration should be included in the sampling schedule.

Most of the dissolved inorganic materials are present as discrete ions, and specific analytical techniques are required for measurement of the ionic substances present in a water sample. Surface samples of water used for the measurement of the dissolved inorganics may simply be dipped up in the sample bottle. Collections of samples from deeper water or at various depths in a lake are accomplished with a Kemmerer water sampler.

To minimize breakage, small plastic bottles are often used to collect and transport water samples. Many of the plastics adsorb certain of the inorganic materials and this scavenging action must be considered and corrected for. For example, the addition of 0.2 ml of sulfuric acid to each 100 ml of water collected in a polyethylene bottle will remove the phosphorous adsorbed by the plastic.

Dissolved organic substances fall into at least three different categories. Many of the dissolved organics present in waste water are used as an energy source by the heterotrophic microbiota in both the waste stream and the receiving water. These materials often are called biodegradable organics. The second type of dissolved organic includes those which are neither toxic to nor utilized by the aquatic biota. Such substances, which may be present in wastes or may be formed during anaerobic fermentation of organic wastes (25), are often collected on carbon filters suspended in streams. Some of these substances may be responsible for taste and odor problems in domestic water supplies. Materials toxic to the aquatic biota are the third type of dissolved organic commonly found in both natural waters and waste streams. Organic pesticides are an example of this type of pollutant.

Organic dissolved materials are usually found in much more dilute concentrations than are the dissolved inorganics. More precise and sophisticated analytical techniques must be used to identify and measure the dissolved organics, and usually a larger sample volume is required. The diurnal and seasonal variability of these substances depends on the constancy of their source and on the changes in the rate of biotic utilization of those that are biodegradable associated with seasonal changes in temperature.

Samples to be used for analysis of dissolved organic materials can be collected by the same methods used for dissolved inorganics. However, those samples containing biodegradable organics cannot be stored for any length of time prior to analysis. Bacteria utilize the organics during the period of storage, and samples to be analyzed for biochemical oxygen demand (BOD) should not be stored longer than 1 day even at temperatures as low as 4°C (26). Misleading results are often obtained from frozen samples because freezing ruptures algal and bacterial cells, causing the cellular contents to increase the concentration of dissolved organics.

Collection and preservation techniques for nonbiodegradable and toxic dissolved organics are dictated by the type of material and by the requirements of the specific analytical method.

C. Particulate Solids

The suspended or particulate solids in water include both inorganic and organic materials. The inorganic fraction is made up largely of silt, sand, and clay soil particles, while the organic fraction may be either living or dead organic matter.

Turbidity caused by particulate solids reduces light penetration into water. This shading, along with the smothering and abrading action of these materials, reduces production of both autotrophic and heterotrophic portions of the biotic community (27). Both inorganic and organic particulates eventually settle to the bottom of lakes and streams and this sediment often changes the type of benthic substrate. Inorganic silt and sand change the physical nature of the bottom materials, and the anaerobic sludge beds often resulting from organic accrual alter both the physical and chemical features of the benthic environment. Such alterations of the benthic substrate are accompanied by changes in the types of organisms present. Constant water movement may delay final deposition of particulate solids, and the bed load – the heavier particles moving along the bottom – has a marked effect on the ecology of streams.

Collection of samples from lakes for analysis of particulate materials can be accomplished in a fashion similar to that used for the dissolved solids. The moving water of streams complicates the sampling for suspended materials because it is difficult to collect a representative sample in a changing flow field. It is especially difficult to collect meaningful samples of the bed load materials. For such samples the water must be withdrawn at a rate equal to the flow rate to avoid resuspension of bottom sediments in the sampling area. An alternate method is to place a small cup in the center of a large flat concrete or plastic surface with the lip of the cup and the flat surface level with the benthic substrate. The bed load materials fall into the cup, from which they are removed for analysis.

Several methods are available for the collection of the zooplankton and phytoplankton which make up the bulk of the living suspended organic material in water. Samples of the total plankton can be obtained with any method used to collect water samples. For surface samples, the water can be dipped up in a 1- to 4-liter wide-mouthed bottle with the volume required depending on the abundance of the plankton. Samples from deeper water can be collected with a Kemmerer or Nansen water bottle lowered to the desired depth.

Other collection methods which allow field concentration of the net plankton are available, e.g., the Wisconsin plankton net, the Juday plankton trap, and the Clark-Bumpus plankton sampler. Detailed instructions on the use of each of these samplers are given by Welch(12). All of these samplers have a fine mesh net, usually size 25 silk bolting cloth, which strains the larger plankton from the water. However, in many lakes the bulk of the standing crop biomass is composed of nannoplankton which pass through the net. Until the relative importance of each size of plankton has been evaluated, samples collected with fine mesh nets should not be considered to be representative of the total plankton. Whenever samples of net plankton are collected, companion samples of the water should be taken from the same location for determination of nanno-plankton numbers, types, and biomass.

The total plankton present in water samples can be concentrated with a centrifuge such as the Forest plankton centrifuge(11). If it is operated at maximum speed, this centrifuge will remove 98% of the plankton, including those as small as the larger bacteria(12).

Preservation of plankton samples is required if there is much of a delay between collection and analysis of the sample. In most cases the sample will not deteriorate appreciably in 4–8 hr if it is maintained at the original or even a colder temperature. Warming of the sample should be avoided. Samples of plankton can be preserved by adding 4–5 ml of commercial Formalin to each 100 ml of sample volume.

The abundance and type of plankton present in any surface water are subject to considerable seasonal variation associated with changing climatic and environmental factors. These small organisms also may exhibit a significant diurnal vertical variation. Figure 1 represents the diurnal

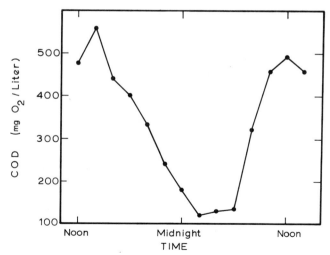

Fig. 1. Diurnal variation in chemical oxygen demand (COD) in the effluent from a sewage lagoon caused by vertical movement of plankton algae.

change in concentration of chemical oxygen demand (COD) in the effluent withdrawn from the 8-in. depth of the highly enriched regime of a sewage lagoon. This variation is due to the diurnal vertical movement of the plankton algae. The phytoplankton were most abundant at the 8-in. depth during periods of greatest sunlight intensity and were most abundant at the surface during the dark hours. As solar intensity increased, the organisms moved downward, maintaining a more favorable position with regard to the light intensity required for photosynthesis. Even in highly enriched environments, the phytoplankton often are virtually absent in the upper 3–5 in. of water during the periods of brightest sunlight. These diurnal and seasonal variations should be recognized, evaluated, and compensated for in any investigation of plankton communities.

A thorough treatment of the procedures and precautions involved in collecting water samples for bacterial examination is given elsewhere (*11*). The main considerations are the use of sterile glassware and the protection of the sample from contamination.

IV. Benthic Samples

The biota which are associated intimately with the bottoms of lakes and streams play a considerable role in determining water quality, but water quality also exerts a marked influence on the type of benthic community present. In deep lakes the organisms at the mud–water interface accomplish appreciable organic reduction and are responsible for most of the regeneration of essential plant nutrients. The mixed communities attached to stream bottoms and the littoral zones of lakes serve a dual role. The algal fraction is the source of large amounts of chemical energy and oxygen, while organic decomposition and nutrient release are associated with the heterotrophic fraction. This benthic assemblage, which includes algae, bacteria, protozoa, and aquatic insect larvae, represents the bulk of the biological activity occurring in most streams. The importance of the benthic community should not be overlooked in any sampling plan, for an understanding of any aquatic system is incomplete without knowledge of the physical, chemical, and biological interactions at the bottom of the body of water.

The collection of adequate samples of bottom deposits is, in many ways, more difficult than collection of representative water samples. It is difficult to obtain representative samples of bottom muds, and after they are gathered they often must be transported through several meters of overlying water without loss or exchange with the water mass. Although there is considerable interplay between the physical, chemical, and biological factors in bottom muds, it is often necessary to obtain benthic samples for specific analytical measurements.

A. Physical and Chemical Measurement

It is very difficult to collect and retrieve benthic samples for physical and chemical analyses. The bottom muds usually contain dissolved gases and reduced materials which may be released or altered during the collection and subsequent travel through the more oxygenated surface waters. For most physical and chemical analyses, a core sampling device(12) is probably the best method of sampling bottom deposits. The core, when delivered intact, can be used to study the deposition pattern over periods of several seasons or many years, depending on the rate of deposition. There is less chance of material loss to the water during the retrieval of the compact core than with the flocculent sample collected with the more popular dredges. The use of a core sampler also minimizes oxidation of the reduced materials during the ascent of the sample.

Once the sample is at the surface there is still considerable difficulty in preserving it in its original condition. Attempts have been made to freeze the core both at the surface and at the bottom and to store the core under inert gas or in deoxygenated water. Regardless of the method used, there is little assurance that the concentrations of gases and reduced substances measured in the sample truly represent those at the bottom. Disturbance of the bottom muds appears to alter the entire benthic ecology(28).

B. Biological Measurement

The portion of the benthic biotic community most commonly included in aquatic sampling programs is the macrofauna, comprised primarily of aquatic insect larvae and worms. In lakes or deep rivers such samples usually are taken with one of the variety of dredges available for this purpose. For soft bottom muds in shallow water the Ekman dredge(11) is often used, but larger and heavier dredges, such as the Petersen dredge (11), are favored for deeper waters. Beeton et al.(29) discussed some of the problems associated with the use of dredges to collect benthic macrofauna from deep waters.

Samples of the benthic macrofauna of streams can be collected with a simple dip net, with dredges, or with Surber or Hess-type samplers(12). Each of these methods allows collection of benthic organisms for taxonomic purposes, but the use of the dip net precludes consideration of the area factor. All samples collected from the bottom of lakes and streams should be collected from known areas. The results can then be expressed as number or weight of organisms per unit area, which allows much better comparisons of different bodies of water than do lists of species present.

To facilitate transportation of the benthic samples, the macrofauna are often separated from the finer bottom material with 20- or 30-mesh screens at the collection site. Many of the smaller insects, especially the small chironomids, also may be lost through such screens. Thus, extreme care must be taken in any field separation technique so that the sample collected is truly representative of the benthic macrofauna.

As was noted previously, the benthic sampling program ideally should include the collection of samples from all different types of bottom materials and current velocities. If time is not available for such a complete sampling scheme, all stream samples should be taken from similar benthic substrates in areas of similar current velocities. Macrofauna from lakes and reservoirs ordinarily should be collected along specific transects.

Although the macrofauna is the most obvious portion of the benthic community, the other biotic levels are also important in the investigation of any aquatic ecosystem. Butcher(30), Patrick et al.(31), and others (32–34) have used artificial substrates to collect samples of the attached algae indigenous to streams and lakes. Clean glass or Plexiglas slides are suspended in the water under investigation and are soon colonized by the native periphytic organisms. After a predetermined period the slides are removed and the attached organisms are counted and identified to a convenient taxonomic level. This method is especially useful for collecting stream periphyton, which is dominated by the diatoms. The silica frustules of the diatoms allow identification of the algae after they are dried, and changes in diatom species composition can be used to show alterations in water quality.

The bacterial and protozoan components of the benthic community are included in any bottom sample, and the number of types and individuals present can be obtained from any such sample, provided the proper taxonomic expertise is available. Although changes in protozoan density and species composition have been used to delineate changes in water quality(35), the more conventional index to nonpathogenic bacterial activity is measurement of BOD of the bottom muds. In many ways this estimate of community respiration is more informative than lists of bacteria present.

C. Variability

All natural waters and most waste streams are subject to considerable diurnal and seasonal variation. Changes in temperature, photoperiod, discharge rate, and dilution capacity are accompanied by changes in the biodynamics of all portions of the benthic community as well as alterations of some of the physical and chemical parameters. Analyses taken during the summer may not even approximate conditions on the bottom during the winter. In general, any alteration in the environment will cause change in the benthic community. Thus, to adequately evaluate benthic conditions, samples should be collected whenever there are measurable changes in the environment.

V. Measurement of Community Metabolism

Much of the preceding material has been devoted to discussion of sample collection for specific analyses, and most of the techniques discussed are simply methods for obtaining grab samples. The current state of the art is such that most investigations of aquatic systems are based entirely or almost entirely on grab samples. Regardless of the care involved in the collection and analyses of such samples, the results represent static measures of specific environmental parameters. Aquatic ecosystems are not static; in fact, they may be described as being in a constant state of dynamic equilibrium. Measures of standing crop of organisms or concentration of specific ionic substances help describe the body of water but tell little about the dynamic, physical, chemical, and biological interactions which characterize the living ecosystem. A slight change in a physical or chemical parameter often is followed by large changes in community metabolism, and likewise, changes in community metabolism often lead to marked alterations in one or more of the physical and chemical factors.

When waste materials are added to natural waters, the response of the indigenous community and the effect on water quality depend entirely on the interaction of specific wastes with the delicate balance of all the physical, chemical, and biological factors which characterize and limit the native aquatic ecosystem. The addition of organic matter leads to increased bacterial activity, a greater diurnal variability in dissolved oxygen content, and usually an increased algal production rate. The addition of even small amounts of toxic materials will have a direct effect on both community metabolism and water quality by limiting the activity of one or more of the biotic levels. Increased turbidity may cause a marked decrease in photosynthetic energy fixation and oxygen production with very little change in species composition, although if continued, there may be a marked reduction in standing crop biomass.

In most bodies of water, especially those which receive wastes, the two most important measurement parameters are the rate of community respiration and the rate of organic addition including both photosynthetic activity and the inflow of allochthonous material. Photosynthesis by the algae and macrophytes produces a chemical energy source for the remainder of the community, and oxygen is produced as a by-product. Community respiration includes the oxygen demand of all aerobic biota present, but in most systems the bulk of the oxygen utilization is accomplished by the night respiration of the plants and by the small heterotrophic microorganisms, i.e., bacteria, protozoa, fungi, etc. The addition of organic material at a rate greater than that required by the heterotrophic community results in benthic deposition of organic matter which serves as an energy substrate for additional bacterial metabolism. Increased bacterial activity requires increased amounts of oxygen to satisfy the bacterial respiratory requirements. Thus, increases in the accrual rate of organic matter ultimately lead to an increased respiration rate, regardless of whether organics are added directly or accumulate as a result of excess photosynthetic activity due to increases in plant nutrient levels.

Continued deposition of both extrinsic material and excess aquatic plant production leads to continued increase in the aerobic respiratory rate until the thickness of the organic debris exceeds the oxygen transfer capabilities and the organic muds become anaerobic. Increased organic content of bottom deposits can be measured from core samples and in most cases shows good correlation with increased community respiratory rate and decreased dissolved oxygen concentration near the bottom.

The mixture of organic material with the native inorganic bottom materials alters and stabilizes impermanent benthic substrates. This type of benthic stabilization in streams often allows additional attached macrophyte growth, and in those areas of the stream containing dense beds of aquatic vegetation the diurnal dissolved oxygen pulse may range from supersaturation during peak photosynthetic activity to a low of 2.5–3.0 mg/liter 3 hr after sunset (36).

These massive changes in community metabolism will always be accompanied by change in species composition, and in such cases examination of alterations in species composition is not an adequate assessment of the overall impact of the pollutant on the aquatic ecosystem. In most instances the problems associated with pollution of natural waters are those of alteration of either the water quality or some portion of the biotic community. Variations of production or respiration rate occur in many aquatic ecosystems prior to change in species composition. In fact, measures of the metabolic rates of the community or of the various biotic levels within the ecosystem give a much better evaluation of the well-being of bodies of water than do extensive lists of the organisms present.

Well-trained individuals can correlate changes in species diversity and composition with changes in water quality caused by the inflow of waste materials, but to the average investigator, who lacks the required taxonomic training, such lists of species and numbers are largely incomprehensible. Many different levels of the biotic community have been used as indices of ecosystem alteration. For this purpose Patrick et al. (31) rely heavily on changes within the diatoms, Mohr (35) has used the protozoa, Brinkhurst (37) uses the tubificid worms, and Wilhm (38) uses change in the macrofauna. Such parameters are useful in showing changes in single-community levels but give little information about the biotic activity of the entire community within a body of water. A slight change in species composition is not necessarily indicative of a great or serious change in water quality. If the new species fills the same role in the community as the one it replaced and maintains about the same level of production, little harm is done to the aquatic community. However, any permanent change in production or respiration rates, with or without change in species composition, will result in a change in the biotic community and most probably a change in water quality as well.

Changes in water quality can lead to changes in both species composition and community metabolism. Neither of these measures should be used exclusively, and in most investigations of aquatic ecosystems attention should be given to both species diversity and community metabolism. However, much of the current activity is devoted to delineating changes in species number and type, and little attention is paid to measurement of production and respiration rates within specific bodies of water. To better understand and control conditions in natural waters, more effort should be made to obtain measures of the diurnal, seasonal, and annual variability of the metabolic activity within polluted, enriched, and clean water ecosystems.

A. Biochemical Oxygen Demand

The oldest measure of community metabolism is the 5-day biochemical oxygen demand (BOD) test. (Chapter 15 deals with the measurement of BOD.) This technique has been used for many years for all types of water and waste water. As a comparative parameter, BOD is an important measure of water quality, but the values obtained from the standard test may not adequately reflect the utilization of oxygen in nature. The use of a specified dilution medium and seeding of the sample do much for the standardization of the BOD method, but the chemical environment and the biota present may be greatly different in the bottle than in nature.

While the BOD test is an important and useful measure of community activity, it cannot be used for all types of water and waste water. The presence of toxins in an industrial waste stream may result in a low BOD when in fact the waste may contain significant amounts of biodegradable material. Increased BOD with increased dilution suggests that toxic materials are present in the waste. The BOD test has been used with considerable success as a means of evaluating effluent from most waste water treatment facilities, but it underestimates oxygen demand in lagoon effluents and other waters containing large amounts of algae. A large percentage of the algae live for periods longer than the 5 days required for the standard BOD test, and the oxygen demand of the algal protoplasm is not included in the measured BOD.

Samples for the analysis of BOD of water or benthic muds may be collected with any of the common sampling gear. Surface water samples can be obtained with any clean container, and samples from deeper strata normally are collected with a Kemmerer or Van Dorn water sampler (*38a*). Benthic muds can be collected with either a core sampler or one of the dredges, but the core sampler minimizes loss of any reduced materials which may yield an appreciable immediate oxygen demand.

These methods of sample collection provide grab samples, and the results of the analyses of such samples are estimates of BOD for small portions of the system. Daily average values of the BOD of water can be obtained with any of the many different composite samplers (*38b*). Some of these units withdraw water at a constant rate (*38b*), while others withdraw at a rate proportional to the flow of the water being sampled (*38c*). The use of composite or proportional samplers allows inclusion of some of the diurnal variability, and the analyses of such collecting devices yield estimates of the average BOD for the period of sampling. While such estimates of BOD are useful indices of community respiration, they do not include measures of the diurnal variability unless samples are analyzed for 1- or 2-hour intervals for a full 24-hr period. The BOD of the water in a given stream or waste stream may be subject to considerable diurnal and seasonal variation; and while the BOD of the bottom muds also may vary seasonally, it is relatively constant over a 24-hr period.

Despite these drawbacks, BOD is a useful and versatile measure of water quality suitable for a wide range of water types. This estimate of the activity of the aquatic community is usually more informative than lists of bacteria species isolated from water samples. The isolation techniques provide near optimum growth conditions for these small organisms, and it is difficult to evaluate the activity of the natural bacterial population from lists of bacterial species isolated in the laboratory. The mere presence of an organism tells little about its role in community metabolism.

B. Diurnal Variability

One of the best indices of community metabolism is the direct measurement of diurnal variability in the dissolved oxygen concentration. The rate of increase in dissolved oxygen concentration during the light hours is a measure of the photosynthetic production, while the rate of decrease during the night is a measure of community respiration. In general, the more enriched or polluted the body of water, the greater the diurnal variability in oxygen concentration. There may be little or no measurable change in the oxygen content of an oligotrophic lake or a mountain stream, but the concentration in a sewage lagoon may range from 35 mg/liter to less than 1 mg of oxygen/liter in a 12-hr period. In most waters the daily change lies between these extremes. Typical curves of the diurnal variability in oxygen content with different degrees of enrichment are shown in Fig. 2.

This variation in oxygen content can be measured for a given body of water by chemical titration of the oxygen(11) in grab samples collected at 1- or 2-hour intervals for a full 24-hr period. Where they can be used, recording polarographic oxygen probes are an alternate, and certainly easier, means of obtaining such curves.

In many systems the oxygen content is at the same level at 6 a.m. as it was 24 hr earlier. This does not mean that the ecosystem is balanced but only that there is enough net oxygen produced during the day to meet the

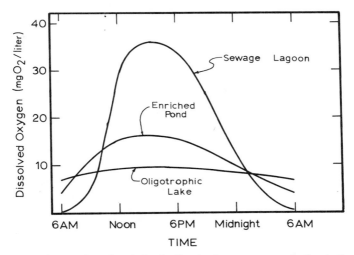

Fig. 2. Comparison of diurnal variation in dissolved oxygen concentration in three bodies of water with different levels of enrichment.

night respiratory demand. Each of the curves in Fig. 2 ends at the same level from which it started, but the data indicate that oxygen production, and hence algal production, is considerably greater in the sewage lagoon than in the oligotrophic lake.

The measured change in oxygen concentration during the light hours includes only net production. Gross oxygen production is equal to the sum of net oxygen production and respiration. Since oxygen is produced as a by-product of the photosynthetic process in which solar energy is converted to chemical energy, the amount of algal protoplasm formed is equivalent to the gross oxygen production less daytime plant respiration. In enriched or polluted waters a significant fraction of the gross oxygen production is used to support daytime bacterial respiration, and considerable algal protoplasm is stored in the system. Some of this stored organic matter is used to support algal respiration at night, but the bulk of it remains in the system where it stimulates further bacterial activity which, in turn, increases the respiration rate. Carbon dioxide evolved from the increased bacterial respiration provides the carbon source for additional photosynthesis. Thus, both production and respiration rates will increase until plant nutrients or some other environmental factor becomes limiting. This acceleration of community metabolism increases the turnover rate of carbon and results in an increased algal standing crop. Even though standing crop biomass is greater, the system may still approximate a balanced condition unless the factor limiting production is removed.

The addition of biodegradable organic material increases bacterial respiration, which supplies more carbon dioxide to the algae. The addition of phosphorus, nitrogen, or any other limiting plant nutrient allows increased algal production which is eventually followed by increased bacterial activity. These increased metabolic rates appear as a greater diurnal variability in the oxygen concentration.

Diurnal change in pH is another parameter which can be used to monitor community metabolism. During maximum photosynthesis, carbon dioxide is withdrawn from the bicarbonate-carbonate alkalinity system and there is a resulting increase in pH. The amount of pH change during the daylight hours is related directly to the amount of photosynthetic production. Night respiration supplies carbon dioxide which restores the alkalinity, and pH declines. The daily change in pH is given in Fig. 3 for the same three systems shown in Fig. 2.

In general, increases in community metabolism are associated with change in the environment and can be measured as increases in the diurnal variability of oxygen or pH, or, with greater enrichment, as diurnal changes in bicarbonate alkalinity.

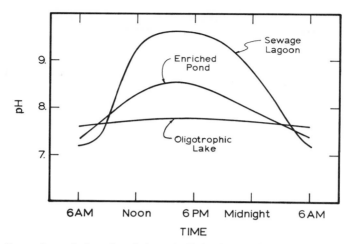

Fig. 3. Comparison of diurnal variation of pH in three bodies of water with different levels of enrichment.

C. Light Bottle–Dark Bottle

Incubation of companion samples of water in light and dark bottles, a technique first used by Gaarder and Gran(39), is another means of estimating community metabolism. For this method, samples of water are collected with a Kemmerer or Van Dorn water bottle. The dissolved oxygen concentration of the sample is determined and two ground-glass-stoppered bottles are filled with water from the sampler. One of these bottles is of clear glass, and the other is darkened with aluminum foil, tape, or black paint so that it is impervious to light. Both bottles are then suspended at the depth from which the sample was taken and left there until there is a measurable change in oxygen concentration in both bottles. An exposure period of 2–4 hr usually is sufficient, but the length of time required depends on the rate of community metabolism.

Sunlight penetrates the light bottle, allowing both photosynthesis and community respiration to continue, while in the dark bottle photosynthesis is prevented and change in dissolved oxygen is due only to community respiration. At the end of the exposure period both bottles are retrieved, the dissolved oxygen content in each bottle is determined, and these values are compared with the original oxygen concentration of the sample. Negative change in oxygen concentration in the dark bottle is an estimate of community respiration, while net algal production is recorded as a positive change in oxygen content in the light bottle.

This method is often used to gain estimates of community metabolism at various depths in lakes and reservoirs but is not directly applicable to streams. The imprisonment of the water in the bottles is atypical of the constant water movement and increased atmospheric exchange characteristic of streams.

D. Algal Growth Potential

Increased algal production is one of the prime manifestations of eutrophication, and estimates of the ability of a given water to grow algae would be useful in any investigation of enriched aquatic ecosystems. Oswald and Golueke (40) proposed such a measure with their method for determining algal growth potential (AGP). Basically this approach involves seeding filtered samples of the water in question with an algal suspension and incubating this mixture in the light for periods of 2–3 months. The measurement parameter is the dry weight or packed cell volume of the algal biomass at the end of this period.

The residue remaining in an aerobic system after this length of time would be largely biologically inert or at best only slowly utilized by the aquatic community. Although this technique yields an estimate of ecosystem enrichment, the long incubation period and the use of artificial light and a semistandard seed comprised only of algae common to polluted systems limit its broad application.

E. Benthic Metabolism

The constant movement and mixing of water in streams and the resulting high degree of atmospheric exchange make it particularly difficult to obtain good estimates of stream community metabolism. Diurnal change in dissolved oxygen is a useful parameter, but in shallow or fast-flowing streams the curves constructed from such data are truncated by the enhanced exchange of oxygen with the atmosphere. In deep or slow-flowing streams, measures of diurnal variability of oxygen can be used as an index to community metabolism in much the same manner as in lakes and ponds. In more turbulent water it is difficult to obtain good determinations of the loss of oxygen during peak photosynthesis and of reaeration during the night hours. However, even in the more rapid streams, estimates of community production and respiration obtained from diurnal measurements of oxygen content can be used as a comparative index of biotic activity in similar streams or in areas with similar physical characteristics within the same stream.

Most of the production and respiration in streams is accomplished by the organisms associated with the bottom. Although it is difficult to acquire adequate estimates of the respiratory activity of the benthic community, good measures of benthic production can be obtained by using artificial substrates. When clean glass or Plexiglas substrates are suspended in a body of water, they are soon colonized by the native benthic organisms(*41*). If these substrates are removed at specified intervals, the weight of the accrued material is an estimate of net community production. This method of measuring benthic productivity has been used successfully in many different types of water(*42–45*).

The substrates may be as simple as glass microscope slides, and the attachment racks may be as sophisticated as is desired or necessary. Substrates may be suspended in the water either vertically or horizontally; both types of placement have been used with success. Vertical placement minimizes deposition of debris and appears to be the best approach for streams(*45*). The exposure period required depends on the productivity of the stream or lake, but for comparative purposes periods of 1–2 weeks usually will suffice.

Since current velocity and the amount of available light have a marked effect on production rate, benthic production estimates within a given body of water should be obtained from areas with similar physical characteristics. In streams the best results for comparative purposes are usually obtained from riffle areas where there is less deposition of both inorganic and organic debris. The material which accumulates on the substrates is comprised of autotrophic or photosynthetic and heterotrophic or nonphotosynthetic microorganisms and both inorganic and organic sediments. Expression of the results of gravimetric analysis as grams ash-free dry weight includes only the organic accumulation on the slide. A method of separating all of the various fractions – inorganic and organic sediments and autotropic and heterotrophic biomass – is given by King and Ball(*45*).

Measurement of benthic production, especially if separated into autotrophic and heterotrophic fractions, is a useful index of the general level of benthic activity and the degree of enrichment within natural waters.

F. Variability

Like all other parameters within the aquatic ecosystem, community metabolism is subject to considerable seasonal variation. Light, temperature, and nutrients are the primary factors controlling production while temperature is the main limitation on respiration. Since algal production is directly related to available light, production varies considerably from bright, cloudless days to dull, cloudy days. Community respiration is not affected much by available light. In many systems organic material deposited during the winter is utilized during the summer, and, in general, the maximum metabolic rate occurs during the summer and the minimum value is recorded during the winter. If measurements of community metabolism are included in any comprehensive investigation of a natural water, samples for the appropriate analyses should be acquired at weekly intervals during the summer and at least once a month during the winter.

VI. Current and Future Trends

Increased concern about the deterioration of natural waters has been accompanied by demands that water quality be controlled and managed. Successful management of water quality requires frequent and some-times continuous quantitative measures of the condition of the aquatic environment. While samples collected from natural waters and waste effluents are subjected to increasingly complex and sophisticated physical and chemical analyses, in most cases the biological examination is conducted in a fashion similar to that used by Birge 60 years ago. The keystone of many current investigations of water quality is the biological examination of water samples. The use of indicator organisms (31, 35, 37, 38) has proved useful in the qualitative description of aquatic ecosystems, but this is the one analytical area which has not been, and probably cannot be, automated. It still takes a large amount of a well-trained expert's time to sort and identify the biota collected in each grab sample. This time requirement limits the number of samples which can be processed, which in turn limits the frequency of measurement. With the increased demand for rapid measures of water quality useful in the management of aquatic systems, increased reliance by necessity will be placed on physical and chemical determinations which can be obtained in a short period of time.

Methods of sampling also will have to be altered, for the current grab sample techniques will not meet the demand for operating data imposed by those in charge of maintaining water quality. These requirements pose special sampling problems which probably will be met by contin-uously recording the output of such devices as the polarographic oxygen probe and the specific ion probes currently under development. The use of such recording and telemetering devices will reduce the collection of samples, but extreme care will be required in the placement of the probes. If these measuring devices are not placed in representative portions of the ecosystem, the data collected will be of little or no value.

Although much of the water quality data collected in the future probably will be physical and chemical determinations, proper selection and interpretation of these data will yield excellent measures of community metabolism. Correlation of these measures of metabolism with information from well-designed field and laboratory studies should result in methods for accurately estimating community production, organic storage, and respiration rates from such physical and chemical determinations. These metabolic rates will have a prominent place in the computerized control of water quality in the future.

There is not now, nor is there ever likely to be, a single method of sampling and analysis which can be used to describe aquatic ecosystems. The type of ecosystem and the availability of time and equipment limit the number of environmental variables which may be considered, but the choice of methods lies with the individual investigator. The number of specific analytical and sampling schemes available to evaluate various physical, chemical, and biological parameters in natural waters is well over 1000, and this number is being expanded constantly. In addition, new and better sampling devices are continually being developed. But the prime requirement of all samples, regardless of the method of collection, is that they be representative of the body of water from which they are taken. For in all cases, the quality of any investigation of an aquatic ecosystem is no better than the sampling program used.

REFERENCES

1. H. B. N. Hynes, *The Biology of Polluted Waters*, Liverpool University Press, Liverpool, England, 1960.
2. L. Klein, ed., *River Pollution, II. Causes and Effects*, Butterworths, London, 1962.
3. K. M. Mackenthun and W. M. Ingram, *Biological Associated Problems in Freshwater Environments — Their Identification, Investigation, and Control*, Federal Water Pollution Control Admin., Washington, D.C., 1967.
4. C. N. Sawyer and P. L. McCarty, *Chemistry for Sanitary Engineers*, 2nd ed., McGraw-Hill, New York, 1967.
5. L. E. Keup, W. M. Ingram, and K. M. Mackenthun, *Biology of Water Pollution: A Collection of Selected Papers on Stream Pollution, Waste Water, and Water Treatment, Publ. No. CWA-3*, Federal Water Pollution Control Admin., Washington, D.C., 1967.
6. P. S. Welch, *Limnology*, 2nd ed., McGraw-Hill, New York, 1952.
7. G. E. Hutchinson, *A Treatise on Limnolgy, Vol. 1, Geography, Physics, and Chemistry*, Wiley, New York, 1957.
8. G. E. Hutchinson, *A Treatise on Limnology, Vol. 2, Introduction to Lake Biology and the Limnoplankton*, Wiley, New York, 1967.

 9. F. Ruttner, *Fundamentals of Limnology* (transl. by D. G. Frey and F. E. J. Fry), University of Toronto Press, Toronto, 1953.
10. G. K. Reid, *Ecology of Inland Waters and Estuaries*, Reinhold, New York, 1961.
11. *Standard Methods for the Examination of Water and Wastewater*, 12th ed., American Public Health Association, New York, 1965.
12. P. S. Welch, *Limnological Methods*, Blakiston, Philadelphia, 1948.
13. P. R. Needham and R. L. Usinger, *Hilgardia*, **24**, 383 (1956).
14. A. R. Gaufin, E. K. Harris, and H. J. Walter, *Ecology*, **37**, 643 (1956).
15. T. A. Olson, *Trans. Am. Fisheries Soc.*, **62**, 278 (1932).
16. G. W. Prescott, *Hydrobiologica*, **1**, 1 (1948).
17. C. M. Tarzwell and A. R. Gaufin, *Proc. Ind. Waste Conf. 8th, Purdue University, Lafayette, Ind., 1953*, p. 295.
18. H. A. Hawkes, in *River Pollution, II. Causes and Effects* (L. Klein, ed.), Butterworths, London, 1962, pp. 311–432.
19. R. W. Butcher, *J. Ecol.*, **21**, 58 (1933).
20. C. M. Allen and E. A. Taylor, *Trans. ASME*, **45**, 285 (1923).
21. L. M. Berner, *Ecology*, **32**, 1 (1951).
22. H. T. Odum, *Limnol. Oceanog.*, **1**, 102 (1956).
23. W. J. McConnell, *Limnol. Oceanog.*, **7**, 335 (1962).
24. D. L. King, in *Advances Toward Understanding Lagoon Behavior, Eng. Extension Ser. No. 6*, University of Missouri, Columbia, 1966, pp. 88–110.
25. D. L. King and D. R. Bunn, *Proc. Ind. Waste Conf., 21st, Purdue University, Lafayette, Ind., 1966*, p. 248.
26. F. J. Agardy and M. L. Kiado, *Proc. Ind. Waste Conf., 21st, Purdue University, Lafayette, Ind., 1966*, p. 226.
27. D. L. King and R. C. Ball, *Limnol. Oceanog.*, **12**, 27 (1967).
28. J. E. Stein and J. G. Denison, in *Advances in Water Pollution Research*, Vol. 3, Water Pollution Control Federation, Washington, D.C., 1967, p. 181.
29. A. M. Beeton, J. F. Carr, and J. K. Hiltunen, *Publ. Great Lakes Res. Div. No. 13*, 1965; in *Water Pollution Abstr. (Brit)*, **40**, 1104 (1967).
30. R. W. Butcher, *Ann. Bot. (London)*, **45**, 813 (1932).
31. R. Patrick, M. H. Hohn, and J. H. Wallace, *Notulae Naturae*, No. 259, 1954.
32. V. S. Ivlev, *Arch. Hydrobiol.*, **25**, 177 (1933).
33. C. L. Newcombe, *Trans. Am. Microscop. Soc.*, **68**, 355 (1949).
34. R. W. Castenholz, *Limnol. Oceanog.*, **5**, 1 (1960).
35. J. L. Mohr, *Sci. Monthly*, **74**, 1 (1952).
36. R. L. Vannote, Ph.D. Thesis, Michigan State University, East Lansing, 1963.
37. R. O. Brinkhurst, *Publ. Great Lakes Res. Div. No. 13*, 1965; in *Water Pollution Abstr. (Brit)*, **40**, 1229 (1967).
38. J. L. Wilhm, *J. Water Pollution Control Federation*, **39**, 1673 (1967).
38a. J. P. Riley, in *Chemical Oceanography* (J. P. Riley and G. Skirrow, eds.), Vol. 2, Academic, New York, 1965, pp. 295–304.
38b. H. S. Kline, *Proc. Ind. Waste Conf., 5th, Purdue University, Lafayette, Ind., 1950*, p. 191.
38c. H. D. Brailsford, *Water Sewage Works*, **115**, 408 (1968).
39. T. Gaarder and H. H. Gran, *Conseil Intern. Exploration Mer. Rappt. et Proc.- Verb.*, **42**, 3 (1927).
40. W. J. Oswald and C. G. Golueke, *J. Water Pollution Control Federation*, **38**, 964 (1966).
41. J. C. Peters, M. S. Thesis, Michigan State University, East Lansing, 1959.

42. A. R. Grezenda and M. L. Brehmer, *Limnol. Oceanog.*, **5**, 190 (1965).
43. N. R. Kevern and R. C. Ball, *Limnol. Oceanog.*, **10**, 74 (1965).
44. A. Sladeckova, *Botan. Rev.*, **28**, 287 (1962).
45. D. L. King and R. C. Ball, *Trans. Am. Microscop. Soc.*, **85**, 232 (1966).

Chapter **11** **Concentration and Separation Techniques**

Julian B. Andelman
GRADUATE SCHOOL OF
PUBLIC HEALTH
UNIVERSITY OF PITTSBURGH
PITTSBURGH, PENNSYLVANIA

S. Charles Caruso
MELLON INSTITUTE
CARNEGIE-MELLON UNIVERSITY
PITTSBURGH, PENNSYLVANIA

I. Introduction

In the analysis of natural and treated water the need frequently arises to concentrate the sample, so as to improve the sensitivity of the analytical method or to separate the constituent of interest from species that interfere with its analysis. Although there are certainly some constituents and methods that do not require concentration or separation prior to analysis, many do, particularly those involving trace concentrations of both organic and inorganic species. To illustrate the need to concentrate, Table 1 compares the concentrations of several trace metals in seawater and fresh water to detection limits of two widely used methods of analysis. Although the useful range of concentration of an analytical technique will vary significantly with the instrument, method, and analyst, so that the detection limits noted in Table 1 are somewhat variable, nevertheless they indicate that in most instances there is a need to concentrate prior to analysis, particularly if any reasonable degree of precision and accuracy is to be obtained. Indeed, several of the colorimetric detection limits noted in Table 1 apply to methods which involve preconcentration, such as by solvent extraction.

Other methods of analysis are also likely to require preconcentration. Thus, conventional dc and square wave polarography have detection limits in the vicinity of 100 and 1 μg/liter, respectively(4), and emission spectroscopy is generally sufficiently insensitive for trace elements so as to require preconcentration(2). Inverse polarography (anodic stripping voltammetry) has considerably lower detection limits, of the order of $10^{-10} M$(4); however, it involves concentrating the sample by plating onto a microelectrode. Although this technique has been shown to be sensitive to less than 0.1 μg/liter of lead(II) in a natural fresh water(6),

TABLE 1

Typical Concentrations of Several Trace Metals in Fresh Water and Seawater Compared to Detection Limits of Atomic Absorption Spectrophotometry and Colorimetry

Element[a]	Typical concentration in seawater[b]	Some minimum concentrations in fresh water[c]	Atomic absorption detection limits[d]	Colorimetric detection limits[e]
Ba	30	2–20	50	> 100
Cr	0.05	1–10	5	5
Cu	3	1–2	5	20
Fe	10	2–10	5	20
Mn	2	3–9	2	5
Ni	2	1–10	5	4
Pb	0.03	3–10	30	10
Ag	0.1	0.2–1	5	2

[a] All concentrations in micrograms per liter.
[b] From Ref. 1.
[c] From Ref. 2.
[d] From Ref. 3.
[e] From Refs. 4 and 5.

even this highly sensitive technique would require preconcentration in order to measure lead in seawater. Neutron activation analysis is another highly sensitive technique which, however, requires equipment not available to many laboratories. Its sensitivity for copper, nickel, and barium (4) is generally sufficiently high to permit analysis of these metals at the levels indicated in Table 1 without preconcentration. Nevertheless, even using this technique, the need for separation often arises because of the formation of activation products that can interfere with the analysis of the element of interest.

The organic constituents of fresh water and seawater are sufficiently numerous and usually at low enough concentrations to require preconcentration and separation prior to analysis (7,8). In a tabulation of methods for the determination of a variety of organics in seawater, only carbohydrates and amino acids were listed as being capable of direct analysis; all other methods involved concentration and/or separation techniques (9).

Although there are many inorganic species in fresh water and seawater whose concentrations are such that they are above the sensitivity limits of currently available analytical methods, many interferences can arise from other substances which should be removed prior to analysis. Indeed the great majority of the currently used methods of analysis are subject to numerous well-known interferences which are noted in reviews and standardized procedures for the analysis of a variety of waters (5,9,10). The need to separate organic constituents prior to analysis is frequently even more critical than for inorganic species because of the relative lack of specificity of the analytical techniques used.

In addition to the need for separating soluble species that may interfere with an analysis, it is frequently desirable to distinguish between soluble, insoluble, and colloidal species. For this purpose such techniques as filtration or dialysis are useful.

There are many techniques available for concentrating and separating species of interest in water. It is the purpose of this chapter to consider the major techniques that are used. Frequently more than one procedure is required for a particular analysis. A thorough knowledge of the scope and limitations inherent in each is necessary to allow the judicious selection of the most appropriate method. Where it is useful, the principles of each method are considered, followed by examples to illustrate typical applications. This chapter is not designed to provide any new insights to the practitioner already involved in using concentration and separation methods. Rather, it is meant to orient readers with relatively little direct experience with these methods, to their utility and range of application. To assist in that respect, a general bibliography appears at the end of the chapter, with subdivisions for the various concentration and separation methods that are discussed. In the order in which they appear the methods are: precipitation techniques, liquid–liquid extraction, freeze concentration, adsorptive bubble separations, chromatography, ion exchange, membrane techniques, carbon adsorption, and distillation, evaporation, and sublimation.

II. Precipitation Techniques

A. Introduction

Precipitation has been used for many years as a separation technique in analyzing complex mixtures, and many gravimetric analyses have been developed. This discussion, however, focuses primarily on coprecipitation and related techniques, mostly for concentrating but to some extent for separating trace inorganics in water prior to their analysis by other methods. Direct precipitation, which depends upon the solubility product being exceeded and which, therefore, is generally usable only for macroscopic concentrations of elements, is not discussed here.

The applications of these coprecipitation and similar techniques for concentrating trace inorganics in seawater have been reviewed(9,11), as have the principles of coprecipitation(12), the latter discussion primarily focusing on the contamination process in direct precipitation, rather than on the utilization of coprecipitation as a concentration technique.

B. Principles

The principles of precipitation developed by Kolthoff and others are discussed in great detail by Laitinen(12). In coprecipitation an ion is removed from the solution phase with a precipitate (carrier), even though its solubility is not exceeded. The two principal mechanisms for this process are *adsorption*, in which the ion coprecipitating is adsorbed onto the surface of the primary precipitate; and *occlusion*, in which the ion is found in the interior of the primary precipitate, this category including both solid solution formation and ion entrapment.

1. ADSORPTION MECHANISM

There are different types of adsorption that can occur in coprecipitation. A potential-determining ion, for example, hydroxide, can adsorb onto the surface of a precipitate. In this process the amount adsorbed is related to the solution concentration, and the ion is called potential-determining because the electrical double-layer potential associated with the solid-solution interface is determined by the solution activity of that ion.

Another important adsorption process is ion exchange. There can be exchange of lattice ions with the coprecipitated ion; e.g., lead can exchange at the surface with barium in a primary precipitate of barium sulfate. There can also be counter-ion exchange. An example of this process is a silver iodide precipitate having an excess of iodide ions adsorbed on the precipitate surface. These adsorbed iodide ions must be balanced in charge by nearby positively charged counter-ions. Thus, a counter-ion, sodium, may be exchanged with ammonium in solution and these latter ions are considered as coprecipitated when they then act as counter-ions for the excess iodide in the silver iodide.

In the case of the lead adsorbed on barium sulfate, the exchange equilibrium can be written

$$X = K(Pb^{2+})/(Ba^{2+}) \tag{1}$$

where X is the amount of adsorbed lead per unit weight of precipitate. The (species) refer to concentrations in solution at equilibrium, and K is an equilibrium constant for the adsorption process.

In ion exchange adsorption at the surface of precipitates, the greater the concentration or charge of an ion, the more is adsorbed. Also, for two ions of equal charge and concentrations, the ion most strongly attracted by the lattice ion is preferentially adsorbed (Paneth-Fajans-Hahn rule). Thus, for example, acetate adsorbs more strongly than nitrate on silver iodide precipitates, because the silver acetate is less soluble and more covalent than silver nitrate. Other types of adsorption occurring in coprecipitation are molecular or ion pair adsorption, in which the process may follow a Freundlich adsorption isotherm, and monolayer adsorption, following a Langmuir adsorption isotherm.

Adsorption-type coprecipitation is prevalent for primary precipitates with large surface areas, such as colloidal hydrous oxides of aluminum and iron. Such precipitates have a great tendency to adsorb hydroxide ions as potential-determining ions and heavy metals as ion exchange counter-ions. They have been widely used to coprecipitate trace metals from seawater.

2. OCCLUSION MECHANISM

Solid solution formation is an important mechanism in the occlusion type of coprecipitation. It has been noted that this is likely to occur if the foreign ion does not differ greatly in size from a major ion in a precipitate that it is replacing, providing the two salts crystallize in the same habit. An example is the isomorphous replacement of bromide by chloride in silver bromide. If such a crystalline precipitate forms slowly or diffusion within it is rapid, the solid solution crystal is homogeneous in composition throughout. However, there may be a continuous gradation in composition of solution as it forms. In such a case the solid solution is said to be heterogeneous. The distortion between the isomorphous ions in the solid and solution phases is different in homogeneous and heterogeneous solid solution formation, and, hence, so is the quantity of material coprecipitated. A colloidal precipitate may form a homogeneous solid solution, while a coagulated colloid is likely to form a heterogeneous one. Aging generally helps a crystal to reach a homogeneous solid solution equilibrium.

Another kind of solid solution formation occurs when two ions of a pair replace two other ions in a crystal lattice. An example of this is barium sulfate, which can form a solid solution with potassium permanganate.

Another occlusion type of coprecipitation is ion entrapment. In this case a precipitate can grow around an adsorbed ion and the foreign ion may represent a lattice imperfection. In general, this type of occlusion increases with speed of formation of a precipitate and is reduced with high temperature aging of the precipitate.

A technique called "cocrystallization" has been developed by Weiss and Lai (13) in which an organic reagent is added to water and precipitated, incorporating a metal ion into it, probably by "anomalous mixed crystal formation". The organic reagent is chosen so as to have limited solubility when associated with the metal which is "cocrystallized" with the precipitated organic reagent. The precipitate is collected and treated in a variety of ways for subsequent analysis. Many metals can be cocrystallized simultaneously, although generally an organic reagent can be selected which is specific for one, two, or a group of elements.

Several techniques have been developed whereby metal ions are complexed with organic reagents and the complex is precipitated, thereby concentrating the metal (9). The advantage of these techniques, as with cocrystallization, is that a large quantity of an inorganic carrier is not associated with the concentrated metal.

C. Applications

The adsorption type of coprecipitation is widely used for concentrating trace metals, particularly in seawater. In one technique it is not necessary to add a carrier, such as iron(III); instead, the seawater is made alkaline, precipitating out such naturally occurring carriers as magnesium hydroxide and simultaneously coprecipitating several elements (11). Subsequent extraction of the redissolved precipitate and analysis by atomic absorption spectrophotometry indicated that the recovery for manganese, iron, nickel, cobalt, copper, and zinc is 98–100%.

Coprecipitation with ferric hydroxide as the carrier is a commonly used technique. It is relatively unspecific, adsorbing, for example, beryllium, aluminum, uranium, many transition metals, and the lanthanides (9). In such a method ferric chloride may be added to seawater, for example, 5 mg of iron/liter, precipitating out colloidal ferric hydroxide, which coagulates naturally. After a second dose, followed by centrifugation, the total precipitate is then frequently further treated by other separation methods prior to analysis. This technique can recover trace elements in concentrations as low as 0.02 μg/liter with 98–99% efficiency (9). In many analyses iron may interfere and it is necessary to remove it. For example, one recent technique for the analysis of vanadium in seawater and other natural waters involved coprecipitation with iron(III) hydroxide, re-solution of the precipitate, and separation of the iron from the vanadium by ion exchange prior to analysis of the vanadium (14).

A variation on the adsorption type of coprecipitation involves adsorption of iron or manganese onto an ion exchange column and precipitating them within the column by passing through a basic solution. Seawater is then passed through the column and the trace metals are adsorbed onto the hydroxide precipitate(9). The advantage of this technique is that large volumes of seawater can be passed through the column to improve sensitivity; a disadvantage is that the column may be contaminated with high concentrations of those trace elements being concentrated.

Other primary precipitates used in adsorption-type coprecipitation of seawater include the hydrated oxides of aluminum and manganese, the sulfides of copper, lead, and iron, and the mixed carbonates of calcium and manganese(9). Coprecipitation has also been widely used for concentrating radioactive trace elements in environmental samples. In one such method for the analysis of radium, the sample is made basic and lead and barium carriers are added, followed by sulfuric acid to precipitate out barium and lead sulfates, causing the radium to be coprecipitated(15).

A recent application of cocrystallization with an organic reagent used 5,7-dibromo-8-hydroxyquinoline as the primary precipitate to cocrystallize several trace metals from pure water and seawater(16). This reagent was chosen because of its low solubility in water and its ability to complex the metals of interest, which in previous cocrystallization techniques were not efficiently recovered. The reagent was added to the test water sample as a saturated solution in acetone, the latter being boiled from the solution, precipitating out the crystals. After standing overnight, the solution was filtered and the metal analyses were performed after redissolving the precipitate and separating the metal species by ion exchange. For precipitation from seawater at a pH of 8, recovery for copper, zinc, iron, cobalt, and chromium was 98–100%; for manganese(II), 85%; for lead(II), 42%; for silver, 60%; and for cerium(III), 7%(16).

Concentration by precipitation of organic complexes was used for the analysis of 17 trace elements in natural waters(17). Since the final analysis was performed by dc arc emission spectroscopy, a known amount of indium was added as an internal standard prior to precipitation, which followed after mixing the sample with 8-quinolinol, tannic acid, and thionalide. After standing overnight, the precipitate was filtered with ashless paper and ashed at 450°C prior to analysis. The results indicated an average analysis error of $\pm 15\%$ and a standard deviation of $\pm 3.3\%$ for metals when a range of 0.0025–0.25 mg was present in the electrode. It was noted that this method is suitable for waters with small or large quantities of total dissolved solids (up to 100,000 mg/liter). A disadvantage is the relatively long time required for the precipitation.

The various types of coprecipitation techniques for concentrating trace metals have great utility and have seen particularly wide use in the analysis of seawater. With the growing interest in the incidence, geochemistry, and epidemiological aspects of trace elements and chronic disease, it is expected that these techniques will gain use in the analysis of fresh and drinking water as well.

III. Liquid-Liquid Extraction

A. Basic Concepts

Solvent extraction is a physical separation process based on the selective distribution of a substance or substances in two immiscible solvents. Under ideal conditions, the partitioning of a solute between the two liquids occurs in accordance with the distribution law when the system is at equilibrium. Temperature, pressure, and composition must be specified to describe the equilibrium system. At constant temperature and pressure, only the composition is necessary to describe the system completely.

Nernst(18) was the first to state the distribution law quantitatively. This law requires that the concentration of a solute in one solvent has a direct relationship to its concentration in the other solvent with which it is in contact. A derivation is beyond the scope of this brief section on liquid–liquid extraction. The interested reader is referred to one of the general references listed at the end of the chapter. The modified Nernst "partition isotherm" is given mathematically by the expression

$$P = \frac{a_1}{a_2} \tag{2}$$

where P is the partition coefficient and a_1 and a_2 are the activities of the solute in the respective liquid phases, 1 and 2. This ratio, P, is precisely defined thermodynamically. However, for practical application the approximate form suggested by Nernst,

$$K = \frac{C_1}{C_2} \tag{3}$$

is used, where K is the distribution constant and C is the concentration in each solvent. This relationship holds true for dilute solutions and ideal behavior, or where the activity of the solute is the same in each solvent. However, this expression has been found to be adequate for many practical applications. The distribution coefficients are sometimes observed to vary due to the formation of different molecular species in either phase.

Some solutes are subject to a change in molecular form due to chemical reaction, association, or dissociation. Where a number of solutes are present, interactions may also cause results which deviate from the predictions obtained from distribution coefficients. Such systems require a more complicated expression of the distribution law.

B. Solvent Selection

The main consideration involved in the choice of a solvent for extraction is its selectivity; that is, the solvent's capability to extract one component of a solution in preference to another. The selectivity of a solvent for a given molecule can be determined by use of phase diagrams. However, this approach is seldom taken in practice because only a small number of phase diagrams are available in the literature and it would require an extensive study to produce phase diagrams for the possible combinations of solutes in two-phase liquid systems. Similarly, only a relatively small number of distribution coefficients can be found in the literature. Thus, the choice of a solvent for a given extraction procedure is usually based on experience or semiempirical considerations.

Knowledge concerning the polarity of the solute to be extracted can prove useful in the choice of an appropriate solvent. The concept that "like dissolves like" has been found by experience to be helpful. Thus, polar solvents are used for the extraction of polar solutes from nonpolar liquids and vice versa.

Consideration of the interaction of solute and solvent will influence the choice of a solvent. For example, a solute that is readily solvated by a solvent will be soluble in that solvent. Similarly, hydrogen bond formation between solute and solvent will affect solubility and specificity.

If the solute system to be extracted consists of known materials, the measurement of the distribution coefficients of potential extraction solvents should be carried out. A solute requires a high coefficient for it to be easily removed from solution. Also, the coefficients of other components in solution must be distinctly different to allow separation of a specific solute from all others present.

The recoverability of the solute from the solvent is another important consideration. This is generally accomplished by distillation or stripping, i.e., extraction of the solute from the solvent using a second solvent. If the solute is nonvolatile and thermally stable, then distillation is feasible. Stripping is practical when the solute or a more convenient form (salt of an acid or base, a chelate, etc.) can be readily recovered by distribution between the extractant phase and the stripping solvent.

The density differential of the two phases should also be considered in selection of a solvent. If the densities of the two phases are similar, troublesome emulsions may result. Often such emulsions can be prevented or destroyed by the addition of a strong electrolyte to the aqueous phase.

The most important solvent characteristics are that it dissolve the solute to be extracted and that it be completely immiscible with the aqueous phase. Although complete immiscibility is rarely obtained, solvent extraction is predictable in practice by premeasurement of the distribution coefficient in the mutually saturated phases.

It is extremely important that the solvent be of high purity when isolating trace organic constituents from samples. Reagent grade liquids contain many impurities in sufficient concentration to complicate the analysis of the isolated organic mixtures. Thus, solvents should be purified before use, or a high purity solvent should be obtained from a commercial source. These solvents should always be tested for purity before use as an extractant by evaporating a volume of solvent equivalent to that used in the procedure and examining the concentrate or residue. This will eliminate the embarrassment of identifying solvent impurities as sample components.

C. *Extraction Techniques*

The relationship between extraction efficiency and the distribution coefficient is easily established to be

$$\text{per cent extracted} = \frac{100 K V_s}{V_a + K V_s} \tag{4}$$

where $K = C_s/C_a$, V and C are the volumes and concentrations, respectively, in the solvent (s) and aqueous (a) phases. This relationship is very useful in determining the number of extractions required to quantitatively remove a specific solute. It also can be used to demonstrate that one extraction with a given volume of solvent is less efficient than two extractions using half of the solvent each time. For example, if one assumes that w grams of solute are to be recovered from V_a milliliters of aqueous phase by extraction with V_s milliliters of extractant, and w_2 is the weight of solute remaining in the raffinate after the second extraction, then, by the appropriate substitution in Eq. (4), and solving for w_2, the result is

$$w_2 = w \left(\frac{V_a}{K V_s + V_a} \right)^2 \tag{5}$$

On the other hand, when one extraction with $2V_s$ milliliters of solvent is carried out, an amount of solute, w_x, remains in the raffinate:

$$w_x = \frac{wV_a}{2KV_s + V_a} \tag{6}$$

A comparison of the values of w_x and w_2, when V_a and V_s are equal, clearly shows that $w_x(=w/2K+1)$ is greater than $w_2[=w(1/K+1)^2]$ since

$$\frac{1}{2K+1} > \frac{1}{K^2+2K+1} \tag{7}$$

If the distribution coefficient of a solute is large, multiple extractions are usually not required. The above relationship shows that for distribution ratios of 100 and equal volumes of raffinate (phase remaining after extraction) and extractant, the extraction is quantitative.

The effectiveness of an extraction technique for resolving mixtures containing two solutes can be determined by the calculation of the separation factor for the system. The separation factor β can be defined as

$$\beta = \frac{K_1}{K_2} \tag{8}$$

where K_1 and K_2 are the distribution coefficients of the solutes. The separation factor is a measure of the degree of separation of two substances in solution. If $K_1 \neq K_2$, separation is possible and the greater the difference between K_1 and K_2 the easier that resolution of the two components can be accomplished. Since K is determined by the solubility of the solute in each of two phases, altering the solubility characteristics will change the value of the ratio (K_1/K_2) and can produce more favorable extraction conditions. For example, for some systems K can be influenced by pH, complexing agents, or salting-out agents. Thus, the utility of liquid-liquid extraction can be enhanced by a knowledge of the condition which can alter the distribution constants to make extraction of one component more effective in an analytical procedure.

Extractions can be carried out by using batch or continuous techniques. Batch extraction is simplest and is conveniently carried out in a separatory funnel. The extracting solvent is added to the aqueous solution in the funnel and the phases are thoroughly mixed by shaking. After the solutions have separated, the denser phase is removed through the stopcock. The process is repeated by addition of fresh solvent until the desired degree of separation is realized. The distribution coefficient of a solute will have to be large to effect quantitative removal in one or two extraction steps. By judicious selection of solvents, many organic compounds can be extracted from aqueous solutions in one or two equilibrations. Also, many metal chelates have been separated from solution by one extraction.

A continuous extraction technique is useful for the efficient extraction of solutes which have an unfavorable distribution coefficient. Many such devices have been developed. The apparatus of Kutscher and Stendel (19) is useful for solvents lighter than water, and Wehrli(20) modified this apparatus for use with solvents heavier than water.

The countercurrent extraction technique has been successful in resolving solutes whose separation factors are quite close to unity. In this method the immiscible phases come into contact with each other as they flow in opposing directions. Craig and Craig(21) have developed the theory and technique of the intermittent countercurrent procedure. In this process, contact of the raffinate and extractant occurs in a series of tubes containing equal volumes of the two phases. The tubes are shaken gently to bring the solutes to equilibrium in both phases. Equilibration is repeated by successive transfers of each phase with fresh solvent. Craig and Post(22) designed a multiple-stage apparatus for making a large number of equilibrations. Multiple extractions are achieved rapidly with this equipment. Separations of complex mixtures of natural products have been realized with this technique. For example, amino acids, peptides, aromatic bases, alkaloids, lipids, steroids, vitamins, hormones, porphyrins, phenols, flavins, and many other classes of compounds have been separated by this procedure(21).

Kolfenbach et al.(23) developed a countercurrent extractor of the continuous type. This type of extractor is very efficient since fresh solvent is continuously brought into contact with solute-depleted aqueous phase followed by the extraction of fresh aqueous phase by solute-containing solvent. Although an equilibrium state is approached by this procedure, it is difficult to predict the efficiency of resolution since the theory has not been adequately developed.

D. Applications to Environmental Analysis

Liquid–liquid extraction is very useful for the extraction of both organic and inorganic compounds. In the field of environmental analysis, it has been widely applied to concentrate, isolate, and separate organic compounds present in trace concentrations in aqueous systems. Its inherent simplicity and versatility recommend this process for many analytical purposes. Extraction steps are used to concentrate the substrate, to separate it from interferences, or to transfer it to a more suitable matrix. Examples of these can be found in the standard manuals(5, 10) for water analysis.

1. ORGANIC SOLUTES

Solvent extraction has been used extensively for the isolation and concentration of pesticides(24) from environmental sources prior to analysis. Lamar et al.(25) have described an extraction procedure with hexane for the analysis of chlorinated pesticides in water by electron-capture gas chromatography. Kawahara and associates(26) developed a method for parathion and methyl parathion in the presence of chlorinated hydrocarbons using a mixture of solvents for extraction of river water. Holden and Marsden(27) reported a scheme for the examination of surface waters and sewage effluents for chlorinated pesticides which utilizes a solvent extraction step. Organophosphorous pesticides(28) in water have also been analyzed after separation with diethyl ether. The literature contains many other references along these lines; these were selected to serve as typical examples.

Solvent extraction has proved to be useful for the extraction of many types of organic compounds from surface water for subsequent analysis. Hoak(29) has used a Scheibel(30) 18-stage countercurrent extraction column to remove and concentrate the taste- and odor-producing compounds from large volumes of river water. This column consists of a central rotating shaft with agitators spaced at intervals and stationary wire mesh packing between the agitators to effect the phase separation.

Bunch and Ettinger(31) developed a field countercurrent extractor for water contaminants. This apparatus incorporates the Podbielniak model 6000 SP centrifugal contactor as the heart of the unit. The authors suggest that this extractor should prove useful for concentrating carcinogenic polynuclear hydrocarbons and pesticides, and in isolating "slug" doses of organic pollutants from river water.

More recently, Caruso et al. (32) have demonstrated the use of solvent extraction of small volumes of surface water to concentrate the trace organics present for gas chromatographic separation and spectrometric identification. This technique has proved useful for river and lake surveys, to assess the pollution load present in a water system, to trace sources of the contaminants present, and to evaluate the efficiency of waste treatment processes.

Several investigators have used solvent extraction in oceanographic studies. Slowey et al.(33) isolated carboxylic acids and hydrocarbons from the Gulf of Mexico by extraction with ethyl acetate and chloroform. Williams (34) concentrated fatty acids of chains lengths varying from 10 to

22 carbons from Pacific Ocean samples. Cronin (35) used petroleum ether and methyl isobutyl ketone to recover organic substances from samples taken off the Oregon coast. He found that a small pulse extraction column (36) was efficient and practical for isolating organics from seawater.

2. INORGANIC SOLUTES

Liquid-liquid extraction techniques are also used prior to analysis for the separation of inorganic substances dissolved in water. Metals must be present in the form of a neutral or molecular species to be extracted by nonpolar liquids. The metal ions in solution are often converted to metal chelates or ion association configurations before isolation. The β-diketones, 8-hydroxyquinoline, and α-dioximes form chelates with many metals. These complexes are readily formed and are usually insoluble in water but dissolve in many organic solvents. They are generally pH dependent and by the selective control of pH can be used to obtain specific metal separation. Recently, Kopp et al. (37) reported a method for the quantitative determination of microgram amounts of 15 minor elements in natural water. The chelating reagent, ammonium pyrollidine dithiocarbamate, is used to form complexes with traces of zinc, cadmium, arsenic, iron, molybdenum, manganese, aluminum, beryllium, copper, silver, nickel, cobalt, lead, chromium, and vanadium. These complexes are extracted with chloroform, concentrated by solvent evaporation, and subsequently subjected to spectrographic analysis. Iron in seawater has been isolated with 1,10-phenanthroline, 4,7-diphenyl-1,10-phenanthroline, and 2,4,6-tripyridyl-sym-triazine complexes by Stephans and Suddeth(38). A Japanese study(39) utilizes a dithizone-chloroform extraction to separate zinc-65 from contaminated water prior to analysis.

Many metals form extractable ion association species or complex moieties with halogens, nitrates, and thiocyanate ions. An example is the removal of iron from hydrochloric acid solution by diethyl ether in the form of $FeCl_3$ or $HFeCl_4$(40). In this system the distribution ratio depends on the partition coefficient and the quantity of the partitionable species present. At low acidities the degree of formation of $FeCl_3$ and $HFeCl_4$ is very low, resulting in a small distribution. ratio. In 4–6 M hydrochloric acid, the degree of formation of the complex species increases considerably, and extraction approaches 100% at 6 M. However, at acidities of 7 M and higher the miscibility of the phases increases, producing a concomitant decrease in extraction efficiency. Iron has been removed as the chlorocomplex to reduce its concentration in steel samples prior to the determination of the nonferrous metals present(*41*). Arsenic, antimony, gallium, germanium, platinum, palladium, rhodium, gold, mercury, and thallium are also known to form extractable species with the chloride ion(*40*). In general, this process is not as selective as the extraction of chelates.

Another extraction technique involves the reaction of the anionic complexes of metals to form salts with the triphenylmethyl-arsonium cation. Iron, antimony, cobalt, copper, and manganese form salts which are soluble in organic solvents. This procedure has been utilized to extract permanganate ion(*42*) at the end point of permanganate titrations involving other colored substances.

Long-chain tertiary amines have been used for the isolation of sulfate and chloride from aqueous solutions(*43*). For example, the quantitative determination of straight-chain and branched-chain alkylbenzene sulfonates (*44*) in detergents and waste waters can be carried out by conversion to the heptylammonium salt and selective extraction from solution with chloroform prior to infrared analysis. Amines have also been used to isolate anionic complexes of many metals(*45*). These amine salts are soluble in chloroform.

IV. Freeze Concentration

A. *Introduction*

Freezing as a technique for concentrating solutes in water to facilitate subsequent analysis has not been widely used. Nevertheless, in recent years it has been studied in the laboratory by several investigators and some of its limitations and efficiencies for various solutes have been examined. It has been shown to be applicable to inorganic and organic solutes, as well as microorganisms. In addition to its use as a concentration technique, freezing may also be used to obtain water relatively free from trace organic and inorganic impurities.

There are two broad types of freeze concentration: zone melting and normal freezing, both of which have been utilized for concentrating materials in water. Zone melting involves slowly heating and melting a narrow zone in a previously frozen sample and gradually moving the zone along the length of the solid, the melted zone carying any solutes or impurities with it and leaving behind a relatively pure frozen component, such as water. Normal freezing starts with a liquid sample which is slowly frozen either longitudinally or radially inward, the liquid region generally becoming more concentrated in solute as it reduces in volume. The zone melting process is more readily adaptable to a multistage procedure, but the equipment is generally more elaborate and costly than that used in normal freezing. When both techniques are used as a single-stage process, normal freezing can sometimes achieve as efficient a separation as zone melting, and in much shorter times(46). Most of the applications to water analysis have utilized the normal freezing technique, which is the focus of this discussion and which has been recently reviewed(46). However, occasional references to zone melting are made herein.

B. Principles

The basis of the freeze concentration technique is the phase equilibria between the liquid and solid phases. The discussion that follows is taken, the most part, from the review by Gouw(46). In order to examine this phenomenon, it is useful to consider a binary system, such as water containing a small amount of a solute. More complicated systems containing more than one solute may sometimes be considered and treated as "pseudo binary." Examples of two pertinent binary phase diagrams are shown in Fig. 1; both examples show only that portion of the diagram where the solute concentration is small. In these diagrams x refers to the mole fraction of a component.

Figure 1 (a) represents a system with eutectic formation. When the temperature of an aqueous solution at point A is lowered to point B, the

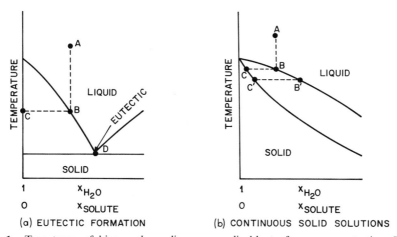

(a) EUTECTIC FORMATION (b) CONTINUOUS SOLID SOLUTIONS

Fig. 1. Two types of binary phase diagrams applicable to freeze concentration. The diagrams are given only in part. The symbols x_{H_2O}, x_{solute} refer to mole fractions of the indicated species, and A, B, B', C, C', and D refer to various phase compositions.

solid material formed is represented by point C, namely, pure water. As the temperature is further lowered, pure solid water continues to form, the liquid becomes enriched in solute, and the system moves along the composition-temperature curve from B to D, the eutectic point. At this point further solidification on removal of heat from the system results in solid formation (containing ice and solute) of unchanging composition, namely, that of D. For such a phase diagram, then, it is theoretically possible, providing that the initial solution composition is to the left of D, to freeze out pure water until the solution composition reaches D, thereby concentrating the solute in the process. Further solute concentration beyond that represented by D is not possible.

Figure 1 (b) represents a similar binary phase diagram in which water and the solute are mutually soluble in all proportions in the solid phase forming solid solutions in the region of the phase diagram shown. For a liquid solution represented by point A, as the temperature is lowered to point B, the composition of the solid freezing out is represented by point C. This solid is not pure water, unlike the previous case involving a eutectic. As the temperature is further lowered, the liquid phase becomes more concentrated in solute, reaching, for example, point B'. However, the freezing solid has a higher content of solute, represented by point C', than that initially formed at point C. For such a system it is not possible to freeze out pure water; some of the solute is also being frozen. However, even though recovery of solute is not complete, it does become concentrated in the liquid phase.

A similar analysis may be applied to ternary and more complex aqueous solutions. Thus, for example, with a ternary system containing two eutectic points, initially pure water may freeze out, then a eutectic solid containing water and one solute, and finally a eutectic solid containing water and the two solutes. With continuous solid solutions of water and two solutes, there may also be a continuous variation in the composition of the solid phase, with one solute being frozen out more readily than another. This analysis of the equilibria phenomena indicates that for complex solutions one can obtain different recoveries of the different solutes, complete for some and with various degrees of completion for others.

In practice these theoretically attainable separations are frequently not achieved because of phenomena occuring at the solid-liquid interface. As the solid freezes, the ejected solute is at a higher concentration in the liquid at the interface than in the bulk of the solution. If the solid front is "moving" at a faster rate than the ejected solute can diffuse across the unstirred liquid boundary layer, the solute concentration at the interface will remain higher than in the bulk solution. Thus, if continuous solid solutions are formed, as in Fig. 1(b), although the bulk liquid composition corresponds to point B, that at the solid-liquid interface may be represented by point B', so that the composition of the freezing solid is that of point C', rather than C, and the recovery and concentration processes are less than those theoretically attainable.

In addition, there may be dendritic growth of the solid phase and entrapment of solution in it. Thus, even when a eutectic diagram indicates that pure solid water should be crystallizing from solutions, experimentally solute may be incorporated in the solid phase. Entrapment may also occur due to supercooling, followed by very rapid crystallization in some regions. In general, the freeze concentration process can approach the equilibrium process when the growth of the solid phase is kept slow and the stirring near the solid-liquid interface is rapid. The latter reduces the thickness of the unstirred boundary layer, thereby facilitating the diffusion of the ejected solute back into the bulk solution.

The apparatus used in normal freeze concentration are of two basically different types. In "column crystallization" the liquid is placed in a vertical column which is slowly lowered into a freezing zone with continuous stirring in the liquid phase; an example of such an apparatus has been described by Mathews and Coggeshall(47). The other basic type, which will here be called "stationary normal freezing," involves inserting a cylindrical or spherical vessel into a cooling medium so that the ice forms initially at the walls of the container and grows inward. The cylindrical apparatus generally utilizes a propeller type of stirring (48); also, a description has been given for a spherical vessel rotated at a 45° angle in an ice bath, the rotation providing the necessary agitation of the solution(49).

C. Applications

Zone refining has been used to separate such impurities as thiophene, propionic acid, o-bromotoluene, and o-xylene from water(50). A similar technique has also been used for concentrating a wide variety of materials from aqueous solution, including ascorbic acid, quinone, aldehydes, bacteria, bacteriophage, and plankton(51).

Column crystallization has been utilized for concentrating solutes from water. In one example a 0.1% solution of $KMnO_4$ was concentrated to 2.2%, while in another experiment hydroquinone in water was separated from resorcinol and pyrogallol by a multistage process(52).

There have been several recent studies of stationary normal freezing for concentrating aqueous solutions. One of the early reports described a basic cylindrical type of apparatus, the technique being used on samples as large as 300 liters and as small as 100 ml; stirring was necessary, and in one case 16 liters of aqueous solution were reduced to 1 liter in about 50 hr(48). In a study of the chemical properties and structure of organic materials responsible for color in natural water, this cylindrical type of apparatus was used to concentrate such materials as fulvic acid, hymotomelanic acid, and humic acid, although recovery efficiencies were not stated(53).

The efficiency of recovery for aqueous solutions of sodium chloride and Rhodamine B was studied using the cylindrical arrangement(54). For initial chloride concentrations in the range of 2.6–11 mg/liter, with volume reductions, V_R, of up to 12, the recovery was essentially complete. However, with Rhodamine B initially at 10–55 μg/liter and V_R up to 10, recovery was typically 90%. It was noted and should be emphasized here that recoveries can vary for different solutes. Iodine has been recovered with approximately 90% efficiency for V_R of about 4; a distilled water solution containing acetone, isopropyl alcohol, and sodium chloride was concentrated to a V_R of 5 with 89, 90, and 100% recovery, respectively(55). It was suggested that this method was useful for preparing organic free water, and it was noted that Rhodamine B dye could be reduced in concentration in water by a factor of more than 20,000 using this technique.

A recent study using the cylindrical apparatus measured the recoveries of ^{14}C-labeled glycine, glucose, citric acid, and phenylalanine in distilled water and lake water and lindane in distilled water(56). In the distilled water experiments with the ^{14}C-labeled compounds, initial volumes ranging from 800 to 1300 ml were reduced by V_R factors of 3.3–6.3 in about 4 hr. These compounds were concentrated up to factors of 22 with recoveries in the range of 88–100%. Similar experiments with lindane and V_R of 5 resulted in similar recovery efficiencies. Using filtered lake water and ^{14}C-labeled compounds initially in the range of 0.12–0.15 mg/liter, recoveries were 91–100% for V_R up to 15.

A systematic series of studies of recovery of organics from aqueous solution using the rotating spherical vessel apparatus described previously has been presented(49, 57, 58). In the initial study(57) ternary mixtures of phenol, m-cresol, and 2,4-dichlorophenol in distilled water were concentrated by V_R of 57 in 24 min with recoveries of 63, 72, and 40%, respectively. However, it was also noted that for V_R up to 10, recovery was "quite efficient." For a similar mixture with added salts it was found that for V_R of 3.2, the recovery of organics ranged from 81 to 97%, while that of aluminum, calcium, sodium, and potassium ranged from 72 to 97%. It was concluded that the presence of salts can affect the recovery of organics due to "spontaneous ice crystallization."

The second study of the series concerned measurements of recoveries of phenol, o-,m-, and p-cresol, 2,3-dichlorophenol, acetophenone, and fatty acids from solutions with low concentrations of inorganics (49). In one case m-cresol recovery was essentially complete up to V_R of 5. With increasing V_R up to 50, recovery decreased (to about 60%), and varying the rate of rotation had no effect. For higher V_R, increasing the rate of rotation increased recovery. With mixtures of fatty acids, each with an initial concentration of 10 mg/liter, essentially complete recovery was obtained for V_R up to 20. It was noted in general that, when the residual liquid solution volume was reduced to 30 ml or less (initial volumes were usually 200 ml), recovery began to decrease. For the different solutes studied, recovery efficiencies generally did not vary.

The third study in the series investigated the possible effect of added inorganic salts and variation in pH on recovery of organics (58). For acetophenone initially at 0.09–0.9 mg/liter in water and with rotation rates of 80 rpm, recovery was essentially complete for V_R up to 5 and with NaCl initial concentration varying from 0 to 165 mg/liter. However, at higher values of V_R the recovery was reduced as the initial salt concentration was increased. In studying m-cresol in tap water it was found that recovery became incomplete at V_R greater than 3, compared to 5 in distilled water; increasing the rotation rate increased recovery, as did reducing the pH to 3, compared to 7 and 10. The addition of copper, calcium, magnesium, and iron had no effect on recovery. The possible reasons for the effect of added salt on efficiency of recovery of organics were considered.

Although freeze concentration has not been widely used to concentrate materials from water, the growing number of studies have indicated some of the ranges of applicability, and problems as well. The ability to avoid high temperatures and phase changes is one advantage of this technique. Also, the apparatus can be relatively simple and inexpensive. However, since complete recoveries are frequently not attained, for quantitative work it may be necessary to measure recovery efficiency in each case, or at least utilize an internal reference material of chemical structure similar to that of the compound being studied (57).

V. Adsorptive Bubble Separations

A. Introduction

Adsorptive bubble separation methods may be used for separating and concentrating such diverse materials in water as surfactants, other soluble molecules and organic and inorganic ions, colloids and other particles, and microorganisms, as well as removing them in waste treatment. These methods involve passing gas bubbles in a vertical column through a solution or suspension and collecting the concentrate either at the top or as an overflow, such as a surfactant adsorbed at the bubble-solution interface, or as a particle attached to the bubble. In foaming systems the foam may be collected and collapsed, or in non foaming systems the surface may be skimmed for collection, such as in flotation processes. For concentration or separation purposes these techniques may be used in a batch or continuous mode, as well as with several stages or in cascade.

The nonfoaming methods include (59) "bubble fractionation," in which the rising bubbles carry material to the surface where it may be collected by overflow, and "solvent sublation," where the material attached to the rising bubble is trapped in an immiscible solvent placed above the main liquid. Foam separations include "foam fractionation" and "froth flotation" (59). Foam fractionation may be used for concentrating both naturally surface-active solutes and soluble inorganic or organic ions or molecules associated with the surfactant (a collector), which tend to concentrate at the bubble-solution interface. Froth flotation involves trapping and concentrating a solid or particulate material in the foam, and includes such categories as "microflotation," the removal of microorganisms and colloids; "ion flotation" and "molecular flotation," the removal of nonsurface-active ions and molecules, respectively, which form an insoluble product with a surfactant collector; "precipitate flotation," the removal of a precipitate not formed by added surfactant collector; and "adsorbing colloid flotation," the removal of a solute adsorbed onto a colloid.

It has been pointed out (60, 61), however, that for inorganic colloids and microorganisms the distinction between foam fractionation, which is a partitioning process, and flotation may be blurred, and that it may be convenient to classify the foam separation processes broadly according to the gas flow rate, with subcategories for the initial state of subdivision of the material to be removed or concentrated. The high gas flow rate systems utilize tall columns with considerable foam and refluxing, while the low flow rate units provide for foam collapse in the cell and subsequent removal, e.g., by skimming, of the insoluble layer at the surface (60).

B. Adsorption Theory

The removal of soluble materials from the bulk solution by adsorptive bubble techniques depends essentially on their ability to concentrate at the gas-solution interface. Both naturally surface-active materials and those which may be rendered so by associating with surface-active compounds, such as a metal ion forming a complex with a surfactant, will concentrate at this interface. For a simple binary system of a surface-active solute in water, this behavior may be described(62) by the Gibbs isotherm

$$\Gamma = -\,(1/RT)\,(d\gamma/d\ln a) \tag{9}$$

Where R, is the gas constant, T is the absolute temperature, γ is the surface tension in dynes per centimeter, and a is the bulk activity of the solute. Γ, the surface excess in moles of solute per square centimeter, may be considered as referring to that outermost portion of the surface containing a monolayer of the solute. For a solution sufficiently dilute so that the solute behaves ideally, the activity, a, may be replaced by C, the solute concentration in moles per cubic centimeter. Furthermore, if the solute is an electrolyte, Eq. (9) must be further modified, such that for a dilute uni-univalent electrolyte a factor of one-half must be added and Eq. (9) becomes

$$\Gamma = -\,(1/2RT)\,(d\gamma/d\ln C) \tag{10}$$

However, it has been noted(62) that, for some measurements with ionic surfactants, Eq. (10) without the factor 2 applies, and that other isotherms, such as that of Langmuir, may describe this behavior.

For very dilute solution, $d\gamma/dc$ is frequently constant, so that Eq. (10) can be simplified to give

$$\Gamma = KC \tag{11}$$

with K as the adsorption equilibrium constant expressed in centimeters. However, as the bulk surfactant concentration is increased so as to reach the critical micelle concentration (cmc), the surface adsorption levels off; with addition of surfactant at this point the surface tension undergoes very little change and Γ remains essentially constant(62). Thus, as the bulk surfactant concentration increases above that of the linear region described by Eq. (11), the value of the adsorption constant K decreases and the adsorptive bubble technique becomes less effective as a concentration process.

C. Foam Fractionation

In using an adsorptive bubble technique, such as foam fractionation, for concentrating a solute, one is interested primarily in the enrichment ratio, E, which is defined as

$$E = C_D/C_F \tag{12}$$

with C_D as the solute concentration in the collapsed foam product, and C_F, the solute concentration in the feed (sample). This enrichment factor may be related to the adsorption equilibrium constant in, for example, a simple mode batch foam fractionation operated with recycle, as shown schematically in Fig. 2(a). Although this system does not achieve high enrichments, it may serve to measure Γ_W, the steady-state surface excess concentration in the liquid pool, and illustrates the essential features of foam fractionation (63, 64). After the solution containing the surfactant is placed in the cell region labeled "liquid pool," the gas is bubbled through the pool, generating a foam, which overflows into the foam breaker. The foam is collapsed by a mechanical stirring mechanism or other techniques. In this simple mode the collapsed foam is returned to the liquid pool, and the cell is operated until the steady state is achieved. For such a system it may be shown (63) by material balance that

$$\Gamma_W/C_W = (C_D/C_W - 1)(Qd/6G) \tag{13}$$

where the subscript W refers to the liquid pool, Q is the overflow rate of the collapsed foam in cubic centimeters per minute, d is the diameter of the average spherical bubble, and G is the volumetric gas flow rate. Thus, by measuring C_D and C_W in the steady state and knowing Q, d, and G, one can measure Γ_W. This has been done, for example, with the surfactant monobutyl diphenyl sodium monosulfonate in distilled water (64). In the steady state, Γ_W is 2.6×10^{-10} moles/cm^2, corresponding to a bulk liquid concentration of about 10^{-3} M, which was above the cmc region. This system may also be used to indicate the effects of Q, d, and G on the enrichment ratio by deriving a new expression. This is done by substituting Eqs. (11) and (12) into Eq. (13) and using C_W in place of C_F (since there is no continuous feed) to obtain the equation

$$E = 1 + (6G/Qd)K \tag{14}$$

Thus, it is seen from Eq. (14) (applicable in the region of constant K, i.e., low concentration of surfactant) that decreasing the bubble size, d, and foam flow rate, Q, will increase E, as will increased gas flow, G. It has been indicated that, for the purpose of measuring Γ by this technique, a high gas rate is useful in that it reduces internal reflux and foam residence time in the column, both of which may lead to erroneous values of Γ (62).

A more practicable mode of operation utilizes a continuously fed foam fractionation enriching column with reflux, as shown schematically in Fig. 2(b). In this apparatus, as some of the collapsed foam is refluxed through the rising foam, the interstitial liquid of the latter is enriched by countercurrent contact with collapsed foam. It may be shown (63), for a theoretically infinitely tall column and from material balance considera-

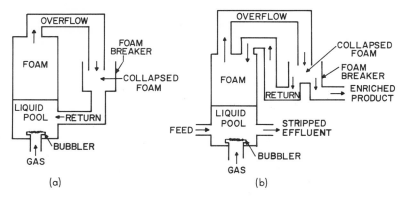

Fig. 2. Two modes of foam fractionation. (a) Simple mode batch separator with recycle, and (b) continuous enriching column with reflux.

tions, that

$$E = 1 + K_F G/d(6.59 - 0.59/(R_r + 1))(1/D - 1/F) \qquad (15)$$

where D and F are the volumetric flow rates of the collapsed, enriched foam product and the feed, respectively, and R_r is the reflux ratio. In this case, as an approximation, it is assumed that the pool concentration is the same as that of the feed, so that for a given K_F, as with the simple mode batch technique, increasing the gas flow rate and decreasing the bubble diameter will increase the enrichment ratio, as will increasing the reflux ratio. The enrichment ratio may also be increased by taking smaller fractions of the input flow as enriched product (reducing D compared to F). In practice, a column several feet long is sufficient to meet the requirement of an infinitely high column for the above treatment, provided that the reflux ratio is not too high(64).

Concentration and separation of a variety of solutes have been studied using foam fractionation. This technique has been applied to phenol using a simple mode batch separator without recycle or reflux(65). Since phenol is only weakly surface active, the collector, a quaternary ammonium cationic surfactant at concentrations ranging from 50 to 600 mg/liter, was added to the solution to form a surface-active moiety with the phenol, and the fractionation was performed over a pH range of approximately 6–13; the effects of added chloride and sulfate were also evaluated. In this batch process the fraction recovered, F_r, is

$$F_r = C_D V_D / C_F V_F \qquad (16)$$

where V_D and V_F are the liquid volumes of the collapsed foam and liquid feed, respectively. At a pH of 12.9, F_r values of 0.99 were attained for feed concentrations of phenol ranging from 11 to 672 mg/liter, provided that sufficient surfactant was added. Generally, the greater the phenol feed concentration, the more surfactant is required. F_r attained a maximum at pH 11.6. Since increasing the pH results in the formation of the phenolate ion, it was expected that the higher pH would result in better recovery, which depends on the interaction of phenolate with the positive surfactant ion. The addition of chloride and sulfate reduced the fraction recovered. In one set of experiments 17 mg/liter of chloride reduced it by about 50%, and 14 mg/liter of sulfate by about 75%. From the point of view of using foam fractionation as a concentration technique to facilitate analysis, the enrichment ratio, E, is of equal importance. For aqueous solutions without excessive quantities of interfering anions and with feed concentrations of phenol of 25 mg/liter at a pH of 11–12, E values from 6 to 14 were obtained.

A similar simple mode batch foam fractionation apparatus was used to concentrate 1-naphthylamine using an anionic surfactant, sodium lauryl sulfate, and reflux times up to 3 hr(66). This amine is a potential carcinogen for man and has been found in a Japanese river polluted by dye wastes(67). With initial concentrations of 1-naphthylamine of 10^{-4} M, a pH of 2, and $2 \times 10^{-3} M$ added surfactant, recoveries of essentially 100% were obtained, provided the reflux time was 1 hr or more, with enrichment ratios of about 100(66). The authors noted that this initial concentration of $10^{-4} M$ 1-naphthylamine was by no means a lower limit, since foam fractionation frequently becomes more efficient with reduced feed concentrations. Subsequently, using the same technique, these authors concentrated methyl orange and obtained 98% recovery for $C_F = 5 \times 10^{-7} M$ and only 81% for $C_F = 1 \times 10^{-5} M$. The foam fractionations were carried out at pH 10 and reflux times of 90 min, using a cationic surfactant(68). They obtained enrichment ratios as high as 210.

An example of the concentration of an anionic surfactant, monobutyl diphenyl sodium monosulfonate, by batch foam fractionation has been described with reflux ratios ranging from zero to infinity(64). With initial surfactant concentrations ranging from $5 \times 10^{-4} M$ to $3 \times 10^{-3} M$, enrichment ratios as high as 10 were obtained and they generally increased with reflux ratio. Another study compared the effects of surfactant feed concentration, nature of surfactant, and the effects of air and feed rate on removal in continuous foam separation. This process was primarily designed for stripping the surfactant so as to reduce its concentration in the effluent(69). The reduction in surfactant concentration in the stripped effluent, compared to that in the feed, ranged from 14 to 67%. Increasing the gas flow rate generally increased the removal in the treated effluent, and there was no pronounced effect of surfactant feed concentration.

Similarly, at comparable feed concentrations of about $10^{-3} M$, alkyl benzene sulfonate and two cationic surfactants showed comparable removals of 20–30% in their effluents.

D. Ion and Precipitate Flotation

Several concentration and separation methods using ion and precipitate flotation, with and without foaming, have been described and are of interest in water analysis. The ion flotation technique involves introducing a surfactant, the collector, at concentrations below the cmc, into a solution containing oppositely charged ions, the colligends. The insoluble colligend-collector pair is adsorbed onto the surface of the solution and is carried by the rising gas bubbles. The insoluble soap or sublate is then removed from the solution surface(70). An extensive discussion of this process is available, including a review of applications (71). An interesting application of this technique is the analysis of cationic and anionic surfactants below their cmc. A photometric measurement indicates the reduction in concentration of an added dye due to the stoichiometric removal of the dye by the oppositely charged surfactant in the ion flotation process(72). For four cationic surfactants in the range of 10–50 mg/liter, the relative standard deviation of the analysis was about 1%, but it was only 5–8% for potassium laurate. Dodecyl ammonium chloride was also successfully analyzed by this technique in the range of 1–5 mg/liter.

Ion flotation has also been developed as a treatment technique for removing trace quantities of strontium-89 using a continuous flotation circuit at pH 3.7 with α-sulfopalmitic acid as the collector(73). With $5.7 \times 10^{-5} M$ strontium added as a carrier, 97% removal was obtained under steady-state conditions.

Cyanide has been separated and concentrated by a batch foam ion flotation technique in which the cyanide forms a complex with ferrous ion(74). With initial cyanide concentrations ranging from 1.5 to $3.1 \times 10^{-3} M$, the pH was varied from 5.8 to 11.4, ferrous sulfate from 0.2 to $1.1 \times 10^{-3} M$, and cationic surfactant from 0.3 to $1.6 \times 10^{-3} M$. Increasing the concentrations of surfactant, at least up to $6.5 \times 10^{-4} M$, significantly improved the removal of cyanide. Decreasing the pH also increased removal, as did increasing the initial ferrous/cyanide molar ratio from 0.21 to 0.35 (at pH below 8). The cyanide reduction was about 85% in one series of runs at pH between 6 and 7.

There have been studies comparing the relative efficiencies of ion and precipitate flotation(60, 75, 76). It has been noted that in ion flotation using foam fractionation there is a marked dependency on gas flow rate, collector-colligend ratio, and ionic strength, whereas precipitate flotation is insensitive to these variables(60). For the purpose of comparing ion and precipitate flotation of iron(III), copper(II), and lead(II) with initial concentrations of about 10^{-4} M, a batch cell was utilized and the pH, ionic strength, and collection times were varied, with sodium lauryl sulfate as the primary collector(60). Comparisons were made with foam separations reported previously(75, 76). For iron it was found that there was considerable difference in the removal as pH was varied. In the vicinity of the precipitation pH of 2.7, the efficiency changed rapidly; at pH 4 the removal by precipitate flotation was 99.9% complete, compared to 37.8% removal at pH 2.75 and no removal at pH 2.65. Copper removal was somewhat different from that of iron in that the latter was much less sensitive to ionic strength. Also, at an ionic strength of 0.013, copper removal by foam fractionation at pH 6.3 was less than that at pH 4.4. The precipitation pH was about 7. At the lower pH values there was about 90% removal at an ionic strength of 0.0013 and 60% at 0.013. However, at pH 9.5 removal of copper by precipitate flotation was essentially complete and was not affected by ionic strength ranging from 0.0013 to 0.26. Lead removal by the flotation technique was 75% at pH 7.0 and 48% at pH 5.8.

A separation of aluminum from beryllium in aqueous solution using precipitate flotation has been described(77). In this technique sodium salts were added to solutions initially containing 1.1×10^{-3} M beryllium, 2.2×10^{-3} M aluminum, and 3×10^{-2} M fluoride (as a complexing agent), so as to precipitate sodium fluoroaluminate, the latter being floated by bubbling with the slow addition of a cationic surfactant. Provided that the initial aluminum–beryllium ratio was greater than 2, the separation was good and more than 90% of the aluminum was recovered.

E. Flotation of Microorganisms

The separation of a variety of microorganisms by flotation has been reviewed(78), with particular reference to the separation of spores and vegetative bacterial cells. It was noted, for example, that, depending on the choice of fatty acid collector and pH, as high as 64% recovery of spores and 99.9% recovery of cell debris was attained.

Microflotation was used in a preliminary study to remove the bacterium *Escherichia coli* and two species of algae, *Chlamydomonas reinhardtii* and *Chlorella ellipsoidea,* using fatty acids and amines as the collector and absolute alcohol as the frothing agent(79). For *E. coli* the removal was highly pH dependent, essentially 98% removal being attained at pH 7.2 in 15 min. The removal was also dependent on added alum and alcohol concentration, as well as gas flow rate. It was proposed that the principal function of the aluminum was the flocculation of the organisms. Depending on gas flow rate and time, as much as 99% removal of *Chlamydomonas* was obtained and no alum was required. With *Chlorella*, however, cell clumping was observed, but only 50% removal was attained, the removal being insensitive to pH in the range of 3.5–8.0.

The separation of *Aerobacter aerogenes* was also studied by micro-flotation with foaming, using lauric acid and laurylamine as well as alum (*80*). With lauric acid, maximum removal of about 90% was achieved, the optimum pH being between 4.0 and 7.5 in the presence of 50 mg/liter of added alum. Although the removal rates were slower with laurylamine, close to 100% removal was obtained at an initial pH of 4.0 using 20 mg/liter of laurylamine and 50 mg/liter of alum. Generally, the removal decreased with increasing pH, although there was efficient removal at pH 11, which was regarded to some extent as an artifact.

F. Conclusions

Although these adsorptive bubble separation techniques have thus far seen relatively limited application in concentration and separation for the purpose of facilitating analysis, they are potentially useful, particularly since their efficiency frequently increases as concentration is reduced. In this respect they may be competitive with some other techniques, such as ion exchange or various chromatographic processes. Although they were initially used primarily for concentrating, separating, and purifying naturally surface-active materials, more recently they have been applied to nonsurface-active materials as well, such as metal and other inorganic ions. To the extent that they may be utilized for organics, adsorptive bubble separations are useful compared to techniques which involve interactions with solid surfaces or methods involving elevated temperatures, both of which may result in the degradation of labile compounds.

VI. Chromatography

A. Introduction

1. HISTORY

The technique of chromatography was first reported by the Russian botanist Michael Tswett in 1906(*81*). He applied this process to the separation of plant pigments by percolating a petroleum ether extract of plant leaves through a column of powdered calcium carbonate. By adding a stream of pure solvent to his column, he found that the pigments were separated into a variety of colored zones. The individual components were isolated by extruding the adsorbent from the column, dividing it into sections containing the different pigments, and extracting each pigment from the adsorbent with alcohol. He named the process chromatography.

This new separation process remained largely unexploited until 1931, when Kuhn and Lederer(*82, 83*) demonstrated the value of the technique for complex separations in the field of natural products. In subsequent years the method was successfully applied to the resolution of mixtures of pigments, sugars, amino acids, and proteins. From 1943 on, the number of publications reporting chromatographic separations has increased rapidly to the point where thousands of reports are published annually.

2. DEFINITION AND SCOPE

Chromatography can be defined as a separation process based on the differential migration of substances due to their selective retention in a fixed phase while subjected to movement by a flowing bulk phase. This is a very general definition which includes all differential migration processes based on adsorption (see Sec. VI. C.1.a), partition (Sec. VI. C.2.a), and ion exchange (Sec. VII. B.1) mechanisms. The mechanism for the migration is the flow of a suitable gas or liquid.

Chromatography has a wide range of applicability, as exemplified by its ability to separate the smallest molecules (hydrogen and deuterium) and the largest, such as proteins and nucleic acids. In addition, particulate matter, such as subcellular fractions, mitochondria, and bacteria have been successfully resolved.

The chromatographic process is also capable of separating a wide range of sample sizes. Nanogram (10^{-9} g) amounts can be separated by gas chromatographic methods, while preparative column chromatography is extensively used in industry to separate large quantities of components. Recent reports indicate that preparative gas chromatography will eventually compete with fractional distillation on a commercial scale.

B. *Principles of Chromatography*

1. GENERAL CONSIDERATIONS

In the chromatographic process the solute migration rates are determined largely by the affinity of the solute for the fixed and moving phase, but other factors such as the dynamic equilibrium involving solute, solvent, and adsorbent must also be considered. Both the solvent and solute molecules compete for the surface of the adsorbent. For the separation of a mixture, the solute must be adsorbed reversibly and the adsorbent must have a selective affinity for the compounds present. Also, the compounds to be separated must be soluble in the developing solvent to provide a medium for the movement of the solutes through the column. The inherent slight differences in adsorbability or solubility of chemically similar compounds cause each solute to migrate at different rates, resulting in the fractionation of the mixture. It is theoretically possible to separate any mixture by the chromatographic technique, but there are practical difficulties that restrict this universal potential.

Over the years, chromatography has developed largely as an empirical science. Progress in the development of the theory was hampered by insufficient knowledge concerning the relationship between adsorption and chemical structure, as well as the lack of reproducible adsorbents. Similarly, the nature of partition systems has been only superficially understood.

In recent years the theory of chromatography has advanced at a rapid rate, producing concepts for new chromatographic systems and refinements in the ability to optimize and extend the present techniques. This has brought about increased column efficiency, speed, selectivity, and other practical benefits. Space limitations prohibit a detailed theoretical discussion in this chapter, and the reader is referred to Giddings' excellent reviews on this subject(84, 85). Only a brief presentation of some significant concepts is included in this discussion.

2. THEORETICAL CONCEPTS

a. Distribution Coefficient

Chromatographic separations are based on the selective retardation of the components of a mixture. This is brought about by the inherent differences in adsorbability or solubility of different substances. A chromatographic system consists of two phases, one of which is fixed. A solute added to such a system is distributed between the phases in a characteristic manner. The distribution coefficient, K, of a substance partitioned between the two immiscible phases is determined as the ratio of its concentration in each phase [see Eq. (3)]. The distribution coefficient is generally a function of temperature and concentration. However, in the very low concentrations usually found in most chromatographic separations, the distribution coefficient can be treated as a constant. The values of K may be determined from a plot of C_1 vs. C_2, which is termed the distribution isotherm. The distribution coefficient is a very useful constant in chromatography. The value of K determines the rate of migration of a solute down the column, and the variation with concentration affects the shape of the chromatographic band. Also, the ease of separation of a pair of solutes can be predicted from the ratio of the distribution coefficients [see Eq. (8)].

b. Adsorption Isotherm

A completely satisfactory theory of adsorption has not yet been elaborated. The dependence of chromatography on the adsorption process is best illustrated by the adsorption isotherm. This is a plot of the equilibrium amount of solute taken up per unit weight of adsorbent versus the concentration of solute in the moving phase at constant temperature. There are three types of isotherms of interest in chromatography. These are illustrated in Fig. 3. This isotherm classification of Brunauer et al. (86) describes adsorption from the gas phase. Type A is a linear isotherm, which results when the ratio of the equilibrium concentrations in the two phases is independent of concentration. With a linear isotherm a symmetrical peak is formed, as is shown in Fig. 3(a). Such behavior is also characteristic of partition systems. Type B is a generalized Langmuir isotherm. This type produces bands with sharp fronts and long, diffuse tails (Fig. 3(b)). Such tailing is the principal disadvantage of adsorption chromatography. Type C is best described by the Freundlich equation and produces bands with diffuse fronts, termed fronting (Fig. 3(c)). Most substances in adsorption systems produce type B isotherms.

The effectiveness of the adsorbent is determined by several factors,

ISOTHERM TYPE

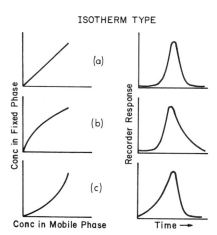

Fig. 3. Adsorption isotherms and corresponding chromatographic peaks. (a) Linear type, (b) Langmuir type, and (c) Freundlich type.

of which the more important are the surface area, the chemical composition of the surface, and the geometrical arrangement of surface atoms. Best results are obtained with adsorbent-adsorbate systems which produce a linear adsorption isotherm. Isotherm linearity is favored for adsorbents with high surface area, surface sites of uniform energies, and reversible rapid adsorption-desorption processes. Conditions of separation and the type of sample also influence linearity. Higher temperatures and more effective eluants generally produce more linear isotherms. Normally, the surface area should exceed a value of 50 m²/g. Overly reactive surfaces can be deactivated by the addition of water or various other saturators(87). The amount of deactivation can be controlled by the careful addition of known quantities of a saturator.

c. The Plate Concept

Chromatographic separations depend on the differences of distribution of two materials in the two phases at equilibrium. Thus, if two solutes are equilibrated between two phases, an enrichment of one of these components in one of the phases will result. The degree of separation realized will depend on the number of equilibrium steps the mixture is subjected to before elution. The portion of the column in which one equilibrium step takes place is called a plate. This is the region in which a single separation effect occurs.

The plate concept has proved to be very useful in chromatography, even though it is only an approximation for continuous processes. True equilibrium is not realized in a continuous process, and a plate is considered as the region in which the average concentration of the component in the two phases is equal to the value at equilibrium. The length of the column in which this occurs is termed the height equivalent to a theoretical plate. A chromatographic column can then be considered as composed of adjoining sections containing a fixed phase through which a fluid percolates and travels from plate to plate. This concept allows the mathematical treatment of the chromatographic process. The larger the number of theoretical plates for a unit length, the more efficient is the column. The height equivalent to a theoretical plate, H, is equal to the length of the column, l, divided by the number of theoretical plates, n,

$$H = \frac{l}{n} \qquad (17)$$

The number of plates in a column for a specific solute can be calculated from the ratio of the chromatographic band width, W, to the elution volume, V, (the volume of mobile phase needed to elute the substance from the column), by the following expression (*88,88a*):

$$n = 16 (W/V)^2 \tag{18}$$

The plate theory was developed for liquid–liquid partition chromatography by Martin and Synge (*88*) using Craig's approach (*89*) for explaining distribution in countercurrent liquid–liquid extraction. The plate concept has been more thoroughly developed in the field of gas–liquid partition chromatography. However, most of the information obtained is applicable to the various types of liquid chromatography.

3. CLASSIFICATION

All chromatographic procedures incorporate two phases, a stationary phase and a mobile phase. The fixed phase may be a solid or a liquid, whereas the moving phase is always a fluid (a gas or a liquid). One may classify chromatographic methods (*90*) according to the types of phases involved in the separation process. Thus, there are four main types with several modifications, as follows:

1. Liquid–solid
   Column adsorption chromatography
   Thinlayer chromatography
   Gel exclusion chromatography
   Ion exchange chromatography
2. Liquid–liquid
   Column partition chromatography
   Paper chromatography
3. Gas–solid
   Gas–solid chromatography
4. Gas–liquid
   Gas–liquid chromatography

This section of the chapter discusses the main features of column adsorption, thin layer, gel exclusion, column partition, paper, and gas chromatography. This last technique is discussed only briefly in this section since Chap. 28 is devoted to this valuable technique. Ion exchange procedures are discussed in Sec. VII.

C. Chromatographic Techniques

This section briefly discusses the main types of chromatographic techniques. For detailed descriptions the reader is referred to the selected bibliography at the end of this chapter.

1. LIQUID–SOLID CHROMATOGRAPHY

a. Column Adsorption Chromatography

This technique was the first chromatographic process reported by Tswett(81). In this procedure the mixture to be separated is adsorbed in a narrow region at the top of a column containing a suitable adsorbent, and the chromatogram is developed by percolating a solvent through the porous medium. As the solvent flows down the column, successive equilibrium steps occur among the solute, solvent, and adsorbent. This continuous adsorption-desorption equilibration with the flow of liquid causes the solutes to move down the column. Since each substance has a characteristic adsorption isotherm, each solute moves through the column at a specific rate. The solvent flow is continued until the desired degree of resolution is obtained or the solutes are eluted from the column.

The relative migration rates are defined as the ratio of the distance traversed by the solute to the distance traveled by the solvent in the same time interval. LeRosen(91) called this ratio the R value. In practice, the retardation factor was introduced by Martin and Synge(88) to specify the criterion for obtaining the measurements. They designated this value R_f, and it is mathematically expressed as

$$R_f = \frac{\text{distance traveled by the leading edge of solute}}{\text{distance traveled by the leading edge of solvent}} \qquad (19)$$

Such values are characteristic and reproducible for a given substance and a specified solvent–adsorbent system. However, the temperature, the flow rate of solvent, and the concentration of solute must also be specified. For best resolution the sample should be adsorbed in a narrow zone, the concentration of sample should be small, and the rate of solvent flow should be slow enough to allow equilibrium to be established. It is necessary to keep the quantity of sample small because of the limited surface available for adsorption and the greater adsorption efficiency realized with lower concentrations. The greater the difference in R_f values of the components of a mixture, the easier it is to separate them. Generally, two components can be resolved if the R_f values differ by at least 0.1.

The separated components can be recovered by the collection of successive small volumes of the effluent solution. Each component is detected by a suitable means and collected as it leaves the column. This technique has been called elution analysis and is perhaps the most useful of the column adsorption processes. A plot of the concentration of each component versus the effluent volume required for elution is termed the chromatogram. Some modern methods of detection allow automatic recording of the chromatogram while the separation is in progress. An alternative method of recovery of the separated components often used involves extrusion of the adsorbent column, dividing it into sections containing the individual components, and recovery by extraction with a suitable solvent. This is especially simple with colored compounds. Three other methods for developing the chromatograms have been devised. These are frontal (92), displacement (93), and gradient elutions analysis (94).

Frontal analysis is carried out by the continuous addition of the original sample solution to the adsorbent column. Although this process is not effective for the separation of mixtures, it can provide information not realized by the other techniques. Its main use is for the determination of adsorption isotherms. Also, the number of components present in a complex mixture is equivalent to the number of steps in the chromatogram. Thus, it is especially useful in the analysis of substances that are irreversibly adsorbed on the column.

In displacement analysis the chromatogram is developed with a solution containing a substance with greater attraction for the adsorbent than any of the components in the sample mixture. All of the components move down the column at the same rate as the developer, and under equilibrium conditions each substance moves as a zone of relatively pure material. Thus, the bulk of the component can be obtained in relatively pure form, especially for materials which exhibit excessive tailing [see Fig. 3(b)]. However, if substances show Freundlich-type isotherms, then the bands will overlap. This procedure will determine the components in the sample not irreversibly adsorbed on the column. With proper calibration, the displacement technique can be used for quantitative analysis of separated components.

Gradient elution analysis (94) is the technique of developing the chromatogram by eluting with a solution whose composition is continually changing. Generally, a more polar component is mixed with the developing solution at the same rate as the developer is added to the column. This procedure has been found to be effective in reducing or eliminating tailing and thereby increasing resolution.

(1) *Absorbent.* One of the most critical considerations for a given separation by liquid-solid chromatography is the selection of the adsorbent. The origin of all adsorption phenomena resides in the forces of attraction and repulsion between molecules, atoms, and ions. These forces acting at the surface of a solid are merely extensions of those acting within the solid substance. The molecules in a solid surface are in an unbalanced attractive field and, thus, have a surface-free energy. These intermolecular forces, which are considered primarily responsible for adsorption in chroma-

tographic systems, may be classified as London forces, electrostatic forces, charge transfer forces, and hydrogen bonds(95). The first two types are relatively weak forces responsible for physical adsorption, whereas the latter two types are stronger chemical forces, which are responsible for chemisorption(96). Physical adsorption is characterized by rapid reversibility, which is necessary for good chromatographic separation.

Various types of adsorbents possess very different selectivities for solutes(97). Adsorbents such as metal oxides are polar and show preferential adsorption of polar molecules; the reverse holds true for the organophilic carbons, i.e., hydrocarbons are more strongly adsorbed than polar compounds. To avoid problems of chemisorption, acidic adsorbents are used for the separation of acids and basic adsorbents for the chromatography of bases.

The adsorbent capacity of a substance depends largely on the combined effects of surface area and energy. Wide variations in these parameters are found, depending on the preparation and activation procedures used in their manufacture. Differences exist among nominally similar products, so that the surface area of an adsorbent should be known and it should be reactivated prior to use. The activated adsorbent can then be carefully deactivated by the addition of water or some other saturator to the degree required by the chromatographic separation. Adsorbents can be evaluated by determining R_f values of standard sample-solvent combinations(98).

Obviously, it is necessary that the adsorbent be completely insoluble in the developing solvent or the column will be destroyed. Also, the adsorbent must be chemically unreactive with the solvent and solutes. There are only a few materials which meet these requirements for the organic and aqueous solvents used in chromatography. Silica, alumina, and charcoal are the most widely used adsorbents, but others, such as magnesia, magnesium silicate, diatomaceous earth, sucrose, starch, lactose, fuller's earth, and calcium salts, have been employed for special purposes in chromatographic systems.

Some characteristics of the two most commonly used adsorbents are presented in this section.

(a) *Silica.* Silica is the most extensively used adsorbent in liquid-solid systems and can be utilized to separate most types of non-ionic organic compounds. Many excellent reviews (99–103) are available which describe its application in great detail. Studies pertaining to the elucidation of the structural composition of silica surfaces and the mechanism of adsorption on these surfaces have also been reported(104–106). Its adsorptive properties depend largely on the hydroxyl groups bonded to surface

silicon atoms. The hydroxyls interact with polar or unsaturated compounds by hydrogen bonding. When the silica is heated above 200°C the
hydroxyls are changed to siloxane groups(107). These silicas are less
active and nonspecific in their adsorptive properties. Consequently, they
adsorb polar, nonpolar, saturated, and unsaturated substances to the
same degree.

(b) *Alumina*. Alumina is the second most widely used adsorbent in
liquid-solid chromatography. Several recent reviews(101, 108–111)
have reported on the separation characteristics, the nature of the alumina
surface, and the mechanism of adsorption of some molecules on alumina.

Alumina is found in many crystalline forms(111), depending upon the
method of preparation. The temperature of activation has the greatest
influence in this respect. Aluminas used in chromatography are generally
the gamma form mixed with other low temperature forms. Higher activation temperatures produce aluminas with higher adsorbent activity(112),
if the temperature does not exceed 1000°C. Above this temperature the
active forms undergo a transition into inactive alpha forms.

Although some disagreement exists, recent studies(113, 114) indicate
that surface hydroxyls do not contribute to alumina activity. The nature
of the adsorption sites has not been established conclusively, but Peri
(109) suggests that they are due to exposed aluminum atoms or strained
Al-O bonds. The alumina surface contains both acidic sites, responsible
for the adsorption of polar and unsaturated compounds, and basic sites,
which adsorb acids strongly. These latter sites may be surface oxide ions.

A good, general purpose adsorbent can be prepared by heating alumina
at 400°C, followed by addition of half a monolayer of water(115). For
some purposes deactivation by more than a monolayer of water is
preferable.

(2) *Solvents*. In theory there should not be any difference in the action
of the adsorbent toward the solute and solvent. Experience has shown
that the adsorption affinities of compounds are influenced largely by the
polarity of the molecules. Thus, water and the lower molecular weight
alcohols are good eluting agents, since they are preferentially adsorbed
and displace less strongly adsorbed solutes. The simplest method of
varying the relative adsorption of the sample is by changing the solvent;
strong eluants decrease adsorption and weak eluants increase it. The
selection of eluant can influence the order of component separation of a
mixture, but the molecular configuration of the solutes has more affect
on this than either the adsorbent or the solvent.

It is important that the solvent have sufficient solubility for the sample
so that the components will not precipitate during the separation process.
Also, the solvent should not be chemically reactive toward the adsorbent

or sample components. Volatile solvents are generally preferred to enable recovery of the separated components by distillation. Liquid–liquid extraction and other separation techniques can also be used to recover the solute.

Developing liquids are classified as desorbing, eluting, and displacing agents according to the relative adsorbabilities of the solvent and sample components. A solvent may function as a desorbing liquid for one type of molecule and as an eluting or displacing agent with some other compound. Tables listing liquids according to their eluting power have been published and can be found in most standard volumes on chromatography. These elutropic (116) series can be helpful in the selection of a suitable solvent for a given separation. A desorbing solvent must be more strongly adsorbed than the solutes of the sample, whereas for elution chromatography the developer must be less strongly adsorbed than any of the sample components. In the case of displacement analysis, the solvent consists of a mixture of two substances, one more weakly adsorbed and the other more strongly adsorbed than the compounds present in the sample.

It is more difficult to select solvents for use with carbon adsorbents than for silica and alumina, since there are many varieties of carbon. Activation at low temperatures produces a hydrophilic adsorbent, and those activated at high temperatures are organophilic. Polar substances are more weakly adsorbed on organophilic carbon than are the nonpolar hydrocarbons(117).

(3) *Apparatus.* The chromatographic adsorption column consists simply of a glass tube narrowed at the lower end to contain a glass wool plug, a porcelain plate, or a sintered-glass disk. A stopcock at the lower portion is useful to control the flow from the column. The column can vary in size from small glass microtubes, 2 mm by 100 mm, to large preparative columns. For example, stainless steel columns, 4.5 cm in diameter and 19 m in length, have been used to separate large quantities of material(97).

The diameter-to-length ratios vary from 1:5 to 1:100 depending on the analytical problem at hand. Long columns are not practical when it is necessary to extrude the adsorbent, and in the case of wide columns the possibility of liquid channeling increases. When possible, it is desirable to use narrow columns to improve the resolution of the components and decrease the solvent retained by the column. For chromatographic schemes that require extrusion, columns have been constructed in short demountable sections for ease of recovery of the separated material after development.

Various auxiliary equipment is required for efficient operation of a column. Often a reservoir is attached at the top to provide sufficient capacity or constant head for the solvent. Pressure or suction is commonly employed to speed up the flow rate, especially when finely divided adsorbents are used. In the case of gradient elution analysis, a system to introduce and mix the second solvent is required. Several procedures for accomplishing this have been reported (118).

Some means of collecting fractions and detecting solutes are also required. Automatic fraction collectors capable of collecting large numbers of fractions are available commercially. Many methods of determining the amount of material present in each fraction are in use. The method of choice is dictated by the type of material being chromatographed. Weighing, refractive index, and ultraviolet adsorption are three commonly used detection techniques. More recently, Woods and Lantz (119) have described the use of a hydrogen flame ionization detector, which is available commercially. This type of detector has the advantages of ability to detect a broad spectrum of organic compounds, high sensitivity, and application to gradient elution chromatography.

b. Thin Layer Chromatography

(1) *Introduction.* The technique of thin layer chromatography was first described in 1938 by Izmailov and Schraiber (120), who utilized layers of adsorbent spread on glass plates instead of packed in columns. This method was developed further by several investigators (121, 122) for the separation of terpenes. Meinhard and Hall (121) produced a cohesive film of adsorbent by the addition of starch to serve as a binder. However, the thin layer procedure was not generally utilized until 1958, when Stahl (123) published procedures for the separation of many classes of compounds in extremely small quantities. In addition, the availability of commercial apparatus, based on Stahl's designs, provided the stimulus for widespread use of the method. The inherent advantages of thin layer chromatography are speed of development, high sensitivity, and sharpness of solute spots. Separations that require many hours on a column or paper are carried out in a few minutes on a suitable layer.

(2) *Procedure.* A layer of adsorbent approximately $250\ \mu$ thick is formed on a glass plate or other firm and inert support. The adsorbent is prepared in a slurry, normally with water or water mixed with a volatile organic liquid, before being spread on the plate by means of commercial spreading equipment or some other suitable process. Some workers have used slurries made with volatile solvents such as acetone (124) and ethyl acetate (125). A binding agent such as starch or calcium sulfate is generally added to the slurry to improve adhesion to the plate and to increase the

mechanical strength of the film. The plate is dried and activated by heating for a prescribed time period at a specified temperature.

Solutions of the mixtures to be separated are applied with a pipette about 1.5 cm from the lower edge of the plate as a spot or streak. After the solvent has evaporated, the plate is usually developed by placing it in the chromatographic chamber with the lower edge immersed in the mobile phase. The developing liquid rises up the plate by capillary action and moves past the sample spots, and the components of the sample migrate upward at characteristic rates. When the solvent front has advanced a predetermined distance, the plate is removed from the tank and dried. The resolved components are then detected by an appropriate physical or chemical procedure, depending on the types of compounds present [see Stahl (126) for a detailed explanation].

(3) *Adsorbents.* Any adsorbent suitable for liquid column chromatography can be used for thin layer chromatography, as long as the particle size is adequate. Plates can be prepared from particles in the size range of 1–25 μ. For superior results particle sizes between 0.5 and 5 μ are used. Silica gel is the most widely used adsorbent for thin layer chromatography, but other common adsorbents are alumina and kieselguhr. In addition, hydroxyapatite (127), cellulose (128) and cellulose derivatives (129), polyamides (130), calcium sulfate (131), polyethylene (132), and Sephadex (133) have found application for specific separations.

Stahl and co-workers (134) found that the rate of development is influenced by the thickness of the layer. They reported that the rate of solvent movement increased with the thickness of the layer up to about 250 μ. This suggested that retention values of the components can also be influenced by the thickness of the layer. Retention values were found to vary with film thickness, but for film thickness above 200 μ the effect is negligible.

Calcium sulfate, 10% by weight, is generally used as the binder with silica gel plates and should be thoroughly mixed with the adsorbent to obtain a homogeneous mixture. Commercial silica gels containing a binder are available, and purchasing these may be preferable to preparing them. Some special silica gels are manufactured which have sufficient adhesive properties so that a binder is not required. These gels are preferred for applications where the binder may present a problem. Preparations of gels from various manufacturers differ in their chromatographic characteristics. Thus, their properties should be evaluated by separation of a mixture of test dyes (123) on these adsorbents before use.

Alumina has been used extensively in column chromatography and is the next most widely used adsorbent in thin layer studies after silica gel. It may be used with a binder, but it is also manufactured in a form suitable for loose layer work where the plate is prepared by spreading the adsorbent as a dry powder. Most loose layer chromatography(*135*) has been carried out on alumina. This adsorbent is available in acidic, neutral, or basic forms and is more useful than silica gel when a high or low acidity absorbent is required.

A limited amount of thin layer work has been carried out with diatomaceous earths(*136*). A suitable grade of diatomaceous earth (kieselguhr G, Merck) is available commercially. It is prepared so that it has an average particle size of $10\,\mu$ and contains a binder. This adsorbent is used mainly for liquid partition chromatography by impregnation with an organic liquid. For example, Knappe and Peteri(*137*) prepared kieselguhr layers by incorporating the impregnating liquid directly in the slurry. Other ways of preparing plates for partition chromatography include: dipping the plate into a solution of the impregnating substance(*138*); allowing a solution of the liquid to ascend or descend the plate, as in the normal procedure for development(*139*); spraying the material onto the plates(*136*); and exposing the plate to the vapor of the impregnating compound(*140*).

Cellulose powders have been used to some extent in the thin layer technique. These powders have some advantages over the use of paper sheets since the adsorbent surfaces are more uniformly distributed. Paper is fibrous and contains large gaps, which favor diffusion of the components of a sample. With layers of powder, the solvent flow is more uniform, with less diffusion of the solutes, and the rate of flow is faster. The separations obtained on cellulose layers are generally superior to those realized on paper sheets. Modified cellulose powders are also available for use in thin layer ion exchange chromatography. For example, Randerath(*141*) linked triethanolamine to cellulose by means of epichlorohydrin to form a weak anion exchange material useful for the separation of nucleotides.

Several types of prepared plates are available commercially. Adsorbent-coated glass plates containing a number of different types of coatings, both with and without binders, are offered by several manufacturers. Glass fiber sheets impregnated with potassium silicate or silicic acid have also been on the market for several years. Another type of prepared plate is a sheet consisting of silica gel bound by polyvinyl alcohol to a flexible plastic support. However, these plastic sheets are limited in their usefulness since they cannot be treated with charring techniques or with corrosive reagents in order to locate sample spots.

An advantage of thin layer chromatography is that the composition of the adsorbent can be selected on the basis of the requirements of a specific separation. Modified plates consisting of mixtures of adsorbents and containing buffers, complexing substances, or other reagents have been used to obtain efficient fractionation of substances. For example, plates coated with adjacent layers of different composition (*142*) and with gradient layers (*143*) have proved highly successful.

(4) *Development of the Chromatogram.* The selection of the developing solvent is dependent on the principle of chromatography to be used for the separation and the type of compounds present in the sample. In adsorption chromatography the solvents used for liquid–solid chromatography on columns can be used successfully. These are listed as "elutropic series" in the standard works on chromatography (see general references at the end of the chapter). Solvent mixtures rather than individual solvents are often used to obtain improved separations. It is generally best to avoid mixtures of more than two components, since phase changes with temperature are more likely to occur with multi-component solutions. Solvent combinations employed in paper chromatography have been applied with thin layers of cellulose powders. The purity of the solvents is of more importance in thin layer than in column chromatography because of the smaller quantities of sample involved.

The spotted plate is placed in a suitable chamber with a tight lid [Fig. 4(a)] for development. The lower edge of the plate is immersed in the developing solvent to a depth of 0.5–1.0 cm. The smallest container possible should be employed to keep the volume of the enclosed atmosphere at a minimum. In this way the time required for equilibration of the solvent vapor with the atmosphere is minimal. This saturation can be further hastened by lining the walls of the tank with filter paper. This produces more rapid separation, a uniform solvent front, and the formation of more compact spots, because it prevents evaporation of the solvent from the thin layer surface. Figure 4(b) shows a chromatogram of a four-component mixture and the individual solutes chromatographed on the same plate for comparison.

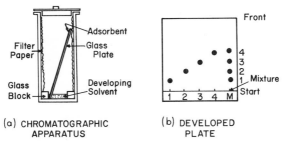

(a) CHROMATOGRAPHIC APPARATUS

(b) DEVELOPED PLATE

Fig. 4. Ascending thin layer chromatographic technique. (a) Apparatus, and (b) developed plate. Spots 1, 2, 3, and 4 are known compounds and M is a mixture of these four compounds.

The plates are generally developed by the ascending technique to a height of 10–20 cm. Difficult separations can be improved by allowing the solvent to flow over the top of the plate where it can be absorbed by a suitable method(144). Similarly, improved resolution can also be realized by repeated development in the same direction with the same solvent system(145) or different solvents(146).

Another technique for improving resolution is two-dimensional development. In this case, the sample is spotted near one corner of a chromatoplate and development is carried out in two directions consecutively. Two different solvents are generally employed to accomplish an increase in separation efficiency. Kirchner et al.(147) were the first workers to apply this technique to thin layer studies. Added versatility can be obtained with this system by modifying the layer prior to the second development. Bergel'son et al.(148) separated isomeric monounsaturated fatty acids by developing in the first direction on silica gel impregnated with dodecane, and then applying silver nitrate to the plate before development in the second direction. Johansson and Rymo(149) applied thin layer separation on Sephadex in one direction, and electrophoresis in the other direction. Kirchner(150) described the application of multiple layers by preparing a plate containing two adsorbents. He separated a mixture of ketones using a charcoal layer for the first development and a silicic acid layer for development in the perpendicular direction.

Additional systems for plate development are descending or horizontal techniques. These require a somewhat more complicated apparatus. One advantage of these procedures is the longer development flow obtained by allowing the solvent to run off the bottom or edge of the plate. Also, the horizontal technique(151) can be modified to effect radial development (120). This process spreads the zones into thin lines instead of spots and thus improves resolution of components with close retention values.

After development is completed, the plate is removed from the container and dried by passing a current of air over the surface. The dried plate is then treated to detect the spots, if they are colorless.

(5) *Detection.* In general, the indicators used for detection of colorless compounds on thin layers are similar to those employed in paper chromatography. These include the use of ultraviolet fluorescence, radioactive counting, spraying with chromogenic reagents, and exposure to iodine vapors. In addition, with inorganic adsorbents, corrosive reagents such as sulfuric acid can be used to char most nonvolatile organic substances. Kirchner et al.(122) were the first to use concentrated sulfuric acid to visualize the solutes. Some compounds appear at room temperature, while others require heating of the acid-sprayed plate. For highly unreactive compounds, 5% nitric acid should be added to the sulfuric acid to

increase the oxidizing power of the solution. A saturated solution of potassium dichromate(*152*) in concentrated sulfuric acid and potassium permanganate(*153*) in concentrated sulfuric acid has also been employed for the same reason. The plates are usually heated to char the spot.

(6) *Qualitative and Quantitative Analysis.* Identification of the separated solutes on thin layers can be realized by specific chemical reactions, color-producing reagents, and comparison of R_f values. If careful attention is paid to the variables involved, the reproducibility of retention values corresponds to that obtained for paper chromatography (*154*). Those variables are: the quality of adsorbents used, the activity of the adsorbents, the thickness of the layer, the quality of solvents employed for development, equilibration of chamber atmosphere, the development distance, and temperature fluctuations.

The first application to quantitative analysis was reported by Kirchner and co-workers(*122*). These investigators demonstrated the reliability of the thin layer procedure for quantitative determinations, when conditions and techniques are carefully standardized. They applied the method to measuring the amount of biphenyl in citrus juice in concentrations varying from 0.1 to 600 mg/liter, with an average error of ±2.8%. Since this first report, a large number of publications have dealt with the quantitative determination of many types of organic compounds, including hydrocarbons, aldehydes, ketones, quinones, acids, esters, terpenes, pesticides, phenols, amino acids, indoles, and many others.

Many techniques have been applied to obtain quantitative evaluation of the resolved components on thin layer chromatograms. Estimates have been made from the area of the spot(*155*), which has been found to have a relationship to the quantity of the solute present in the sample. The density of colored spots has been determined with a photodensitometer capable of measuring the intensity of the reflected light as related to that of standards.

For some determinations the portion of the layer containing the component has been removed from the plate(*156*) and eluted with a suitable solvent. The resulting solution can then be analyzed by a spectrophotometric(*157*), colorimetric(*158*), or fluorimetric procedure(*159*).

Radioactive methods have also been utilized for quantitative determinations on thin layers. The sample components can be tagged by reaction with a suitable radioactive substance(*160*) or by an isotope dilution process(*161*). The radioactive emission of the solutes is then measured with a suitable counter or by autoradiometry(*160*). In addition, some other special procedures that have been applied include volumetric analysis(*162*), polarography(*163*), bioassays(*164*), and enzymatic analysis(*165*).

c. Gel Exclusion Chromatography

Gel exclusion chromatography is the term which may be used to describe both "gel filtration" and "gel permeation" chromatography (166). These generally are elution chromatographic processes in which partition takes place principally on the basis of molecular size. A widely used gel for this purpose is Sephadex (167), which is used in the form of beads of cross-linked dextran, an essentially un-ionizable polysaccharide containing, however, a few carboxyl groups. The gel swells in water and the porosity is determined by the degree of cross-linking, which varies among the different Sephadex types.

In the gel exclusion chromatographic process the test solution to be fractionated is placed at the top of the gel bead column, which may then be eluted by aqueous or organic solutions. As the eluant moves down the column, molecules too large to penetrate the pore structure move with it in the interstitial spaces between the beads. Various types of Sephadex are available that have an upper molecular weight exclusion limit from 700 to 200,000. Smaller molecules penetrate and diffuse through the gel structure at rates which depend on their molecular size and shape, resulting in their fractionation in the effluent, the smaller molecules generally appearing later. However, certain molecules have chemical affinities for the gel due to their substituent groups, notably aromatic substances, and may be retarded to a greater extent than nonaromatics of similar size when eluted by aqueous solutions (167). Similarly, organic molecules with hydroxyl and carboxyl groups may be retarded when eluted with chloroform. Since inorganic salts generally elute slowly, gel exclusion chromatography may be used to isolate and fractionate large molecules like serum proteins, and separate them from inorganic salts and low molecular weight organic compounds.

The advantages of gel exclusion chromatography for the analysis of organics in water are its speed, its ability to separate the high molecular weight organics from the salt and low molecular weight constituents, and its avoidance of any phase changes or heat which might affect labile organics. Chromatographic instruments have been developed to automate and optimize this technique (see Sec. 2.a following, on high efficiency liquid chromatography).

2. LIQUID–LIQUID CHROMATOGRAPHY

In this section the two principal methods of chromatography which involve the use of liquid–liquid (partition) chromatography are discussed. These include partition chromatography with packed columns and paper sheets.

a. *Partition Chromatography on Columns*

The partition chromatography process, unlike adsorption chromatography, utilizes two immiscible solvents. One liquid phase (the immobile or stationary phase) is supported on a suitable solid substance and the developing solvent or mobile phase percolates down the column over the stationary phase. As the sample to be separated moves through the column, distribution of the solutes occurs between the stationary and mobile liquid phases. The characteristic partition coefficient of each component produces a differential migration rate which induces separation. Weak adsorbents or relatively inert substances of highly porous structure are used as supporting media for the immobile solvent. Substances such as silica gel, cellulose, starch, celite, powdered rubber, and kieselguhr have found application for this purpose. The columns are operated in the same way as for column adsorption chromatography.

The partition technique was developed by Martin and Synge(*168,169*) for the separation of amino acids of wool on silica gel which had a water content amounting to 50%. This technique is similar to the liquid–liquid countercurrent extraction procedure except that the two phases are in contact over a very large interface and thus show a higher separation efficiency. The above investigators reported an efficiency of 10^4 theoretical plates(*88*) for a 20-cm by 1-cm column, as compared to about 40 plates for an analogous countercurrent distribution system. The mathematical expressions derived for countercurrent extraction can be used to predict the movement of the solutes for a specific liquid phase system.

The support material must retain the stationary phase strongly and allow a large surface area of the liquid to contact the mobile phase. It must be relatively inert, have good mechanical stability, and be of large surface area. The solid support should also have the capacity to retain an appreciable amount of liquid and still retain its flowing properties. Ideally, the sample should not be adsorbed on the solid support. However, some adsorption effects are present with all known support materials. This is the case even though the surface is completely covered with liquid. Thus, adsorption has some influence in the separation phenomenon in partition chromatography.

The elution technique similar to that used in adsorption chromatography is generally employed for separations with partition columns. An eluting solvent of unvarying composition is usually used, although gradient elution has found application for some separations. When water is the stationary phase, the mobile liquid is an organic solvent or mixture. If a hydrophobic support is used, it is coated with an organic liquid such as silicone oils, paraffin, and long-chain hydrocarbons. Solvents more polar than the stationary phase are then used for the mobile liquid, and often it is an aqueous phase. Such a technique is referred to as "reversed-phase" chromatography. This technique has found application for the separation of mixtures of homologous series and substances which are so soluble in organic solvents that it is difficult to achieve adequate resolution with the ordinary partition procedure.

The selection of solvents is more difficult for a partition system than for adsorption chromatography. However, assuming the adsorbent acts merely as an inert support for the stationary phase, the choice of liquids can be based on the principles of the liquid–liquid extraction technique. The separation of two components, then, depends on the values of the ratio of partition coefficients of the substances in the two solvents. The principles involved were discussed in Sec. III.

An important consideration in the selection of liquid phases is the degree of distribution of the sample components between the two phases. If the solutes are very soluble in the mobile liquid, there will be little distribution between the phases and little or no separation will occur. Similarly, if the solutes remain largely in the stationary phase, an excessively large volume of mobile liquid will be required for elution. For satisfactory separations the fraction of the solute in the mobile phase should be in the range of 0.05–0.5. Cassidy(170) presents a useful discussion of the parameters involved in the selection of solvents to furnish the necessary distribution.

Another useful approach to solvent selection is by referring to the extensive literature on partition chromatography. One can usually find examples of separation similar to the chromatographic problem under consideration. Many of the standard works on chromatography contain useful data for this purpose. Although it may be necessary to modify the system to some extent to accomplish the desired separation, this approach is usually the fastest method to the selection of suitable solvents.

(1) *High Efficiency, High Speed Liquid Chromatography.* Recent developments in liquid column chromatography have greatly increased its utility for analytical applications(171–177). Renewed interest in this technique has been stimulated in part by the accomplishments of thin layer chromatography and the knowledge and skills gained in the field of gas chromatography. In addition, recent theoretical studies(175,178–181) have contributed to a better understanding of the principles of chromatography and have led to predictions of potential applications and limitations of all types of liquid column chromatography. These studies have been very useful in the design of highly efficient and rapid systems. Scott et al.(182) have discussed some of the factors affecting the performance of a liquid column chromatograph, and several other

investigators(*173,183–186*) have described suitable instruments. At least two of these(*173,186*) are the basis of commercially available instruments.

The essential features of a high performance liquid-liquid column chromatograph are: (1) a reservoir for the mobile solvent, (2) a pump of the nonpulsating displacement type, (3) a pressure-measuring device, (4) an equilibrium tube or precolumn, (5) an injector system, (6) an analytical column, and (7) the detector and recording device. In addition, units can be equipped with temperature equilibration coils, flow meter, a flow programming system, a temperature control unit for the precolumn and analytical column, and a vacuum system for degassing the carrier solvent. It is essential that dead volume be kept at a minimum throughout the system for maximum resolution.

The column is the most important feature of the chromatograph. It is prepared from a narrow bore tube by packing with the material required for the separation. Borosilicate glass tubes can be used up to 50 atm, but at higher pressures stainless steel tubes are recommended. The precolumn generally consists of a length of tubing packed with the same kind of packing as that used in the analytical column. Its function is to saturate the carrier solvent with the stationary phase under operating conditions.

The high efficiency of these chromatographs is mainly due to the development of long columns of narrow bore and packing materials which have almost ideal theoretical properties in regard to particle size, uniformity of shape, and available surface area. Columns have been prepared which approach the performance characteristics of gas chromatography columns. Such columns have a high pressure drop, and rapid analyses require operation at high pressures. Fortunately, these high pressures have negligible influence on the separation. Since liquids have a low compressibility, the fluid velocity is nearly constant along the column, and the diffusion coefficient as well as the distribution coefficient are only slightly influenced by pressure.

Kirkland(*187*) has recently described a nonporous support particle uniformly coated with a thin, porous layer of sorbent. This is a spherical siliceous particle with a porous surface of controlled thickness and pore size. This controlled surface porosity (CSP) support can be optimized by varying the dimensions of the overall particle and the thickness and porosity of the surface, which covers an impervious core. The particles have high mechanical stability and can be used at pressures of 1000 psi or higher. For liquid-liquid chromatography applications, Kirkland(*187*) coated the support with a suitable liquid and packed the column using techniques developed for preparing high performance gas–liquid chromatography columns.

Tests with the CSP support indicate that columns with internal diameters of 2–3 mm provide maximum efficiency. Above 3 mm, the height equivalent to a theoretical plate (HETP) increases significantly because of poorer transcolumn equilibrium. Below 2 mm, efficiency also decreases greatly, apparently due to wall effects and an unfavorable support particle-to-bore diameter ratio. Efficiencies of more than 2600 theoretical plates per foot for unretained solutes and more than 40 theoretical plates per second for rapidly eluting solutes were reported with columns developed at carrier velocities of approximately 2 cm/sec. Remarkable separations of isomers and homologs can be realized in a few minutes under these conditions. For example, Kirkland(*187*) obtained the separation of a mixture of the closely related substituted urea herbicides (Linuron, Diuron, Monuron, and Fenuron) in less than 6 min at a flow rate of 1.14 cm³/min of dibutyl ether, using a column of 500 mm × 2.1 mm i.d., packed with 1.0% 3,3'-oxydipropionitrile on 37- to 44-μ CSP support (Fig. 5). The sample contained 67 ng/ml of each herbicide dissolved in dibutyl ether. A high sensitivity ultraviolet photometer with a split stream flow cell was used as the detector(*172*). Separation of the same mixture can

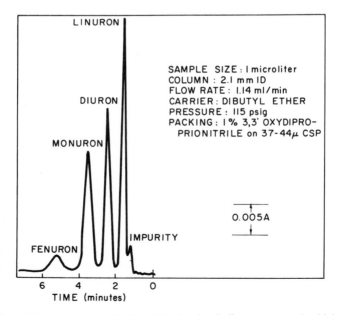

Fig. 5. Separation of urea herbicides with closely similar structures by high-efficiency high speed liquid chromatography. [Reprinted from Ref. *187*, p. 12, by courtesy of Preston Technical Abstract Co.]

be realized in less that 2 min by increasing the carrier velocity, with only a moderate loss of resolution.

Plots of the HETP versus carrier velocity with a CSP support column and acetophenone as the solute show a relatively small decrease in efficiency for a 20-fold increase in flow velocity. Thus, this type of column can be used for separations requiring flow programming, that is, for the analysis of mixtures containing compounds of widely varying partitioning ratios. By programming the carrier flow rate, the components can be eluted at high column efficiencies and the time required for elution of the components can be greatly reduced.

Several types of detectors have been used with liquid column chromatographic systems. Huber(188) has recently reported an evaluation of five types of detectors with respect to minimum detectable peak width, noise level, linearity, and selectivity. The types of detectors evaluated include refractometric, photometric, calorimetric, flame ionization, and argon ionization. All of these detectors can be used with highly efficient columns, but none was found to be best for all analytical separations.

Liquid-liquid chromatography in columns should prove very useful for the analysis of components present in the aqueous environment. With special supports and carefully packed columns operated at high pressures, separations have been realized which are analogous to gas–liquid chromatography with regard to the time required for analysis and column efficiency. Such a system offers three distinct advantages over gas chromatography: (1) It is capable of analyzing nonvolatile substances directly without the necessity of preparing volatile derivatives or pyrolyzing the sample; (2) it can be used for the analysis of thermally sensitive compounds; and (3) greater flexibility can be obtained due to the wider choice available in the selection of solvent used as the carrier.

It should be noted that, although this discussion has dealt primarily with liquid–liquid chromatography, the technique can also be used for liquid–solid and gel exclusion chromatography with narrow bore columns. Excellent separations for these modes have also been reported(173,189).

b. Paper Chromatography

(1). *Introduction.* The use of paper as a medium for the separation of organic mixtures was first reported in the 19th century by chemists of the dye industry. They determined the purity of the dye and the number of components present by spotting solutions on paper and noting the number of concentric rings formed due to the migration of the solvent. In 1861 Schönbein(190) reported that solutes in aqueous solution migrated at characteristic rates when the solution was allowed to rise through the paper by capillary action. Goppelsroeder(191), a student of Schönbein, carried out an extensive investigation of this technique and separated both organic and inorganic mixtures. He tested many adsorbents and found paper to be best for his purpose.

However, capillary analysis was limited by two inherent problems. The development procedure was essentially a "frontal analysis" technique and thus was incapable of the complete resolution of even a two-component system. In addition, this technique was largely based on adsorption chromatography, and as the adsorption capacity of paper for most compounds is limited, the technique is of restricted application.

The next significant developments were reported in the early 1940's by Flood(*192*), who impregnated papers with alumina to improve separations, and Liesegang(*193*), who achieved quantitative resolution by the elution development technique.

Modern paper chromatography developed largely from the classical studies of Consden *et al.*(*194*), who made several important contributions They combined the liquid–liquid partition process on paper with the "elution analysis" technique for development of the chromatogram. When operating under conditions of a linear distribution isotherm, this procedure resulted in the formation of compact, well-defined solute zones on the paper. Consden and co-workers(*194*) also introduced the two-dimensional technique to improve separations of difficult samples.

The many successful separations realized by workers in the field of biochemistry using this partition process stimulated the application of paper partition chromatography in other fields. Since 1946, many thousands of publications have appeared describing the application of the technique to the analysis of a wide variety of substances. Dozens of monographs and review articles have been published which contain detailed information concerning the various modifications and techniques of paper chromatography. Some of these are listed as selected references at the end of the chapter since it is beyond the scope of this short section to include the voluminous information which has been developed in this field.

(2) *Development of the Chromatogram.* Paper chromatograms are generally developed by the technique of elution analysis described in Sec. VI.C.1.a. of this chapter. In this procedure the samples dissolved in a suitable solvent, are carefully spotted near one end of the properly prepared paper sheet so that the initial area of the mixtures is kept as small as possible, preferably less than 0.5 cm in diameter. After the solvent has evaporated, the paper is placed in a suitable developing solution contained in an enclosed chamber. As the developing solvent flows along the face of the paper by capillary action, the sample components will dissolve and migrate with the flowing solvent. Separation is accomplished by the interaction of the solute–solvent–adsorbent system.

Usually the paper is conditioned in the presence of water vapor so that the cellulose will absorb about 20% its own weight of water. Under these conditions the chromatographic process is predominantly a partitioning between a mobile solvent phase and a cellulose-water stationary phase. However, physical adsorption(195) of the solutes and ion exchange of ionic molecules also occur in the complex chromatographic process.

Several types of development procedures can be employed for paper chromatographic separations. These include ascending, descending, horizontal, and radial development. In addition, the first three types can be carried out in one or two directions.

(a) *Ascending development.* This form of development is probably the most frequently employed. It is carried out by dipping the lower edge of the suspended paper in the solvent to a point 1 in. below the line on which the samples are spotted. The solvent rises through the paper by capillary action and development proceeds until it reaches a predetermined height. The rate of ascent is generally slow and allows more time for the solutes to equilibrate between the two liquid phases, resulting in more compact zones. The apparatus required is simpler than for the descending technique.

(b) *Descending development.* In this form of paper chromatography the developing solvent is placed at the top of the chamber in a trough and flows down the paper by capillary and gravitational forces. Thus, the developing liquid moves six to eight times faster than in the ascending mode and chromatograms can often be obtained in 1–2 hr. Slow-moving solutes can be more readily separated by repeated development of the chromatogram. Also, it is a simple matter to allow the solvent to flow off the end of the paper sheet to resolve components with similar retention values. Chromatograms can be developed for several days, if the edge of the paper sheet is serrated to promote an even flow from the end of the paper. Compounds of different polarity have been separated by this technique.

(c) *Horizontal development.* One type of horizontal development(196) is carried out in a shallow glass or metal container. The paper sheet is placed horizontally on glass rods and development can easily be carried out below or above ambient temperature by placing the apparatus in a refrigerator or an oven. Rapid separations can be carried out at the higher temperatures.

Horizontal development can also be accomplished by placing the paper sheet between two glass plates(197). This technique has been found to be especially satisfactory when volatile compounds are chromatographed. Improved reproducibility of R_f values by this method has been reported(198).

Radial development(199) is another type of horizontal development technique. This process involves the use of a circular filter paper with a wick cut parallel to the radius from the circumference to the center. The sample is spotted just above the upper end of the wick and the paper is placed on the edge of a circular disk with the wick dipping into the solvent contained at the bottom. A large petri or crystallizing dish with a cover can be conveniently employed for this method. This technique is frequently used as a rapid test to determine the resolving capability of solvents for a given sample. An interesting modification of radial development is the use of centrifugal force(200) to increase the rate of solvent flow through the paper.

(d) *Two-dimensional development.* Samples can be chromatographed by development in two dimensions by either the ascending or descending technique. For this purpose the sample is spotted near one corner of the paper and the chromatogram is developed until the solvent front reaches the designated position. The paper is then removed and dried and the adjacent edge of the sheet is placed in the chamber so that de-development can be carried out in a direction 90° to the original development. The sample is developed with two different solvents to realize maximum resolution. Also, multiple-development techniques may be used in either one or both directions.

(3) *Paper.* The paper used is a highly purified form of cellulose consisting of 98–99% α-cellulose. The method of manufacture determines the characteristics of the surface and the sorption properties of the paper. A variety of types suitable for chromatography are manufactured. These vary according to thickness, flow rate, purity, absorbence, length of fibers, mineral content, and functional groups present on the cellulose. These variations offer the analyst a choice of properties to fit the requirements of the desired separation. It is usually best to carry out preliminary tests on papers using the test tube technique. The paper which produces the desired separation in the shortest time is selected for the analysis.

If the commercial papers do not have the necessary properties, they often can be modified by impregnation with a suitable substance and by changing the chemical structure of the cellulose. Papers have been impregnated with hydrophobic materials for reversed phase chromatography, with inorganic adsorbents, and with aqueous buffer solutions. The structure of the paper can be modified by acylation of the hydroxyl groups.

(4) *Solvent Selection.* Many factors influence the choice of the solvents used for a desired separation. Partition chromatography is generally employed for separations on paper. Three types of systems are generally used, based on the character of the stationary phase. These are an aqueous phase, a hydrophilic organic phase, and a hydrophobic phase (reversed phase).

In the first type water is absorbed on the paper, usually by equilibrating in a closed chamber which contains a water-saturated atmosphere. If the stationary phase is an aqueous buffer or salt solution, the paper is dipped into the appropriate solution and allowed to dry before saturation with water vapor. Also, the paper may be dipped in an aqueous solution saturated with the immiscible, mobile organic solvent and blotted to remove excess stationary phase. The chromatogram is developed with a solvent, which is immiscible with or saturated with water. For example, butanol and water are partially miscible, but butanol saturated with water is often used as a mobile phase. The water content of this developer can be increased by addition of a third mutually miscible substance. The stationary phase can be made acidic or basic or remain neutral by the appropriate selection of the third component.

For systems in which the stationary organic phase is hydrophilic, it can be incorporated into the paper from the chamber atmosphere if it is sufficiently volatile, or the paper can be dipped into a solution of it in a volatile organic solvent (acetone, methanol, etc.). The diluent is then removed by evaporation before the sample is applied and the chromatogram developed. Formamide is a frequently used stationary phase of this type, and it is generally impregnated into the paper from a 40% ethanolic solution. Chloroform, benzene, cyclohexane, or a mixture of two or more of these solvents have been employed as the mobile phase.

In the reversed phase chromatographic system the hydrophobic liquid is generally applied by dipping the paper in a solution of it, and the volatile solvent is removed before use. Development is carried out with a hydrophilic liquid. A typical system is paraffin oil impregnated on paper, with dimethylformamide-methanol-water (10:10:1) as the mobile phase.

The advantage of a system with an organic stationary phase is that control of the quantity of the fixed phase is possible so that the rate of development and the degree of resolution can be varied to suit the needs of the analysis. Also, the shape of the spots can often be improved by altering the amount of fixed phase applied to the paper.

There should be as few volatile components as possible in a solvent system, since it is necessary to maintain a saturated atmosphere in the chamber. Compatibility with the detection system to be employed is often the deciding factor in the selection of the liquid phases. The solvent system should not possess the chemical, physical, or biological properties of the sample components being used in the detection scheme. Similarly, impurities in the solvent may interfere with the detection method. Thus, only pure solvents should be used for chromatographic separations. If a solvent of the required purity is not available, purification should be carried out by a suitable method(201).

The capacity of the partition system limits the quantity of sample that can be separated and is a function of the solubility of the sample components in both phases. If more than one solvent system can be used, the one with the greatest capacity should be selected. Methods for evaluating the capacity of solvents have been reported(202).

Since there are a large number of papers and many books available dealing with the applications of paper chromatography, the selection of a solvent system is often made on the basis of reported separations on the same class of compounds present in the sample. Often some modification is required to obtain adequate resolution of the sample components. These modifications may include the dilution of the mobile phase, the variation of the amount of stationary phase, and adequate adjustment of the pH of the solvent system. One author(203) suggests 10 basic solvent systems useful for most separation problems.

(5) *Apparatus*. The equipment required for paper chromatography is basically simple and inexpensive. All that is required is an airtight chamber sufficiently large to hold the filter paper in the proper position and a tray for the solvent. The apparatus that have been employed range from a simple test tube to elaborate commercial cabinets. The only limitation on the choice of material for construction of the chamber is its inertness to the developing solvent. Glass is commonly used due to its chemical inertness to solvents and its transparency, which enables easy supervision of the process. Other materials, such as stainless steel, lead, ceramics, and plastics, have been used for some applications. In addition, an atomizer for spraying indicator reagents on the developed chromatogram and an ultraviolet lamp are often required to locate the separated components on the paper. Other equipment required will depend on the detection and quantitative procedures employed by the analyst.

(6) *Detection Techniques*. After the chromatogram is developed, the paper is generally dried and the separated solutes, if colorless, are located by a variety of techniques, which include color reactions with chromogenic agents, formation of colored derivatives prior to separation, ultraviolet fluorescence, ultraviolet absorbence, infrared absorbence, radioactive tracing techniques, and bioautography. In general, the apparatus required is simple and inexpensive.

(7) *Qualitative and Quantitative Analysis*. Filter paper chromatography has been used extensively for the qualitative and quantitative analysis of complex mixtures. Unknown substances can be identified by a comparison of their relative migration rates (R_f) to those of known compounds. Although R_f values are constant under carefully controlled conditions, it is often difficult to reproduce the many variables in actual practice. Thus, the known compounds are generally chromatographed at the same time as the unknown sample. For positive identification, the chromato-

graphic characteristics of the compounds are usually compared with at least two solvent systems or with systems based on different principles, such as paper and thin layer chromatography. Confirmation of the identity of a solute can also be obtained by specific reactions of the compound directly on the paper, or by spectroscopic and chemical analysis after elution.

Paper chromatography is not only a very effective method of resolving mixtures on a microscale (1 or 2 μg), but by careful control of each step of the separation process and the use of a sensitive detection scheme it can furnish reliable quantitative data(204). The most common methods of quantitative analysis are the visual comparison of the solute color intensity with standards, area measurement of the spots by planimetry, densitometry and fluorometry directly on the paper, elution of the solute followed by chemical analysis, and elution followed by the measurement of a specific physical property.

The accuracy of the quantitative procedure depends on the chemical nature of the compounds, the reproducibility of the detection scheme employed in situ, and the error of the analytical method used after elution. For example, measurement by visual comparison methods can have an error of 10–25%, whereas photometric determinations of the solute on the paper are accurate to ±5%. However, measurements made after elution of the solute may have an error as low as 1–2%.

3. Gas Chromatography

The chromatographic process wherein the mobile liquid phase is replaced by a moving gas phase is termed gas chromatography. The mobile phase or carrier gas is generally an inert gas such as nitrogen, helium, or argon which is allowed to flow at a constant rate through a column composed of a small-diameter tube containing the sorbent. Gas chromatography can be subdivided into two general categories: gas-solid chromatography, in which the adsorbent is a solid of large surface area (carbon, silica, gel, alumina), and gas-liquid chromatography, which consists of a liquid immobilized by absorption on an inert, finely crushed solid (celite, crushed firebrick) or coated on the walls of a capillary tube.

Gas-solid chromatography has been applied primarily to the separation of gases or relatively nonpolar compounds of high volatility, whereas gas-liquid chromatography has proved very useful for the analysis of a large number of liquids and solids. Also, many compounds of low volatility can be separated by preparing a derivative of increased volatility, i.e., esterification of carboxylic acids or analysis of the products formed on pyrolysis.

Gas-liquid chromatography offers some advantages over the gas-solid technique. The elution bands are sharper and often symmetrical compared to the skewness of the bands generally obtained in gas-solid chromatography. A wide choice of stationary phases is available, which theoretically allows the resolution of almost any mixture by the appropriate selection of the liquid phase. In addition, the gas-liquid partitioning mechanism is more clearly defined than solid adsorption and this has produced a more rapid theoretical and experimental development.

Gas-liquid chromatography has been the most widely used chromatographic method in recent years and has enjoyed an amazingly rapid growth and development since its invention by James and Martin(205) in 1952. As would be expected, this technique has been extensively applied to the analysis of environmental contaminants. Since Chap. 28 is devoted to gas chromatography, only this brief introduction is given in this section.

D. Application of Chromatographic Systems to Water Analysis

Chromatography has been widely employed for the qualitative and quantitative analysis of complex organic mixtures. It has proved highly useful for separations covering the whole range of organic compounds, from the nonpolar hydrocarbons to the highly polar compounds, such as amino acids and carbohydrates. Its inherent selectivity, extraordinary resolving power, and high sensitivity usually make chromatography the method of choice for difficult analytical separations.

The chromatographic technique best suited for a given separation is generally indicated by the nature of the sample components, the quantity of sample available, and the speed required for the analysis. For components which have sufficient volatility and are thermally stable, gas chromatography is usually the preferred method for the analysis. Solid absorbents are used for the fixed gases and gas–liquid partition columns for liquids and volatile solids.

For labile substances, liquid–liquid partition chromatography is indicated since this is the mildest form of chromatography. The effect of temperature and the catalytic effects of the active adsorbents are at a minimum with this type of system. Also, special additives such as buffers, inhibitors, salts, etc., which may be necessary for the stability of the components or for adequate separation, can be easily incorporated in the developing solution.

The separation of large sample quantities is usually carried out with liquid–solid and liquid–liquid chromatography in columns. A wider selection of substrates is available, and generally better resolution is obtained than with the other chromatographic systems. Usually, solid adsorbents have a greater capacity than most partition systems, so that larger samples can be accommodated with the same size column. In addition, adsorbents are highly selective and are preferred for difficult separations such as the resolution of stereoisomers.

Paper and thin layer chromatography have been most useful for the separation of small quantities, for rapid screening, for nonvolatile compounds, and for analysis of a large number of samples. An important advantage of these chromatographic systems is the inexpensive nature of the equipment required for the analysis.

Chromatography has been used extensively for the analysis of contaminants present in the environment. All types of chromatographic systems have been applied for the detection, separation, and identification of organic substances present in surface waters. Procedures have been reported for the analysis of pesticides(206–216), phenols(217–223), amino acids(224–226), detergents(227,228), volatile fatty acids(229–231), fatty alcohols(232), volatile neutral compounds(233), petroleum products(234), hydrocarbons(235,236), nonvolatile carboxylic acids (237), humic substances(238,239), sterols(240,241), vitamin B_{12}(242), and other organic compounds(243,244). The literature is too extensive to summarize in this short discussion. The references noted are selected from the recent literature.

Generally, chromatographic separations are used after a suitable concentration procedure, such as liquid–liquid extraction, carbon adsorption, or freeze concentration. In many cases two or more types of chromatographic techniques are used to obtain adequate separation of the components of interest. For example, Goodenkauf and Erdei(212) described a procedure for the identification of chlorinated hydrocarbon pesticide concentrations of 2 ppb or less in river water. They concentrated the pesticides from 2000–4000 gal of water by the carbon filter technique and separated the carbon chloroform extract into general classes of compounds by differential solubility methods. The neutral fraction was chromatographed through a column, 19 mm in diameter and filled to a height of 10 cm with silica gel, and was separated into three groups by elution with 2,2,4-trimethylpentane, benzene, and a 1:1 chloroform-methanol mixture. The trimethylpentane eluted the aliphatic compounds, the benzene eluate contained the aromatic components, and the chloroform-methanol mixture removed the oxygenated substances. Most of the chlorinated hydrocarbon pesticides in general use were found in the aromatic fraction. Some pesticides, weed killers (e.g., chlorobenzilate), and a part of the atrazine and propazine were present in the oxygenated fraction. Final identification of the pesticides was accomplished by ascending paper chromatography. An immobile solvent system of ethyl ether-dimethylformamide was impregnated on the paper and developed with 2,2,4-trimethylpentane. After development and drying, the paper was sprayed with a solution of silver nitrate and 2-phenoxyethanol in acetone followed by exposure to ultraviolet light. Semiquantitative results were obtained by comparison of the spots with known quantities of the pesticides.

Similarly, Smith and Eichelberger(210) have developed a thin layer chromatography procedure to remove interfering substances prior to gas chromatographic analysis of pesticides. They found that thin layer chromatography was more effective than steam distillation or column chromatography as a cleanup procedure for the analysis of pesticides present in the aromatic fraction of carbon chloroform extracts. Glass plates were coated with silica gel to a thickness of 0.25 mm and the chromatogram was developed with carbon tetrachloride by the ascending technique. Three to six samples, each in duplicate, were spotted on a plate. One sample was used for corroborative identification by visualization of the spots by bromination, followed by spraying with silver nitrate and fluorescein solutions, then exposure to ultraviolet radiation. The chlorinated pesticides produced brown to black spots, and other pesticides appeared as yellow or white spots. The duplicate sample was used for elution of the separated pesticides from the silica gel with acetone for gas chromatographic analysis. This analysis was carried out with a 90-cm by 3-mm column of Chromosorb W, coated with Dow 11 silicone grease, and an electron capture detector. Recoveries from the silica gel were shown to be quantitative, and the procedure is applicable to a wide variety of pesticides.

Irudayasamy and Natarajan(211) were able to detect thiophosphate insecticides on paper chromatograms at the 0.5-μg level. They separated a mixture of baytex, diazinon, malathion, and parathion by the reversed phase technique. Whatman No. 1 paper was impregnated by soaking in a 15% (v/v) liquid paraffin B.P. in petroleum ether and then allowing the solvent to evaporate at room temperature for 1 hr. The treated paper was spotted with the sample and developed by the ascending solvent technique with dimethylformamide-n-butanol-water (14:1:5) mixture as the mobile phase over a 9-cm distance. After development, the paper sheet was dried, exposed to bromine vapor for 20 sec, and sprayed with 0.4% Congo red solution. The eluates formed clear blue spots on a red background. The spots were stable for at least 10 days if protected from light. The R_f values had a standard deviation of less than ±4%.

When concentrations of the organic contaminants are sufficiently high (ppm range), direct aqueous injection gas chromatography can be employed to great advantage. Baker and Malo(220) reported a rapid and accurate gas chromatographic method for the analysis of volatile fatty acids directly from aqueous solutions. The procedure employs a 5-ft by 1/8-in. column packed with a polyester-type free fatty acid substrate on Chromosorb W and a flame ionization detector. Replicate quantitative values are obtained which deviate by no more than ±1% at the 10-mg/liter level.

Chau and Riley(226) determined the concentration of 11 different amino acids in seawater after vacuum concentration, demineralization by cation exchange, and separation by thin layer chromatography. These authors obtained recoveries of about 90% and a reproducibility of ±10% for concentrations of 1 μg/liter each of 19 amino acids. Irish Sea samples contained 11 amino acids in concentrations of 2–16 μg/liter.

Gel exclusion chromatography using Sephadex has been used in an attempt to fractionate and characterize by molecular size nonfilterable organic matter in streams and lakes(239). After liquid particles were glass filtered above 1 μ, the test water filtrate was concentrated by a factor of 400 using evaporation, and the resulting liquid phase, containing 60–95% of the total organics, was placed on the top of a Sephadex column, which was then eluted with distilled water. The effluent fractions were analyzed for chemical oxygen demand, color, conductivity, and, in some cases, organic nitrogen. Depending on the Sephadex grade used, recovery was between 87 and 100%. As many as 10 separate elution fractions were obtained. It was concluded that a significant number of compounds associated with color in natural water have molecular weights above 50,000, and that low colored waters have most of their color in the low molecular weight fraction, while more color is associated with the high molecular weight fraction in moderately or highly colored water.

The ability of gel exclusion chromatography to separate salts from large organic molecules offers a useful tool for oceanographic researchers because the analysis of organic substances is often hindered by the salts present. Daisley(242) used gel filtration chromatography to both concentrate and separate vitamin B_{12} from seawater. Since sodium chloride interferes with the microbiological assay test for vitamin B_{12} and neither molecule can be separated by a 72-cm by 3.6-cm Sephadex column, a mucopolysaccharide was added to complex with the vitamin and then separation from the salt was accomplished on the Sephadex G-25 column. The complex of vitamin B_{12} was concentrated after separation by the addition of dry Sephadex G-25, since the swelling beads take up only water and the low molecular weight materials. The concentration in the supernatant increased sufficiently for the application of the microbiological assay technique.

The tremendous growth of chromatographic methods over the last decade has provided the chemist with powerful, new, and comparatively simple tools for the separation of small amounts of complex mixtures. Separation processes are an essential part of analytical chemistry, and chromatography has been used extensively in combination with physical measurements, e.g., spectrometric techniques, for trace analysis. Recent developments have added new techniques to the ever-growing number of chromatographic processes available to the analyst, and the extensive research effort in all phases of chromatography offers great promise for additional improvements in the future. For example, the recent developments in high efficiency, high speed liquid–liquid chromatography in columns are sure to find application for analysis of trace contaminants in water as the necessary instrumentation becomes more generally available.

VII. Ion Exchange

A. Introduction

Ion exchange as a concentration and separation technique has been in use for some 50 years. One early method, devised by Bahrdt in 1927, used a sodium zeolite column to remove calcium and magnesium from a natural water because of their interference in a sulfate analysis (245). The use of synthetic zeolites in ion exchange is limited, however, by their narrow range of pH and the difficulty in achieving quantitiative elution.

In the 1930's organic cation and anion exchange resins were synthesized and analytical applications were developed, principally by Samuelson (246). In recent years there has been renewed interest in synthetic inorganic ion exchangers because of their ability to be utilized at high temperatures and to withstand ionizing radiation. Some of the properties and applications of these newly developed inorganic materials have been discussed by Amphlett (247). Within the past 10 years there has also been a growing interest in the use of organic and aqueous-organic solvent mixtures for ion exchange separations, which have been reviewed by Moody and Thomas (248).

Ion exchange in water analysis may be used for determining the total equivalents of salt present, to concentrate ions, and to separate ions from nonelectrolytes as well as from other ions of similar or opposite charge. It is applicable to organic and inorganic ions and is particularly useful in removing interferences so as to facilitate subsequent analysis. Ion exchange is a fast and simple technique which usually results in good recovery and requires relatively little judgment, thus making it readily adaptable for routine analyses.

B. Theoretical Considerations

1. ION EXCHANGE EQUILIBRIA

a. Selectivity Coefficient

When an ion exchange material is equilibrated with an ambient solution containing two exchangeable ions (cations, for example), the exchange process is stoichiometric and the equilibrium reaction can be expressed as

$$bA^{a+} + aB_R^{b+} \rightleftarrows bA_R^{a+} + aB^{b+} \tag{20}$$

with the subscript R referring to species in the resin phase. (The term "resin" is used for convenience to designate the ion exchange material, since synthetic resins are the principal ion exchange material in current use.) The absence of this subscript refers to species in the ambient solution phase. For this reaction an equilibrium expression may be written:

$$K_B^A = \frac{(A^{a+})_R^b [B^{b+}]^a}{[A^{a+}]^b (B^{b+})_R^a} \tag{21}$$

where K_B^A is the equilibrium constant, generally referred to as the selectivity coefficient. The terms in parentheses refer to concentrations and those in brackets refer to activities. For cations of equal charge, Eq. (21) can be simplified, and for univalent cations it becomes

$$K_B^A = \frac{(A^+)_R [B^+]}{[A^+](B^+)_R} \tag{22}$$

In this case K_B^A is a simple measure of the ability of the resin to select A^+ over B^+. Furthermore, if, in the ambient solution at equilibrium, $[A^+] = [B^+]$, then $K_B^A = (A^+)_R/(B^+)_R$. The larger the selectivity coefficient, the greater is the efficacy of separating the ions of like charge by ion exchange.

Selectivity scales for various ions and resin types have been constructed. They indicate the relative affinities of a given resin for various ions. For example, with a typical strong acid resin an affinity series (248a) for univalent cations is as follows:

$$Ag > Cs > Rb > K > NH_4 > Na > H > Li$$

A similar scale for divalent ions with the same type of resin is:

$$Ba > Pb > Sr > Ca > Ni > Cd > Cu > Zn > Mg$$

b. Factors Affecting Selectivity Coefficient

The selectivity coefficient for a given pair of exchanging ions is affected by several factors. One of the most important is the basic chemical structure of the resin. When, for example, the cation exchanging sites are of the strong acid type, such as sulfonate, the resin affinity for hydrogen ion is generally low. In contrast, a weak acid cation exchange resin, such as that with carboxyl sites, has a high affinity for hydrogen ion. Chelating resins are available which are highly selective for multivalent cations as compared to univalent ones, and, therefore, these two ion types may be readily separated by such resins(248b–250). As with most chelating systems in solution, the extent of binding or the selectivity of these resins is highly dependent on pH. Chelating resins are useful in "ligand exchange chromatography"(250a). In this process a multivalent cation is fixed to the exchange sites of a cation exchange resin, and then anions or neutral molecules are separated into fractions when eluted from the top of the column. The basis of the separation here is the difference in affinities of the separating species to the fixed metal in the resin by virtue of their acting as ligands and forming complexes with that metal. There are other specialized resins and resin uses, which may be briefly mentioned here, which depend primarily on the ability to adsorb or exclude species based on their size or charge. Amphoteric ion exchange resins (containing both acidic and basic groups) are available. Such resins have been used to separate electrolytes, which are weakly bound to the anionic and cationic exchange sites, from nonelectrolytes in a separation process called "ion retardation"(251). In just the opposite fashion, acid- or base-type resins may be used to separate electrolytes from nonelectrolytes by virtue of the ability of the resin to adsorb the latter and thereby retard its flow compared to that of the electrolyte; this process is called "ion exclusion"(252). Acid and base resins with large pores (called "macroreticular resins"), which are capable of adsorbing high molecular weight organics(253), are available.

Even for a given resin the selectivity coefficient may vary greatly with the relative amounts of the two exchanging ions in the resin phase. For example, for one strong acid resin with a high degree of cross-linking among the polymer chains, K_H^{Na} is 2.0 when the exchange ion composition in the resin phase is 20 mole % Na, and only 1.0 for 90% Na(253a).

For a given resin type the tightness of the resin structure, as reflected by the degree of cross-linking, can markedly affect the selectivity coefficient. For example, one strong base anion exchange resin equilibrated with a 0.1 M ambient salt mixture had K_F^{Br} values ranging from 6 to 40 (these values applying to 1:1 ratios of Br:F in the resin phase), the values increasing with degree of cross-linking(253b).

Ambient solution properties, such as temperature, ionic strength, or total concentrations of exchangeable ions, and the presence of water-miscible organic solvents can markedly affect the selectivity coefficient (253c). For systems with low selectivity, temperature changes have only small effects on ion exchange equilibria; otherwise, with ions of equal valence an increase in temperature is generally followed by a decrease in selectivity, the opposite being true when the exchanging ions have different valences. The ionic strength of the solution can have a great effect on the selectivity coefficient; such variations are generally larger for multivalent exchanging ions or those with different valences, as compared to a uni-univalent system(254). In utilizing this phenomenon for dilute solutions in a removal or separation technique, there may exist an optimum ionic strength to which the influent solution should be adjusted by the addition of acid or a neutral salt. The presence of a miscible organic solvent may also exert a large effect on the selectivity coefficient. For example, for a typical strong acid resin, K_H^{Na} was found to be 1.54 in water, as compared to 20.7 in 4:1 molar ratios of methanol-water and 102 in 4:1 ethanol-water(248). The use of organic and aqueous organic solvents can be efficacious in ion exchange separations that would otherwise be difficult in pure aqueous systems.

2. ION EXCHANGE KINETICS

Most of the ion exchange sites in a typical resin are located within the matrix or pore structure. Thus, for a typical ion exchange process, such as represented by Eq. (20), to occur, the ions must pass through the resin matrix and across a liquid film or boundary layer at the resin-solution interface. The rate-determining step in the exchange process(255) could then be:

1. diffusion in the boundary layer (film diffusion),
2. diffusion in the resin phase (particle diffusion), or
3. chemical exchange at the exchange sites.

In most cases the chemical exchange is sufficiently rapid so as not to be rate limiting.

The factors that determine whether particle or film diffusion will be rate limiting are (1) the ratio of the concentration of resin exchange sites to that of the exchanging ions in ambient solution, (2) the ratio of the effective diffusion coefficient in the resin to that in solution, (3) the ratio of diffusion film thickness to resin bead radius, and (4) the selectivity coefficient(255a). The larger these factors, the greater the likelihood of film diffusion control; the smaller, the greater the likelihood of particle diffusion control. A situation intermediate between the two may occur.

As a resin pore structure is tightened due to increased cross-linking, the diffusion coefficient in the resin phase will decrease, by as much as three orders of magnitude for highly charged exchanging ions(255b), thereby increasing the likelihood of particle diffusion-limiting kinetics. Generally, the greater the ion charge and size, the smaller its diffusion coefficient in the resin phase. Because of the generally higher activation energy for particle diffusion as compared to film diffusion, raising the temperature will increase the ratio of diffusion coefficients in the resin and solution phases. However, the temperature may also affect the selectivity coefficient, so that the net effect could be in the direction of either particle or film diffusion control.

Decreasing the resin particle size will decrease the likelihood of film control. However, increased agitation in batch systems or increased flow in column operation will create turbulence and reduce the film thickness, leading to particle diffusion control. In one study of alkali metal ion exchange it was found that at ambient solution concentrations below 0.003 M, the exchange kinetics could be considered to be film diffusion limited; above 0.1 M the process was particle diffusion limited.

C. Principles of Column Operation

1. Effect of Rate of Exchange Process

The rate of the exchange process is one of the principal factors that affect column operations. The latter are more widely used than batch processes because they lend themselves more readily to continuous operation, the exchange reaction approaches completion because it is continuously displaced, and they can be used in chromatographic separations.

In such a column operation involving a univalent ion exchange process, as represented by Eq. (20), a cation exchange resin in the B^+ state is placed in a vertical column, through which an influent aqueous solution containing A^+ is passed downward. As the solutions moves down the column in the spaces between the resin beads (interstitial spaces), A^+ ions diffuse into the resin, exchanging with B^+, which simultaneously diffuse out into the interstitial spaces. The equilibrium is continuously displaced in the direction of A^+, replacing B^+ in the resin beads because of the replenishment of A^+ in the column by the influent. As the influent first advances through the column, leaving behind only A^+ ions in the beads, the effluent moves at the same rate and contains only B^+, which has been displaced from the resin.

The advancing front of the influent solution at various times is shown in Fig. 6, which indicates the relative fractions of A^+ and B^+ in the resin, compared to the total exchange capacity, T. T is defined as the concentration of exchange sites in the resin expressed in milliequivalents per gram of resin. The advancing front or interface between the resin converted to A^+ and that still in the B^+ state involves a gradual change from the pure A^+ to the pure B^+ state, as indicated by the S-shaped curves of Fig. 6. The shape of these curves and the factors affecting them have been treated both in terms of a kinetic model involving film, particle, and interstices diffusion, and by plate theory ($255c$–$255e$; Sec. VI.B.2.c).

If these curves become too flattened extending over a large distance, as the front reaches the end of the column (as represented by t_3 in Fig. 6), there remains a portion of the column that is not utilized, even though A^+ ions have started to appear in the effluent. This point in time is called the "breakthrough point," and the effective exchange capacity of the column associated with it, the "breakthrough capacity." Since there is unused resin capacity at this point, the breakthrough capacity will always be less than the total equilibrium exchange capacity. As noted by Helfferich($255f$) and others, there are several factors that generally affect the shape of the breakthrough curve and, hence, column utilization.

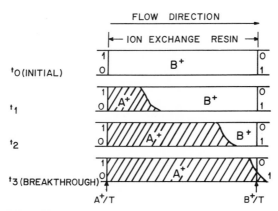

Fig. 6. Ion exchange column operation showing continuous displacement of B^+ by A^+. t_0, column initially in B^+ state; t_1 and t_2, intermediate states as A^+ influent flows through column; t_3, "breakthrough" of A^+ in effluent.

a. Selectivity Coefficient and Solution Composition

When the uptake of A^+ over B^+ is favored by the resin, the boundary is self-sharpening and attains a steady state as it advances. With unfavorable uptake the boundary becomes less sharp with time. (This is generally the case in elution chromatography.) The nature of the influent solution co-ion, that of the opposite charge to the exchanging ion, as well as added electrolyte can either sharpen or flatten the boundary.

b. Geometric and Related Factors

Decreasing the resin bead size generally sharpens the boundary. The use of nonspherical resin particles and particles of nonuniform size may lead to channeling and uneven flow, resulting in a diffuse boundary. A low degree of resin cross-linking will increase the exchange rate and tend to sharpen the boundary. For a self-sharpening boundary in its steady-state shape, increasing the column length will increase the relative fraction of capacity utilized; however, for unfavorable uptake, increasing the column length past a certain point will not increase the relative utilization. Similarly, increasing the length-to-diameter ratio will increase utilization in the former case, but not the latter. Decreasing the flow rate will generally sharpen the boundary, as will increasing the temperature, due to its effect on diffusion.

2. COLUMN USE IN CONCENTRATION AND SEPARATION

If the purpose of ion exchange is primarily to concentrate either a single ion or a mixture of similarly charged ions, the solution may be passed through the column. The resin behind the advancing front is left with, for example, the cation to be concentrated, A^+, or a mixture of such ions, A_1^+, A_2^+, A_3^+, etc. The state of the column containing the A^+ ions with part of the column having been depleted of B^+ is represented by t_2 in Fig. 6. At this point the column may be washed with distilled water, the front remaining fixed in place. Next the column is eluted with an electrolyte, perhaps containing C^+, and the adsorbed A^+ ions move down the column ahead of the newly advancing C^+-A^+ front. If the concentration of the eluant C^+ solution is significantly larger than that of A^+ in the original solution, then A^+ in the effluent will appear more concentrated than in the original solution. This procedure also serves to remove either anions or neutral species originally present in the A^+ solution, since when A^+ is initially adsorbed by the resin, these anions or neutral species continue through the column with B^+ and appear with it in the effluent; any remaining quantities of anions or neutral species are generally removed in the distilled water wash prior to elution.

When ion exchange is being used to separate ions of like charge sign, a useful technique is to adsorb the mixture on the resin, utilizing only a small portion of the top of the column. This is generally followed by washing the column to remove any excess co-ions and neutral species, and finally eluting either by the technique of selective displacement with various eluants or by elution chromatography. Other techniques, such as displacement development chromatography and frontal analysis, which have not been widely used in water analysis, are not discussed here.

In the selective displacement technique, an eluant is chosen which will readily displace one ion of a mixture sorbed on the top of the column, but not the others. Thus, as the eluant moves down the column, A^+ moves along as an ever-broadening band, as shown in Fig. 7, finally appearing in the effluent. By a judicious choice of eluants, all of the adsorbed ions in the mixture may be successively displaced from the column, thereby being separated from each other.

In elution chromatography the mixture of similarly charged ions at the top of the column is eluted by one eluant which displaces all of them, but at different rates depending on their relative selectivities. As the eluant moves down the column, the bands of the various ions being eluted

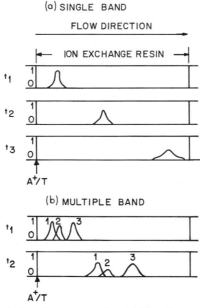

Fig. 7. Ion exchange elution chromatography. (a) Showing spreading of peak of single component A^+ as it moves down the column at successive times t_1, t_2, and t_3. (b) Showing separation of three component mixture of A_1^+, A_2^+, and A_3^+ at successive times t_1 and t_2.

move with it, the peaks broadening as they move. The positions of the bands of such a mixture of three cations, A_1^+, A_2^+, and A_3^+, at two different times in the elution process are shown in Fig. 7. In this case A_1^+ and A_2^+ are not completely separated. Thus, although A_3^+ may be collected in one or more fractions not containing the other A^+ ions, A_1^+ and A_2^+ cannot be completely separated. It should be noted that frequently a combination of elution chromatography and selective displacement is utilized. In such cases one eluant will elute some of the ions, separating them at the same time; one or more additional eluants are then passed through the column, similarly eluting and separating other ions.

D. Applications

There have been numerous reported applications of ion exchange in water analysis, some of which are discussed here in detail to indicate the scope of methods utilized, and others of which are mentioned only briefly. Such applications have been discussed by Samuelson (255g) and Inczedy (255h). Ion exchange procedures for the analyses of radioisotopes in water and other environmental samples have been presented in detail(256, 257). An earlier review of the principles of ion exchange and applications to a variety of waters has been given by Calmon(258).

1. TOTAL IONIC CONTENT

The total salt concentration in natural and boiler waters has been determined by adsorbing the water onto cation exchange resins in the hydrogen form and titrating the displaced hydrogen ions. In one such technique a batch equilibration method was used. Corrections were made for alkalinity, which was determined separately. The expected average deviation was 0.12 meq/liter of total cations; it was noted that, for natural waters with low potassium and sodium content, the total cation content is a good estimate of sodium(259). A similar method using a column technique was used to determine total cation content and was found to give an estimate of total hardness for waters with low sodium content(260).

2. SCHEMES FOR TOTAL ANALYSIS

A scheme of analysis for industrial waters has been presented using strong acid and strong base resins in order to determine calcium, magnesium, copper, iron(III), chromium(III), chloride, sulfate, metaphosphate, orthophosphate, silicate, and chromate(261). The method was developed so as to remove chromate interferences in the colorimetric determinations of orthophosphate, silicate, and metaphosphate, and in the chelometric analysis of calcium and magnesium; it also removed copper and iron(III) which interfered in the latter analysis. In the analysis of the anions, hydroxylamine hydrochloride is added to the test solution to reduce the chromate ion to chromium(III), which is then removed in subsequent passage through the cation exchange resin. The anions in the effluent are then analyzed colorimetrically. Similarly, chromium(III) in the test solution is oxidized with peroxide to chromate and separated from the cations by adsorption on the anion exchange resin. Copper and iron(III) are then determined directly in the effluent. For the calcium and magnesium analyses, the copper and iron(III) are then complexed with cyanide to form $Cu(CM)_4^{2-}$ and $Fe(CM)_6^{3-}$, which are removed in passage over an anion exchange resin, the effluent then being analyzed by EDTA titrations. The complete scheme of analysis generally gave results which agreed well with conventional methods of analysis of cooling water samples.

Using a strong acid and a weak base resin column in series, a field procedure was developed to enrich and analyze natural waters(262). Following uptake on the columns, the columns were eluted by hydrochloric acid and ammonia. It was found that uptake and recovery were complete for sodium, potassium, magnesium, calcium, manganese(II), chloride, and sulfate. Variable amounts of phosphate and iron(III) were adsorbed onto the resin, the remainder passing through as nonexchangeable complexes or "humus"-bound species.

A scheme for the analysis of the major cations in seawater has been developed, using a resin column to adsorb the cations and then successively eluting with a sequence of different eluants(263). After 30 ml of seawater were adsorbed on the resin, potassium and sodium were eluted with 0.15 M ammonium chloride; then calcium was eluted with a solution of 0.35 M ammonium chloride; next, magnesium with 1 M ammonium acetylacetonate at pH 9.6; and finally, strontium with 2 M nitric acid. A variety of analytical methods were used for the different fractions.

3. CONCENTRATING IONS

Several applications of ion exchange primarily for the purpose of concentrating ions have been reported. A chelating resin has been used with industrial waters in order to concentrate multivalent cations by a factor of 10–20 prior to analysis by atomic absorption spectrophotometry(264). It was noted that the metals were held more strongly by the chelating resin than by a typical sulfonic acid resin. In this technique the water samples were buffered at pH 5.5, sorbed onto the resin, and then eluted with 8 M nitric acid. The sensitivity of the method was 5 μg/liter for copper, cadmium, and zinc, and 50 μg/liter for lead(II), nickel(II), and iron(III). This same chelating resin was also used to concentrate molybdenum from natural waters using the thiocyanate method of analysis; the sensitivity of the technique was about 1 μg/liter(265). Cation exchange has been used to concentrate vanadium from river water by a factor of 3.3, at the same time reducing the dissolved solids by 50% so as to facilitate subsequent evaporation prior to neutron activation analysis, the sensitivity of the method was 0.1 μg/liter(266).

Ion exchange has been used to concentrate ions in natural water and simultaneously remove interferences in the subsequent analysis. For this combined purpose a method for barium in seawater was developed in which the test sample was passed through a cation exchange resin column after it was first diluted 1:1 with HCl(267). Subsequent elution with 1 M HCl removed the alkali metals and most of the magnesium; the barium, along with the calcium and strontium, was then eluted with 5 M HCl, the concentration factor being 5:1 compared to the initial sample. The solution was then evaporated to dryness, adding HF, and the residue was analyzed by emission spectroscopy. The efficiency of recovery for barium was 99.9% and the accuracy and reproducibility for the complete method were each within 14%.

Another interesting example of the use of ion exchange for concentration and the removal of interferences is an analytical procedure for nitrate in fresh water using a strychnidine colorimetric analysis(268). It was noted that it is frequently necessary to concentrate natural waters in the determination of nitrate because of the insensitivity of available analytical methods; the authors believe that many methods for nitrate lead to the hydrolysis of organic nitrogen species and result in incorrectly high nitrate analyses. In their method the test sample was adjusted to a pH of 5–7 with buffer in order to prevent flocculation of humic material in the resin bed, and 0.001 M chloride was added which was found to reduce the adsorption of organic matter by the resin. The test solution was then passed through the anion exchange resin column in the chloride form. It was observed that using the resin in the hydroxyl or sulfate forms resulted in almost quantitative adsorption of tannins, which subsequently would be eluted with the nitrate and interfere with its analysis. After the nitrate was adsorbed on the column, the column was washed with distilled water and eluted with 1% NaCl and the analysis was performed. It was found that this method was accurate for nitrate to within 2% in the range of 2–10 μg, and that omitting the ion exchange process frequently gave results higher by several hundred per cent.

4. ANION ANALYSIS

An interesting ion exchange-titrimetric procedure for sulfate and phosphate has been developed which involves conversion of the aqueous solutions of the salts of these anions to their acids and analyzing by titrating the acids with strong base(269). The test solution is passed through a strong acid cation exchange resin in the hydrogen form and the mixture of acids in the effluent is evaporated at 75°C for 2 hr, the nitric, hydrochloric, and hydrofluoric acids distilling from the solution. The remaining solution of about 1 ml containing sulfate and some phosphates is then titrated with strong base, the titer being a measure of the total number of equivalents of sulfate and phosphates. The latter, in the form of ortho- and polyphosphate, may be determined separately by evaporating the residue solution from the first evaporation at a surface temperature of 275°C to remove the sulfuric acid, then hydrolyzing the polyphosphates to orthophosphoric acid and titrating with strong base as before. This phosphate determination may then be subtracted from the results of the first analysis, thereby yielding the sulfate concentration.

A variety of samples from surface streams, wells, reservoirs, sewage, and seawater were analyzed by this technique, with sulfate concentrations in the range of 27–2600 mg/liter, giving excellent agreement with an independent gravimetric analysis. Also, mixed standards of sulfate and phosphate ranging from 1 to 10 mg/liter of each gave results accurate to within 1%. It was indicated that organic interferences could be eliminated by solvent extraction, filtration, or oxidation with bromine water, and that anions of nonvolatile acids, such as arsenate, chromate, molybdate, and borate, would add to the titer in determining phosphate, thereby acting as interferences.

5. REMOVAL OF INTERFERENCES

One of the most prevalent uses of ion exchange in water analysis is the removal of interfering species. One such method involved the use of a cation exchange resin to remove iron(III), calcium, magnesium, aluminum, and manganese(II) ions which may interfere in the spectrophotometric determination of fluoride, involving its ability to bleach a thorium phenylfluorone lake(270). The technique was found to be sensitive to about 1 mg/liter of fluoride and eliminated the need for distillation generally required in many fluoride analyses, provided that there was less than approximately 1 mg/liter of phosphate.

Another ion exchange method for fluoride involved the use of an anion exchange resin, in contrast to the previous technique(271). The test solution is passed through the resin column in the acetate state, the fluoride being retained and potentially interfering cations appearing in the effluent. The fluoride is then eluted from the column with 0.005 M beryllium(II) in 0.1 M acetic acid, the eluted species presumably being BeF_4^{2-}; the SPADNS method is used to analyze the fluoride. If aluminum is present in the test solution it must be chelated prior to the ion exchange step. Using synthetic fluoride solutions of 0.5 and 1.0 mg/liter, the accuracy and precision of the method were each within approximately 10%, even with the following individual or mixed added possible interferences: 200 mg/liter of orthophosphate, 400 mg/liter of calcium carbonate, 1000 mg/liter of chloride, 2 mg/liter of hexametaphosphate, 1000 mg/liter of sulfate, 0.5 mg/liter of chlorine, and 5 mg/liter of aluminum. As with the previous cation exchange method, this technique eliminated the need for distillation.

In using ion exchange for removing interferences of ions of the same charge sign as the test ion, it is frequently necessary to utilize elution chromatography to separate ions. An example of such a technique using a mixed aqueous-organic eluant involves the analysis of lithium in water (272). The purpose of the ion exchange process is to separate the lithium from alakli and alkaline earth metals which interfere in the flame photometric analysis of lithium, particularly at the levels present in seawater. It was found that, after adsorption on the top of the strong acid cation exchange column, using 0.5 M HCl in 80% methanol as the eluant, the lithium eluted first completely, followed by sodium. No alkaline earth metals or potassium were found in either fraction. The advantage of the methanol–water eluant in this case is that it permits the use of smaller resin columns, eluate volumes, and elution times, compared to pure aqueous eluants. The accuracy of the combined ion exchange flame photometry procedure was ±1.5% for 0.3–6.5 mg/liter of lithium added to natural water samples.

A combination of ion exchange, precipitation, and evaporation was used to remove interferences due to sodium, potassium, calcium, and magnesium prior to emission spectrographic analysis of cesium and rubidium in seawater(273). After adsorbing the sample on the top of the cation exchange resin column in the hydrogen form, elution with HCl resulted in calcium being removed in a different fraction from the other cations. The eluate containing the mixture was then concentrated by evaporation and the magnesium precipitated with ammonia and ammonium carbonate. After evaporation and re-solution of the filtrate, a second cation exchange resin was used to chromatographically elute two fractions, one containing rubidium and some potassium, the other containing cesium. These fractions were then evaporated to dryness and the spectrographic analyses performed. On seawater samples spiked with 4 μg/liter of cesium and 200 μg/liter of rubidium, the recoveries were 101.0 ± 0.5% and 98 ± 1%, respectively.

Ion exchange has also been used following other methods of concentration and separation, such as in a reported method for vanadium in natural waters(274). The concentration of vanadium, such as in seawater, is generally too low for direct spectrophotometric analysis. The method reported first used coprecipitation with iron hydroxide to concentrate the vanadium. The precipitate was then redissolved in HCl and passed through a cation exchange resin, and the vanadium was eluted with 0.3% hydrogen peroxide. Iron(III), aluminum, zinc, and other possibly interfering cations did not elute with the vanadium, which was then analyzed spectrophotometrically using diaminobenzidine. In seawater the recovery of vanadium averaged $98 \pm 2\%$; the coefficient of variation was 2.8%.

Ion exchange has been used for the removal of interferences in the low level measurement of oxygen in boiler waters(275). Such waters frequently contain iron(II) and hydrazine, the latter being added as a scavenger for dissolved oxygen. In the Winkler analysis for oxygen in the range of 0.01–0.04 mg/liter, hydrazine and iron(II) were found to interfere when present in the range of 0.04–0.2 and 0.1–1.2 mg/liter, respectively. By first passing the test solution through a cation exchange resin, these interferences were successfully removed.

6. RADIOISOTOPES

Ion exchange has been widely used for the concentration and separation of radioisotopes in natural waters. An example of such an application is the analysis of strontium-89 and -90 in rainwater(276). Using a cation exchange resin, strontium was separated from other radioactive alkaline earths. In analyzing such trace quantities of radioisotopes, it is common practice to add nonradioactive carrier ions, in this case strontium, to avoid losses of the trace materials and, in the case of ion exchange, to facilitate the exchange process, which depends on mass equilibria. In this method strontium carrier was added to the rainwater sample, which was then acidified, filtered, and passed through a cation exchange resin. The column was eluted with an ammonium lactate solution, yttrium carrier was added to the strontium eluate free of other alkaline earths, and the solution was stored for 2 weeks to allow the yttrium-90 decay product sufficient time to equilibrate with the strontium-90. The strontium and yttrium were then separated by precipitating the latter as hydroxide. By counting the radioactivity at different stages, both strontium-89 and -90 could be determined by this technique (see Chap. 25).

7. ORGANIC SUBSTANCES

Ion exchange is also a useful tool in the analysis of organic constituents in natural waters. An example of such an application is the analysis of paraquat, which is the common name for the cation 1,1-dimethyl-4,4-bipyridilium, used as a herbicide for weed control(277). Plant constituents and other organics in water may interfere with the spectrophotometric analysis and are removed by this ion exchange technique. After passing the aqueous test solution through the cation exchange resin column, the latter is washed with $2 N$ HCl, then 2.5% NH_4Cl. The paraquat is then eluted with saturated NH_4Cl and analyzed spectrophotometrically. The selection of the type of resin is critical, the criteria being that the paraquat, but not the interfering species, adsorb well onto the column, that much of the light-absorbing material retained by the resin be eluted prior to the paraquat, and that the paraquat be eluted with high efficiency. The procedure was found useful for waters containing substances absorbing light in the region of 256 mμ, the absorption maximum or unreduced paraquat. For water samples of 50–500 ml the expected recovery of the method is 85–100%.

A method of analysis for amino acids in saline water has been developed, using ligand exchange with a chelating ion exchange resin(278). The latter was used in the copper state and, because of its high selectivity, seawater could be passed through without eluting the copper. In this technique the amino acids interact with the resin by acting as ligands for the chelated copper, which is tightly bound by the fixed negative sites in the resin. In order to test the method, a synthetic mixture of common amino acids, each at a concentration of $1.25 \times 10^{-6} M$ in artificial seawater, was adsorbed on the copper chelate resin column and then eluted. With the exception of cystine, the recovery in each case was complete. In order to use this method for concentrating free amino acids in seawater, a 1-liter sample was first filtered and then passed through the resin column, which was eluted with $3 M$ ammonia. Subsequent analysis was performed by automatic high pressure ion exchange chromatography. Similarly, the total dissolved amino acids were analyzed by first hydrolyzing the total sample, particulate matter included, for 22 hr in $6 N$ HCl, then continuing with the exchange as described previously. It was concluded that the bulk of the amino acids in the seawater analyzed were in a combined state, rather than as free amino acids.

VIII. Membrane Techniques

A. Introduction

Membranes have been used to concentrate and separate soluble ions and molecules, colloidal species, particulates, and microorganisms in natural, treated, and waste water. The capabilities of membranes to exclude species by virtue of their size (dialysis and membrane filtration) and to adsorb or exclude due to specific chemical interactions (ion exchange and osmosis) have been utilized. Rather than deal with the various types of membrane techniques separately in relation to their abilities to concentrate or separate, this section is subdivided into the types of species in water for which such membrane techniques are applicable. Since a variety of membrane types and methods are considered, the detailed theories and mechanisms of operation are not generally discussed, and the reader is referred to the general bibliography at the end of the chapter for more information.

B. Soluble Species

Ion exchange membranes have not seen much use in concentrating soluble species in natural waters, although it has been shown that electrodialysis of seawater with such membranes can recover large percentages of organic matter from large volumes of such water(8). Ion exchange membranes have also been utilized as a preconcentration method for trace metals prior to their analysis by neutron activation and anodic stripping voltammetry(279). In this method the trace metal in a large volume of 0.01 or 0.1 M potassium nitrate solution is placed in contact with a cation exchange membrane and either allowed to reach the exchange equilibrium or the membrane may be removed at a predetermined time. The membrane containing the concentrated metals may then be placed in a vial for neutron activation analysis, or electrolyzed in a supporting electrolyte, so that the metals plate out on a graphite electrode, after which they are analyzed by anodic stripping voltammetry. This membrane technique has the additional advantage of being able to exclude surface-active agents, such as may be found in waste water, from interfering with the anodic stripping technique. The equilibration times varied from approximately 30 min for $10^{-4} M$ metal concentrations to 24 hr for $10^{-6} M$. Smaller concentrations require longer times; however, since the rate of equilibration is known, the membranes may be removed prior to equilibration, although with a loss of sensitivity in the analytical method. The higher charged metals are concentrated to a greater extent. Using 0.01 M potassium nitrate as the bulk electrolyte and irradiation times of less than 5 min, the sensitivity of this technique with neutron activation analysis was found to be approximately $1 \times 10^{-6} M$ for Ag^+, $5 \times 10^{-6} M$ for Co^{2+}, $5 \times 10^{-7} M$ for Cu^{2+}, and $2 \times 10^{-10} M$ for In^{3+}. Using anodic stripping voltammetry an error of $\pm 5\%$ was obtained for Ag^+ in the range of $4-15 \times 10^{-5} M$.

Although it has not been generally used, reverse osmosis with cellulose acetate membranes is capable of concentrating organic species in water. In reverse osmosis a pressure exceeding the osmotic pressure of the solution to be concentrated is applied, forcing solvent across the membrane, with the solute remaining behind. Generally, the solvent, such as water, moves across the membrane by a different mechanism and at a much higher rate than the solute, which thereby becomes concentrated above the membrane. The possible application of this method to natural waters has been demonstrated with sucrose using a batch technique with cellulose acetate membranes and a pressure of 600 psi; it was shown that the percentage of recovery decreases with the volume reduction of the water being concentrated(280). Thus, for example, with volume reductions of 6.2 and 53, the recoveries were 70 and 47%, respectively, and the concentration factors were 4.3 and 25.0, respectively. This method was also studied with sewage effluents and waters spiked with anionic surfactants and lignin(281). The effluent forced through the membrane generally contained less than 0.1% concentration of the soluble species in the feed compared to the original solutions, the feed becoming more concentrated in the process. Recently, reverse osmosis membranes consisting of hydrous gel mixtures of synthetic polyanions and polycations have been developed that permit relatively high flow rates at reasonably low pressures of 100 psi (282). Such membranes may be used to concentrate high molecular weight species, such as proteins, by reverse osmosis (283).

Dialysis has been used in concentrating and identifying high molecular weight material in water and separating it from inorganic salts and low molecular weight species. In this technique the low molecular weight species diffuse across the membrane, leaving the high molecular weight material behind. In one such application, dialysis was used to demonstrate the presence of high molecular weight (greater than 10,000) material in tap water; the polysaccharide and protein assays indicated concentrations for each in the range of 80–100 μg/liter(284). To analyze the composition of organic matter causing a yellow color in a pond, dialysis was used to distinguish between low and high molecular weight species(285). After membrane filtration, evaporation, and freeze drying, 20% of the soluble freeze-dried material was found to be nondialyzable.

Although these various membrane techniques for concentrating, separating, and identifying soluble species have not been widely applied to the analysis of such waters as are of interest here, the few applications noted above show some of their capabilities. Although other techniques are likely to be more useful for low molecular weight species, reverse osmosis and dialysis are powerful techniques for identifying, concentrating, and separating high molecular weight material.

C. Colloidal and Particulate Matter

Membranes which prevent the transport of colloidal and particulate matter by acting as filters or sieves are useful for both concentrating such species and distinguishing between them and soluble material in water. In such applications water and soluble species are forced through the membranes under pressure. A material widely used for this purpose is the so-called membrane filter, which consists of cellulose esters with uniform pore sizes that screen particles larger than the effective pore diameters(286). Such membranes are available commercially with thicknesses of 130–150 μ and porosities of 75–80% (Millipore Filter Corporation, Bedford, Massachusetts; Gelman Instrument Company, Ann Arbor, Michigan). They have limitations, however, for accurate determination of particle sizes because of their ability to retain some smaller particles in their pores due to Van der Waal's interactions(9). Nevertheless, they are useful as a rapid method for grossly distinguishing between soluble and insoluble material in water(9,287). Although they are available with different nominal pore sizes, ranging from 10 mμ to 8 μ, a frequently used membrane in the characterization of natural, treated, and waste water is that with 0.45-μ pores. Other filtration membranes, such as those made of glass fibers or metal, may also be used for this purpose(287).

Membrane filters have been used to concentrate suspended radioactive material in water and industrial wastes(288). In this technique 200–1000 ml are filtered and the membrane is then oven-dried. The alpha and beta radioactivity on the membrane is then measured in an internal proportional gas flow counter; the sensitivity of the method is 10 pCi/liter for beta activity and 2 pCi/liter for alpha activity.

The insoluble concentrations of some trace elements in streams have been determined by separation with 0.45-μ membrane filters and analysis by direct current arc emission spectroscopy(289). In this technique the membranes with the trapped particles are ashed prior to analysis. The low ash content of the membranes, of the order of 0.0001% by weight, is a useful characteristic for such analyses(9). Membrane filters(0.45 μ) have been used to distinguish between soluble and insoluble forms of nitrogen- and phosphorus-containing compounds in estuaries(290). In addition, using this technique, it was found that the recoveries of soluble forms of some types of both nitrogen and phosphorus were improved with prior filtration, presumably because of the interference of suspended matter with the analytical techniques.

A comparison of glass fiber, asbestos, and membrane filters for determining the suspended solids in raw sewage, primary effluent, final effluent, and industrial wastes disclosed that there was no statistical difference in the results obtained among these different filter types (291); it was concluded that the use of the glass fiber filter was the method of choice by virtue of its faster filtration time.

It has been noted that it is frequently desirable to separate suspended and particulate matter in water samples using 0.45-μ membrane filters at the time of collection, rather than waiting until the samples reach a laboratory(292). In this way any subsequent chemical changes that might occur to modify the distribution between the two fractions are avoided. A portable, all-plastic pressure filter apparatus suitable for use with such membrane filters has been described(292). It is capable of use in the field filtration of up to several liters of water and may be operated by hand-powered air pumps. In one application it was reported that a 200-ml sample was filtered in 10 min.

There have been many reported uses of membrane and other filters for separating soluble and insoluble material in water. The examples discussed represent typical materials to which they have been applied. Although the separations are not perfectly defined with respect to the size of species retained or passed through the filter, both because of some degree of heterogeneity in pore size and because of the adsorption of some small particles noted above, nevertheless filtration by membranes is probably the most rapid, simple, and inexpensive technique available to the analyst for separating and distinguishing between soluble and particulate matter in water. Difficulties may arise, however, with the intermediate size range, namely that of colloidal species, due to their notorious property of adsorbing onto surfaces.

D. Bacteria and Viruses

Membrane filters are widely used for the concentration of bacteria in water, and various membrane techniques have been recently utilized for viruses as well. Clark et al.(293) and Goetz and Tsuneishi(286) described the use of membrane filters in concentrating, culturing, and enumerating bacteria in water, and there is now a standardized membrane filter technique for the coliform group(5). It was noted that other methods of bacterial analysis of water are limited in the volumes that can be examined; thus, for plate counts the limit is generally 1–2 ml, and with test tubes, 10–100 ml(286). One of the principal advantages of the membrane filter is that much larger quantities of water can be examined in relatively short times. With a typical 0.45-μ pore size, 10-cm²-area filter, the flow rate is 1000–1200 ml/min using a vacuum developed by a water aspirator.

The upper surface of the membrane, that exposed to the test solution being filtered, contains the relatively uniform, fine pore structure where the particles are trapped. The lower portion of the membrane has a looser pore structure which facilitates the high flow rate. In filtering inert pigment particles it was shown that they are trapped only in the top 10 μ of a membrane with a thickness of 150 μ(286). This ability of the membrane filter to trap bacteria only at the membrane surface is useful in the subsequent culturing and enumeration procedure. Electron micrographs have shown that *E. coli,* for example, are effectively retained on the surface. When the bottom surface of the membrane is placed, after filtration, on a liquid or semiliquid nutrient medium, the medium moves through the membrane pore structure and effectively contacts or wets the bacteria on the other side. With incubation, the colonies on the upper surface of the membrane are free to grow and often develop in as little as 4 hr(286).

In measuring the efficiency of a membrane filter in removing bacteria, it was found that when 50–100 ml containing 2×10^4 to 9×10^5 particles of *Staphylococcus aureus, E. coli,* or *Bacillus subtilis (globigii)* were filtered, generally all the bacteria were trapped; occasionally, one to three organisms were detected in the filtrate, and this was attributed to leakage around the edges or accidental contamination(286). Although 0.45-μ pore size membranes have high efficiency for bacteria generally found in fresh water, there is evidence that some marine bacteria require finer porosity membranes(294). After using a 0.45-μ filter for marine water, filtration of the effluent with 0.22-μ membranes was found to trap an additional small number of bacteria, such as those in the genus *Spirillum,* which are rarely isolated in one-stage filtration with 0.45-μ membranes.

In addition to their widespread use in concentrating and enumerating bacteria of the coliform group, membrane filters have been utilized for other bacteria as well. For example, iron bacteria, *Gallionella* sp., and *Leptothrix* sp. have been identified by this technique in wellwater used for a municipal supply(295). Also, a culturing medium has been developed which is completely selective for enterococci, and this technique is applicable for counting these bacteria in water and sewage(296). Such bacteria are also referred to as fecal streptococci; a standardized method has been developed with such a culturing medium for stream pollution surveys and for determining the sanitary quality of lakes, bathing areas, and wells, since fecal streptococci are indicators of fecal pollution(5).

Some of the limitations of the membrane filtration technique for the bacterial analysis of water and sewage have been discussed(297). Thus, samples with large quantities of colloidal or suspended material can interfere with the filtration or subsequent culturing procedure. In analyzing coliform bacteria, the presence of excessively high concentrations of noncoliform bacteria that grow on Endo-type broth can interfere with the development and enumeration of the coliform colonies; the presence of zinc and copper at concentrations of 1 mg/liter or more can interfere as well.

A variety of membrane techniques have been developed or demonstrated for the purpose of concentrating viruses in water. In one such method a membrane filter was used to concentrate and enumerate a bacterial virus (bacteriophage), T2 coliphage, with the intention of developing this technique as an indicator of the presence of other viruses, just as coliform bacteria are used as a measure of bacteriological contamination in water (298). Although the validity of this technique as a viral indicator is yet to be proved, nevertheless it was found that such a bacteriophage could be enumerated by mixing *E. coli* B with the phage suspension, filtering the mixture, and counting the number of plaques that develop on the bacterial colonies grown on M-Endo broth. The method was compared to a soft agar technique and was shown to be less precise but capable of measuring phage at lower concentrations.

Several other membrane techniques for concentration purposes have been considered in a symposium on the transmission of viruses through water(299). In one such method a 0.45-μ membrane filter was used to concentrate Coxsackie virus A9 in 1-liter suspensions of tap water(300). The virus adsorbed onto the membrane and was eluted from it with 80–90% efficiency by 1 ml of a phosphate-buffered saline solution containing 30–50% agamma chicken serum. It was concluded that the efficiency of recovery was at most 50%, and that there is at least a 50% probability of detecting virus by this method when present at a level of two plaque-forming units per liter.

Osmotic filtration (called "hydro-extraction" by the authors) was used to concentrate echovirus 9 (PL 88) and poliovirus 1 using cellulose dialyzing bags(301). In a typical experiment a 1-liter aqueous sample with a seeded virus suspension was placed in a dialysis bag, which was then inserted in a container filled with moist polyethylene glycol of molecular weight 3000–3700 (Carbowax 4000). As a result of the osmotic gradient, water and other diffusible species (but not viruses) moved across the membrane, thereby concentrating the virus suspension. After approximately 18 hr the reduction in water volume was sufficient to achieve a concentration factor of about 100 for the virus. The method was tested using saline water, clarified sewage, distilled water, and a phosphate buffer solution. With echovirus and poliovirus, recovery efficiencies of 40–60 and 24–61%, respectively, were obtained, with concentration factors of 10 and 50–100, respectively. It was concluded that with further development concentration factors of 1000 or more could be achieved, and that this was a particularly useful technique when ultracentrifuges were not available.

Another filtration technique for viruses uses alginate gel membranes on which the viruses collect and from which they are subsequently removed by dissolving the membrane in a 3.8% solution of sodium citrate(302). The concentrated virus suspension in the citrate-alginate solution may then be cultured in human amnion or monkey kidney cells. With this technique, drinking water, surface and bathing water, and sewage were analyzed, and it was found that when high quantities of suspended matter are present, pretreatment such as by centrifugation or prefiltration is necessary. Depending on the nature of the sample, 10 min to 2 hr are required to filter 1 liter. In a laboratory study of polio virus filtered from 10-liter suspensions, recovery ranged from 25 to 100%. Using this method with raw sewage and effluent from a treatment plant, positive indications of polio, Coxsackie, and other viruses occurred more frequently than when using direct innoculation without preconcentration.

In conclusion, the use of membrane filters to facilitate the analysis of bacteria in water is a well-established and highly useful technique. In recent attempts at similarly isolating viruses in water as possible agents of disease, a variety of membrane techniques have been utilized and show promise because of their simplicity and low cost (see Chap. 13).

IX. Carbon Adsorption

A. Introduction

Active (or activated) carbon refers to any form of carbon that has adsorptive capabilities. Although it was used as early as 1918 as a material for concentrating and separating chemicals in natural waters in order to facilitate analysis(303), active carbon has received wider attention and development for such applications more recently following the publication by Braus et al.(304) describing the active carbon filtration of 5000–75,000 gal of surface water, followed by the extraction of the filter with diethyl ether and then separation of the extract into neutral, acidic, basic, and amphoteric compounds. This technique is now widely used, with chloroform as the extractant, for monitoring raw and finished drinking water quality(5), with 200 mg/liter of carbon chloroform extract (CCE) being the recommended maximum for drinking water(305).

However, filtration by the carbon adsorption method (CAM) has also been used to identify specific organic chemicals in a variety of fresh and treated waters, and large-scale units capable of filtering several hundred thousand gallons of water have been utilized(306,307). The CAM has been shown to be useful for concentrating and recovering chlorinated insecticides because of its ability to sample large quantities of water in a practicable manner, although the recoveries are usually not complete (308). In spite of its known deficiencies, the CAM is still a useful tool for concentrating water samples, particularly when the analyst is confronted with determining the very small concentrations of trace organic chemicals found in most natural waters.

B. The Adsorption Process

1. NATURE OF THE CARBON

The chemical and physical nature of the surface of active carbon is of interest when considering its ability to adsorb specific organic compounds. These properties have been reviewed by Hassler(308a) and Snoeyink and Weber(309), from whom much of the discussion in this section is taken.

Active carbon is a highly porous material with a surface area, most of which is internal, as high as 2500 m²/g. Since it is prepared from a wide variety of carbonaceous materials and different activation processes are utilized, its physicochemical structure and adsorptive properties vary. The first stage in activation involves carbonization to produce a char. This is usually done by heating the raw material at a temperature below 600°C in the absence of air to drive off volatile fractions, producing a porous structure; it is frequently done with the addition of dehydrating metal salts. The char is then activated, for example, by heating with steam or carbon dioxide at temperatures between 800 and 1000°C, to produce the large surface area characteristic of active carbon. The resulting porous structure is heterogeneous, some of the micropores being of the order of 4–10 Å in diameter. The resulting carbon material has been considered to consist of either microcrystals of hexagonal carbon or a complex organic polymer.

Assuming that microcrystals of carbon are present, there would be two distinctly different types of surfaces associated with them: planar surfaces and edges. The planar surfaces would be likely to interact with adsorbing organic compounds through Van der Waals[1] forces, typical of a physical adsorption process. Edges and other raised positions on the crystals would tend to be involved in electron-sharing reactions typical of chemisorption.

In addition to the carbon itself, the inorganic salts utilized in its manufacture can influence and participate in its surface structure. Thus, there is evidence, for example, of iron–carbon centers in active carbons used as catalysts in oxidation processes, and such metal salts would, therefore, be likely to be involved with the sorption by the carbon of some organic compounds in aqueous systems. There is also evidence for a variety of organic oxygen groups due to the interaction of molecular oxygen with the carbon in the activation process, forming surface oxides with characteristics of carboxyl, phenolic hydroxyl, and carbonyl groups (310). These groups can also be formed by oxidation in aqueous solution at room temperature and can influence the sorption capability of active carbon. The presence of such groups can also account for the pH dependence on the equilibrium and kinetics of sorption of some organic compounds. Similarly, there is evidence that the net charge on the carbon particles is affected by pH adjustment, presumably as a result of its effect on the dissociation of such weak acid constituents on the carbon surface (311).

The catalytic and oxidative characteristics of active carbon surfaces can also present difficulties to the analyst, in that sorbed organic materials may oxidize (312) or otherwise react. It has been shown, for example, that phenol sorbed onto active carbon forms quinones (29). Similarly, it has been found that, unless the carbon was pretreated with acid, recovery of some organic solutes may be incomplete due to their destruction on the carbon surface (8).

2. ADSORPTION EQUILIBRIUM

The capacity of active carbon for adsorbing an organic solute will be determined by the equilibrium between that solute in the aqueous phase and on the carbon surface. Such equilibrium adsorption isotherms on active carbon have been measured by Weber and Morris for a wide variety of organic solutes, including various straight chain alkylbenzene sulfonates, phenol, o- and p-nitrochlorobenzene, and DDT (313). It was found that the adsorption isotherm is usually of the Langmuir type (see Sec. VI.B.2.b), the equation for which is

$$X = (X_m bC)/(1 + bC) \qquad (23)$$

where X is the equilibrium concentration of solute adsorbed onto the carbon surface (in moles of solute per gram of carbon), b is a constant which is a measure of the adsorption "affinity," and C is the equilibrium concentration of adsorbing solute in solution. This Langmuir model and its equation assume a maximum adsorption, corresponding to a mono-layer on the surface, of value X_m. It was observed that X_m increased with molecular weight for the alkyl benzene sulfonates, the values being one-half to one-third that of the phenol; it was also observed that b varied among the solutes studied.

At low solution concentrations Eq. (23) reduces to

$$X = X_m b C \qquad (24)$$

such that the adsorption is directly proportional to the ambient solution concentration, the product $X_m b$ being the proportionality constant. Typical values of $X_m b$ were 120 and 1820 liters/g for phenol and 2-dodecylbenzene sulfonate, respectively. For the low solute concentra-tions where this linear region of the Langmuir isotherm is applicable, the $X_m b$ factor is more important than X_m alone in determining the quantity of solute capable of adsorbing onto the carbon. Since $X_m b$ can vary significantly among solutes, it is also expected, at least if equilibrium is attained, that removal of such solutes from aqueous solutions of very low concentrations will vary as well. However, it is also possible that the solution concentration of the adsorbing solute may be high enough to correspond to the nonlinear portion of the isotherm, and even be in the region of monolayer coverage. In such a situation X_m may limit the sorption capability of the carbon for the solute in question. For the various alkylbenzene sulfonates studied, solution concentrations in the range of 3–5 μM resulted in monolayer coverage, whereas the corres-ponding value for phenol was 100 μM. Greater removal of a solute by adsorption onto active carbon may be achieved, if its initial ambient solution is in the linear region of the isotherm, than for the larger concentrations corresponding to monolayer coverage.

In utilizing active carbon for adsorbing organic solutes from natural waters containing a complex mixture, the possible competition between such solutes for the carbon surfaces can influence their respective sorption equilibria(314). It was found, in studying such competition between various pairs of phenol, dodecylbenzene sulfonate, nitrochlorobenzene, and dodecyl sulfate, that there was a mutual reducing effect on X_m, the monolayer or saturation coverage. In each case, nevertheless, Langmuir-type adsorption occurred, and it was concluded that this was a strong indication that the Langmuir model is broadly applicable to the adsorp-tion of water pollutants on carbon. It was also noted that the total capacity of the carbon was greater for these pairs of solutes than for any single adsorbing species in its pure aqueous solution. Elsewhere it was found that on continuously filtering a relatively concentrated mixture of n-butanol and n-amyl acetate through active carbon, the acetate continued to be adsorbed at the expense of the butanol after saturation of the carbon is achieved. This indicates a "preference" of the carbon which may influence the efficiency of uptake in concentrating a complex mixture after a large portion of the available carbon surface is utilized(315).

The pH of the ambient aqueous solution may also influence the interaction with carbon, as was shown for 3-dodecylbenzene sulfonate, such that its adsorption generally decreased with increasing pH; at pH 2 adsorption was 50% higher than at pH 8(313). Similarly, the presence of inorganic salts can affect adsorption; thus, for sodium benzene sulfonate in 2×10^{-4} and $4 \times 10^{-4} M$ calcium chloride solutions, the higher salt concentration significantly reduced the equilibrium adsorption(310). Elsewhere it was shown for dieldrin, lindane, parathion, and endrin that adsorption was lower in river water compared to distilled water, and that the presence of dieldrin and lindane reduced the adsorption of parathion(316).

Pretreatment of the active carbon, especially by oxidation or reduction, can have a significant effect on its adsorption capability(310). Thus, wet oxidation by hypochlorite or permanganate increased the equilibrium adsorption of phenol by a factor of 8, and subsequent chemical reduction diminished the phenol adsorption.

In conclusion, the state of the carbon surface, the solution pH, the presence of various inorganic salts, and the competition with other adsorbing species may affect the adsorption of a solute. In order, therefore, to maximize the adsorption in any active carbon concentrating technique, all of these variables should be controlled or at least recognized as possible influences on removal and, hence, recovery.

3. ADSORPTION KINETICS

Since active carbon particles are porous matrices, similar in some respects to ion exchange resins, some of the factors influencing the rate of adsorption on active carbon should be similar as well (see Sec. VII. B.2). Batch kinetic studies for aqueous organic systems have been made by Weber and Morris, who found that in general the initial uptake of a solute on active carbon was proportional to $t^{1/2}$, in agreement with intraparticle diffusion being the rate-limiting process(317). Such a mechanism requires that the adsorption rate vary inversely with the square of the carbon particle diameter, and this relationship was found to hold as well.

Weber and Morris also found that, for a homologous series of 2-alkyl-benzene sulfonates, the smaller the molecule, the greater its rate of uptake; also, in a study of isomers of dodecylbenzene sulfonate, the molecule with the greater branching adsorbed at a lower rate. The effect of concentration of a solute on its relative rate of uptake is of interest in the use of active carbon as a concentrating material. It was found that, although the absolute rate of adsorption increased with initial concentration of solute, the fraction of solute adsorbed per unit time increased with decreasing solute concentration.

It was shown for 3-dodecylbenzene sulfonate that decreasing the pH increased the rate of uptake; this same phenomenon had been observed in measuring the equilibrium adsorption(313), and in both cases was considered to be due to the effect of pH on the state of charge of the carbon. Similarly, it was shown that for a binary mixture of adsorbing solutes there was a mutual inhibiting effect on the rate of adsorption, just as there had been for the adsorptive capacity(314).

Finally, it should be noted that increasing the stirring rate in these batch kinetic studies increased the rate of uptake, up to 500 rpm. This is an indication that at the lower stirring rate there was probably some influence of film control on the rate.

Since active carbon as a concentration tool is generally utilized in continuous flow systems, these studies have great relevance for its capability for efficient removal. Thus, the selection of carbon particle size and solution flow rate would be expected to influence removal, both because of the intraparticle diffusion-limiting mechanism and the possibility for film diffusion at low flow rates. Just as for the equilibrium case, other solution variables, such as solute concentration, pH, and competition with other adsorbing species, affect the rate. Although it is not possible to favorably adjust all of these variables in using the CAM, the analyst should be aware of their effects.

C. Desorption and Recovery

In addition to the possibility of incomplete adsorption of an organic solute on the active carbon, the desorption process, which is achieved by extraction with a variety of organic solvents, may similarly be incomplete. Also, the possibility of degradation or reaction of the adsorbed solute exists. The nature of the solvent or sequence of solvents, the technique of air drying the water-wet carbon, and the extraction time are all variables that should be considered in optimizing recovery.

It has been found that the desorption efficiency depends on the extracting solvent and the adsorbed compound. Thus, it has been noted that chlorinated hydrocarbons and organics associated with taste and odor problems are usually extracted by chloroform, while carboxylic acids and humic materials are extracted by methanol(306). It was shown that extraction of several chlorinated insecticides by chloroform recovered only 75–85% of that which was adsorbed(308). Similarly, the CAM was used with chloroform extraction for the recovery and analysis of phenol and substituted phenols, and it was found that recovery ranged from 50–80% for carbon that had filtered river waters dosed at the 0.5- to 1.0-μg level(318). It was also noted that other investigators obtained recoveries for such compounds in the range of 54–95% but that the overall recovery for extraction and subsequent separation was 40–60%.

There have been various efforts to maximize recovery by improvement of the extraction procedure. One such study noted that the necessity for air drying the carbon and the subsequent extraction with chloroform and methanol sometimes lead to low and erratic recoveries(319). The study compared the extraction of water-wet carbon by a mixture of propylene dichloride and methanol and the extraction of air-dried carbon by chloroform, followed by methanol. With the former solvent pair the recovery for phenol, substituted phenols, and ABS varied from 84–96%, while with the chloroform-methanol sequence, it was 64–76%. Furthermore, a comparison of the two extracting systems for the carbon filtration of waste water and river water samples indicated that there was 33–50% additional recovery of total weight of extract using propylene dichloride-methanol. It was also noted that 96% of the adsorbed phenol could be recovered by simply pouring two successive 900-ml portions of this solvent mixture over the water-wet active carbon.

Air drying the active carbon prior to extraction can reduce recovery due to evaporation losses or oxidation. In comparing the total weight of extracts of carbon used to filter river water, it was found that direct extraction of the water-wet carbon increased recovery by 22% with chloroform and by 600% with ethanol(320). However, in a similar comparison of the pyridine extraction of acetophenone from water-wet carbon versus air-dried carbon, there was no significant difference(243); with one extraction in both cases the recovery was approximately 65%, and for two successive extractions, 85%.

It is thus apparent that the choice of solvent and extraction method is important in obtaining the maximum recovery of organic compounds adsorbed on active carbon; it is also apparent that recovery is frequently incomplete, and this should be recognized and assessed, along with the extent of initial removal and possible degradation, in utilizing active carbon as a concentration technique.

D. Monitoring with Active Carbon

A standardized CAM for monitoring water quality utilizes both a powdered and a coarse grain activated carbon in a cylindrical pipe 3 in. in diameter and 18 in. long(320a); it recommends a flow rate of 0.25 gpm (gallons per minute) and a total flow of 5000 gal, thus requiring approximately 14 days. Following air drying of the wet carbon, the carbon is extracted with chloroform, which is then evaporated and the residue weighed; the residue is referred to as the carbon chloroform extract (CCE) of the filtered water, expressed in micrograms per liter. It is noted that this method does not, and is not intended to, measure the total organic content in water, that recoveries may range from 50–90%, and that reproducibility is generally within 10%. It is stated that the technique is useful as an indication of undue stress on a water, particularly due to synthetic chemicals from industrial sources, and that the recommended maximum of 200 μg/liter of CCE for drinking water is justified in that waters not meeting this standard are likely to be objectionable, as judged by taste and odor. It is also stated that clean surface waters and groundwaters usually contain 25–50 μg/liter of CCE. It has also been noted that this technique is useful as a screening procedure because of its low cost and ease of use, and that, for surface water samples from a wide variety of sources, generally 90–99% had CCE less than 200 μg/liter(321).

This standardized technique for nonspecific monitoring of organic content has also been utilized with a sequence of chloroform and methanol extractions, the extract from the latter being referred to as the carbon alcohol extract (CAE)(306). It was noted that a nonpolluted water may contain less than 100 μg/liter of CAE, while polluted waters may contain several hundred micrograms per liter; also, for fresh industrial pollution CCE exceeds CAE, whereas otherwise CAE may exceed CCE severalfold.

There have been a variety of studies aimed at improving the recovery of nonspecific organics by the CAM, including studies on the adjustment of flow rates, total flow, pH, pretreatment of the water, and the use of multiple filters in series. One such study investigated the influence of pH, sedimentation, and diatomite prefiltration on the ability of a standard CAM to adsorb organic material(322). It was concluded from the measurement of chemical oxygen demand (COD) and threshold odor number (TON) that the major portion of the organic compounds in the river water was associated with particulate matter. It was found that the combination of sedimentation, prefiltration, and adjustment of the pH to 3.5 prior to the carbon filtration resulted in an increase of more than

80% in the CCE compared to that of the standard CAM; similar increases were found when other solvents were used as extractants. Elsewhere it was found that using a sand prefilter resulted in a 10% increase in CCE, although there was a reduction in CAE(*323*).

The effect of flow rate on the recovery of fluorescein and DDT was investigated and in both cases increasing the flow rate reduced the efficiency of recovery(*324*); with DDT the logarithm of the quantity of DDT adsorbed decreased in proportion to the length along the carbon filter at low flow rates, indicating that adjustment of the length of the carbon filter can improve recovery. It was concluded that, although the adsorption efficiency will decrease with increasing flow rate, more material may be recovered in shorter times by increasing the flow rate, and this may be advantageous in some cases.

Another study of the influence of flow rate and contact time on the standard CAM showed that both the CCE and CAE for river water that had passed through sand filters increased with decreased flow rate(*325*).

A contact time of 5–10 min, which would correspond to flow rates of 60–120 ml/min, was recommended; it was also recommended that the maximum flow be 4000 gal, since much larger flows resulted in lower efficiency of adsorption. It was found that the reproducibility of the CCE among four parallel runs was within 2% and that 84% of the CCE was recovered with an extraction time of 24 hr, the basis being that all is extracted in 72 hr.

An investigation of the effect of total flow and the use of multiple filters in series for analyzing river water found that, depending on the total flow and using a flow rate of 0.5 gpm, 42–67% of the total CCE from five filters in series was recovered by the first filter(*326*); three or four columns in series were required to recover 90% CCE. Using single filters and varying the total flow from 450 to 6635 gal, the maximum CCE of 107 μg/liter was obtained at a flow of 2680 gal. It was recommended that, for greater recovery at flow rates of 0.25–0.5 gpm, two carbon columns be used in series with a maximum sample volume of 2500 gal.

It is apparent that the recovery of CCE and CAE in the standard CAM can be significantly improved by adjustment and control of such variables as pretreatment of the water, flow rate, total flow, pH, length of the filter, and extraction time. It should be remembered, however, that a routine monitoring technique should be kept as simple and inexpensive as possible so as to be usable on a wide scale by untrained operators and with reasonably short sampling times. Certainly, the optimization of recovery by adjustment of many of these variables would reduce the practicability of the method. However, for nonroutine monitoring and the application of the CAM to the recovery of specific organic chemicals, serious consideration must be given to all of these effects.

E. Application to Specific Compounds

Following extraction of carbon by a solvent such as chloroform, the evaporated extract may be separated into groups by the use of differential solubility methods(304). Such separations may categorize the extract according to the weight of ether insolubles, water insolubles, bases, weak acids, strong acids, and neutrals. In petroleum wastes the neutral group was found to be the largest, containing 58–85% of the total(327). It has been noted that the neutral group from the CCE is generally larger than the water-soluble group for polluted waters by factors as high as 11:1(323). The analysis of phenol and substituted phenols in the weak acid fraction of a CCE from surface water has been performed by separation of that fraction using thin layer chromatography on silica gel (318). Several such phenolic compounds were separated and identified at the 0.1- to 25-μg level, depending on the compound and the spray reagent. Eleven compounds identified in CAM extracts from an industrially contaminated river water were associated with odor and all but one were components of the neutral fraction(306).

The CAM has been used extensively in the recovery and identification of chlorinated pesticides. One early study for several such compounds used column chromatography on the CCE to remove oxygen-containing compounds that interfered with the subsequent identification by infrared spectroscopy analysis(308). The procedure was judged to be sensitive to 2–10 mg of insecticide in the original water sample, and the overall quantitative recovery was of the order of 50% for each insecticide (see Chap. 23).

The CAM in conjunction with gas chromatography was used to determine toxaphene and gamma benzene hexachloride in rivers and potable water supplies in an agricultural basin(328). After some cleanup procedures, the CCE was analyzed by microcoulometric gas chromatography and the recovery by the total procedure was found to be 40–50% for water samples spiked at the 0.5- to 1.0-μg/liter level. Similarly, paper chromatography was used to separate and identify several chlorinated hydrocarbon pesticides in CCE at levels of 2 μg/liter or less in river water(212). Most of these compounds were found to concentrate in the aromatic portion of the neutral fraction, relatively free from substances that would interfere with the subsequent paper chromatographic identification. It was estimated that losses in the solubility and chromatographic separations can be as much as 20%.

Silica gel thin layer chromatography has been used as a separation and cleanup technique for the analysis of chlorinated pesticides by gas chromatography(*210*). Recoveries of the pesticides from the aromatic fractions were complete, and it was concluded that this procedure resulted in more accurate analysis of such complex mixtures than was previously possible.

Although the CAM has limitations with respect to the recovery of specific organic compounds, similar to those described previously in the more gross analysis of the weight of the CCE and CAE, it nevertheless has utility by virtue of its ability to concentrate large volumes of water in a practicable manner. However, when accurate determination of a specific compound is required, it is advisable to use spiking with known quantities of the compound of interest so as to determine its efficiency of recovery.

X. Distillation, Evaporation, and Sublimation

A. Introduction

There are a variety of methods for concentrating and separating species in water that involve removal of either a major or minor constituent as a gas or vapor. Thus, evaporation of water from an aqueous solution may serve to concentrate a solute of interest; this may be done as a normal boiling process at atmospheric pressure, or it may be performed at a reduced pressure and temperature, as in vacuum distillation. Water or other solvents may also be removed in freeze drying, where the frozen system is subjected to vacuum, causing the solvent to sublime, leaving a residue of the solute. For some applications water may be removed for the purpose of concentrating a solute, so as to increase the lower detection limit for a sample, while in other instances all the water may be removed in order to determine the total weight of residue or to utilize an analytical method that requires a solid sample.

Distillation may be performed in order to remove a volatile species that interferes with an analysis; or, conversely, a volatile species being analyzed may be distilled from the aqueous sample to separate it from interfering species that remain behind. At one time distillation as a means of fractionation in analysis was widely used; however, this technique currently is not generally used, having been supplanted by various chromatographic methods which are more versatile and efficient.

The theory and techniques of these methods are not discussed here, and the reader is referred to the general bibliography at the end of the chapter. However, various examples are presented to indicate the range of application.

B. Applications

Water is frequently removed by heat evaporation from an aqueous solution to concentrate a solute, so as to improve analytical sensitivity. Thus, in analyzing organic acids in river water, 3–4 liters of a filtered sample, which had been made basic with sodium hydroxide, were evaporated using heat and concentrated to 30 ml(329). Subsequent extraction with diethyl ether and further evaporation to 1 ml were followed by separation with column partition chromatography and analysis with paper chromatography.

In order to improve sensitivity in the analysis of cadmium, copper, nickel, lead, and zinc in wastes from metal plating operations and receiving streams, 100-ml samples were evaporated by heating with concentrated sulfuric acid, occasionally adding concentrated nitric acid(330). After subsequent reduction of hexavalent chromium and precipitation of iron, the sample was filtered and diluted to 10 ml prior to voltammetric analysis with a quiet pool mercury electrode. Concentrations as low as 0.01 mg/liter of each metal in the original sample could be determined.

In considering various techniques for the analysis of molybdenum in fresh water, a spectrographic method was described in which a 1000-ml sample was evaporated to 100 ml prior to subsequent treatment and analysis(265). Similarly, in a spectrochemical technique for the measurement of 19 minor elements, natural waters were composited and passed through a 0.45-μ membrane filter(331). After determining the total dissolved solids, a sample volume was selected, ranging from 100 ml to 2 liters, that contained 100 mg of solids. After adding nitric acid, the sample was evaporated until the volume had reduced to 4–5 ml, in preparation for subsequent spectrographic analysis.

In describing an improvement of a standard method for total residue in water by heat evaporation(331a), it was noted that this technique was time-consuming and inaccurate due to the volatilization, decomposition, or oxidation of organic or inorganic constituents(332). A vacuum rotary evaporation method was developed in which a round-bottomed flask containing the aqueous sample is rotated and heated at 40–50°C, and a vacuum applied. In analyzing four mixtures of known composition containing both organic and inorganic constituents, it was found that the recoveries using the standard method were 75–87%, while with vacuum evaporation they were 97–103%. Also, the total analysis time, including weighing and other manipulations, was considerably shorter for the vacuum method.

An example of a method involving evaporation of water and fusion of the remaining solids is the measurement of low levels of silicon in high pressure boiler waters, with spectrophotometric analysis of reduced β-molybdosilicic acid(333). Samples varying from 20 to 60 ml were heat-evaporated with added sodium carbonate and then fused. After further chemical treatment, replicate analyses of standards indicated that the limits of detection for total silicon were 23.3, 14.0, and 6.0 μg when the initial solution volumes were 20, 40, and 60 ml, respectively.

It has been noted that evaporation of seawater by heating is complicated by possible volatilization of some trace elements, spattering, and fractional crystallization which results in a nonhomogeneous sample(334). In order to eliminate these difficulties, freeze drying was utilized to concentrate seawater samples, leading to a 30-fold increase in sensitivity utilizing neutron activation analysis for trace element detection. A 100-ml sample was rapidly frozen as a thin layer on the walls of a rotating flask, and the ice then sublimed under vacuum. The remaining dry, very fine-grained powder containing the trace elements was then analyzed. Freeze drying has also been utilized in concentrating soluble organic matter in fresh water in order to avoid subjecting this material to the higher temperatures associated with evaporating the solution as a liquid(285).

Several standard methods involve distillation of the test species from water so as to eliminate or reduce interferences(334a). Thus, in the analysis of ammonia, the ammonia is often distilled from the sample, particularly when its concentration is lower than 0.2 mg/liter, when interferences may be present in the analysis by nesslerization or when there is to be a subsequent determination of albuminoid nitrogen. The distillation is usually performed from a buffered sample, and the distillate is collected in a boric acid solution to minimize ammonia losses due to subsequent vaporization. Some volatile organic compounds, such as formaldehyde, interfere with the analysis and may be distilled prior to the ammonia distillation by lowering the pH.

Interferences in the 4-aminoantipyrine analysis of phenol and other hydroxybenzene compounds are frequently eliminated by distilling these "phenols" prior to their analysis(334b). Similarly, cyanide is often distilled from a water sample prior to its analysis, both to separate it from possible interfering agents and to remove the cyanide from the metal ion with which it may be complexed. The sample is first acidified with sulfuric acid, and the cyanide is then distilled as HCN, which is trapped in a sodium hydroxide solution.

Fluoride in water is often analyzed by a colorimetric method involving the decoloration of a zirconium dye lake due to the formation of a zirconium fluoride complex(334c). There are several interferences in such analyses, for example, from iron, aluminum, and phosphate. In order to eliminate these interferences, the fluoride may be distilled and collected. Concentrated sulfuric acid is first added to the sample, to permit distillation at higher temperatures and to vaporize the fluoride. Steam distillation has the advantage of being faster than direct distillation, and it was shown that recovery is complete when the flask temperature is greater than 135°C(335). However, this technique results in dilution of the fluoride in the distillate, and requires preconcentration by evaporation when the fluoride in the original sample has a concentration of less than 0.4 mg/liter. Another example of steam distillation is the analysis of an algicide, phygon(336). Salt is added to the solution to raise the boiling temperature, and the distillate is extracted with chloroform and analyzed by ultraviolet spectrometry.

These various techniques involving evaporation, distillation, and sublimation must be used with care in order to avoid losses or carry over of undesirable material. Also, reduction of temperature is frequently useful to eliminate losses from degradation and chemical reactions in analyzing organic species, and this may be achieved by such techniques as sublimation and vacuum evaporation or distillation. In general, they are simple techniques involving inexpensive equipment and are therefore very useful in concentration and separation prior to the analysis of a wide variety of aqueous systems.

XI. Conclusions

Since most natural and treated waters contain a large number of components, many at trace concentrations, it is frequently necessary for the analyst to resort to concentration or separation techniques. Indeed, in some cases these are an integral part of the analysis, such as in the determination of dissolved solids by evaporation of the water, or the membrane filtration technique for the enumeration of bacteria. Nevertheless, whenever possible, analytical methods should be developed that are applicable to a sample without the need to resort to concentration or separation, which are an added expense and consumption of time. Thus, it is frequently more desirable to eliminate interferences by "masking," such as by complexation methods. A pertinent example of such a development which has eliminated the need for separation is the use of an ion-selective electrode for the analysis of fluoride. Whereas in previous colorimetric analysis it was usually necessary to separate the fluoride from interfering species by such methods as distillation or ion exchange, it is now possible to analyze fluoride with an electrode after complexing iron and aluminum, and this is now the method of choice(337). Comparable efforts are needed to improve sensitivity in many methods in order to eliminate the need to concentrate.

This chapter has attempted to describe and, by examples, indicate the range of applicability of most currently used methods of concentration and separation. However, some techniques which are not widely used or which require expensive or elaborate equipment have not been discussed here. Continuous flow and density gradient centrifugation have been used to separate suspended and colloidal particles, macromolecules, viruses, and bacteria in water(338,339), and are discussed in Chap. 12. Electrophoresis has not generally been used for separating species in environmental waters. Nevertheless, an apparatus using forced flow electrophoresis has been described and shown to be useful for concentrating bacteriophage in water(340). An elaborate instrument for continuous particle electrophoresis is available for separating and collecting colloidal species and particles as large as $100\,\mu$, based on their differing electrophoretic mobilities(341). This relatively expensive instrument is capable of fractionating such diverse species as inorganic colloids, bacteria, and viruses. Most of the other concentration and separation methods described in this chapter are available to modestly equipped laboratories, and all the techniques described are certainly appropriate and usable in nonroutine research. A new technique which should aid greatly in the separation and identification of trace substances in water is high-speed liquid chromatography.

The criteria for the selection of the appropriate technique for concentration or separation are generally the same as in the choice of the analytical method itself: accuracy, reliability, simplicity, speed, and efficiency of recovery. Certainly the experience of others is always useful, and the examples discussed in this chapter should prove useful in that respect. The limitations and advantages of the various techniques have been considered in their respective sections. Some of the methods are more useful for separation than for concentration, and vice versa. Thus, chromatography and ion exchange may be very useful as separation techniques, while freeze concentration and carbon adsorption are generally not selective and are used as concentration methods. Whatever the technique chosen, unless the analyst is experienced in its use, the extent of recovery should be measured and possible interferences in subsequent analysis assessed. Spiking with known quantities of the test species is frequently useful for these purposes.

In spite of the complexity of the aqueous systems with which the analyst is confronted, and the low concentrations of many species of interest, the various techniques available are capable of solving most concentration and separation needs. However, one of the important criteria for assessing an analytical method is simplicity, and this is frequently achieved by eliminating the additional step of concentration or separation. It is in that area that the analyst's energy and efforts should frequently be directed.

SELECTED BIBLIOGRAPHY

A. PRECIPITATION TECHNIQUES

E. W. Berg, *Physical and Chemical Methods of Separation,* McGraw-Hill, New York, 1963. Chaps. 14, 15.

T. Joyner, M. L. Healy, D. Chakravarti, and T. Koyanagi, *Environ. Sci. Tech.,* **1**, 417 (1967).

H. A. Laitinen, *Chemical Analysis,* McGraw-Hill, New York, 1960, Chaps. 6–10.

A. G. Walton, *The Formation and Properties of Precipitates,* Wiley (Interscience), New York, 1967.

B. LIQUID-LIQUID EXTRACTION

L. Alders, *Liquid-Liquid Extraction,* Elsevier, New York, 1955.

E. W. Berg, *Physical and Chemical Methods of Separation,* McGraw-Hill, New York, 1963, Chap. 3.

H. Irving and R. J. P. Williams, in *Treatise on Analytical Chemistry* (I. M. Kolthoff and P. J. Elving, eds.), Part I, Vol. 3, Wiley (Inter-science), New York, 1961, Chap. 31.

G. H. Morrison and H. Freiser, *Solvent Extraction in Analytical Chemistry,* Wiley, New York, 1957.

E. B. Sandell, *Colorimetric Determination of Traces of Metals,* 3rd ed., Wiley (Interscience), New York, 1959.

C. FREEZE CONCENTRATION

E. W. Berg, *Physical and Chemical Methods of Separation,* McGraw-Hill, New York, 1963, Chap. 9.

T. H. Gouw, in *Progress in Separation and Purification* (E. S. Perry, ed.), Vol. 1, Wiley (Interscience), New York, 1968, p. 57.

W. G. Pfann, *Zone Melting,* Wiley, New York, 1958.

D. ADSORPTIVE BUBBLE SEPARATIONS

R. Lemlich, *Ind. Eng. Chem.,* **60**(10), 17 (1968).

R. Lemlich, in *Progress in Separation and Purification* (E. S. Perry, ed.), Vol. 1, Wiley (Interscience), New York, 1968, Chap. 1.

A. J. Rubin, *J. Am. Water Works Assoc.,* **60**, 832 (1968).

E. Rubin and E. L. Gaden, Jr., in *New Chemical Engineering Separation Techniques* (H. M. Schoen, ed.), Wiley (Interscience), New York, 1962, Chap. 5.

F. Sebba, *Ion Flotation,* Elsevier, Amsterdam, 1962.

E. CHROMATOGRAPHY

R. J. Block, E. L. Durrum, and G. Zweig, *A Manual of Paper Chromatography and Electrophoresis,* 2nd ed., Academic, New York, 1968.

I. E. Bush, *The Chromatography of Steroids,* Pergamon, Oxford, 1961.

H. G. Cassidy, in *Technique of Organic Chemistry* (A. Weissberger, ed.), Vol. X, Wiley (Interscience), New York, 1957.

S. Dal Nogare and R. S. Juvet, Jr., *Gas-Liquid Chromatography,* Wiley (Interscience), New York, 1962.

L. S. Ettre and A. Zlatkis, *Practice of Gas Chromatography,* Wiley (Interscience), New York, 1967.

I. M. Hais and K. Macek, eds., *Paper Chromatography,* 3rd ed., Academic, New York, 1964.

J. G. Kirchner, in *Technique of Organic Chemistry* (A. Weissberger, ed.), Vol. XII, Wiley (Interscience), New York, 1967.

E. Lederer and M. Lederer, *Chromatography, A Review of Principles and Applications,* 2nd ed., Elsevier, Amsterdam, 1959.

E. Lederer and M. Lederer, in *Comprehensive Biochemistry* (M. Florkin and E. H. Stotz, eds.), Vol. IV, Elsevier, Amsterdam, 1963.

M. Lederer, ed., *Chromatographic Reviews,* Vols. I–VII, Elsevier, Amsterdam, 1959–1965.

K. Randerath, *Thin-Layer Chromatography,* 2nd ed., Academic, New York, 1965.

I. Smith and J. G. Feinberg, *Paper and Thin Layer Chromatography and Electrophoresis, A Teaching Level Manual,* 2nd ed., Shandon Scientific Co., London, 1965.

E. Stahl, ed., *Thin-Layer Chromatography, A Laboratory Handbook,* 2nd ed., Springer-Verlag, New York, 1969.

R. Stock and C. B. F. Rice, *Chromatographic Methods,* 2nd ed., Chapman and Hall, London, 1968.

F. Ion Exchange

C. B. Amphlett, *Inorganic Ion Exchangers,* Elsevier, New York, 1964.

F. Helfferich, *Ion Exchange,* McGraw-Hill, New York, 1962.

J. Inczedy, *Analytical Applications of Ion Exchangers,* Pergamon, New York, 1966.

G. J. Moody and J. D. R. Thomas, *Analyst,* **93**, 557 (1968).

O. Samuelson, *Ion Exchange Separation in Analytical Chemistry,* Wiley, New York, 1963.

G. Membrane Techniques

E. W. Berg, *Physical and Chemical Methods of Separation,* McGraw-Hill, New York, 1963, Chaps. 12, 13.

A. B. Cummins and F. B. Hutto, Jr., in *Technique of Organic Chemistry* (A. Weissberger, ed.), Part I, Vol. III, Wiley (Interscience), New York, 1956, Chap. V.

A. Goetz and N. Tsuneshei, *J. Am. Water Works Assoc.,* **43**, 943 (1951).

R. E. Stauffer, in *Technique of Organic Chemistry* (A. Weissberger, ed.), Part I, Vol. III, Wiley (Interscience), New York, 1956, Chap. I, Part 3.

S. Tuwiner, *Diffusion and Membrane Technology,* Reinhold, New York, 1962.

H. Carbon Adsorption

J. W. Hassler, *Active Carbon,* Chemical Publishing Co., Brooklyn, N.Y., 1951.

J. J. Kipling, *Adsorption from Solutions of Non-Electrolytes,* Academic, New York, 1965.

F. M. Middleton, A. A. Rosen, and R. H. Burttschell, *Manual for Recovery and Identification of Organic Chemicals in Water,* Robert A. Taft Sanitary Engineering Center, Cincinnati, Ohio, 1959.

V. L. Snoeyink and W. J. Weber, Jr., *Environ. Sci. Tech.,* **1**, 228 (1967).

I. Distillation, Evaporation, and Sublimation

E. W. Berg, *Physical and Chemical Methods of Separation,* McGraw-Hill, New York, 1963, Chap. 2.

G. Broughton, in *Technique of Organic Chemistry* (A. Weissberger, ed.), Part I, Vol. III, Wiley (Interscience), New York, 1956, Chap. VI.

A. Weissberger, ed., *Technique of Organic Chemistry*, Vol. IV, Wiley (Interscience), New York, 1951.

REFERENCES

1. E. D. Goldberg, in *Chemical Oceanography* (J. P. Riley and G. Skirrow, eds.), Vol. 1, Academic, New York, 1965, Chap. 5.

2. R. C. Kroner and J. F. Kopp, *J. Am. Water Works Assoc.*, **57**, 150 (1965).

3. H. L. Kahn, in *Trace Inorganics in Water* (R. F. Gould, ed.), *Advances in Chemistry Series No. 73*, American Chemical Society, Washington, D.C., 1968, Chap. 11.

4. D. N. Hume, in *Equilibrium Concepts in Natural Water Systems* (R. F. Gould, ed.), *Advances in Chemistry Series No. 67*, American Chemical Society, Washington, D.C., 1967, Chap. 2.

5. *Standard Methods for the Examination of Water and Wastewater*, 12th ed., American Public Health Association, New York, 1966.

6. H. E. Allen, W. R. Matson, and K. H. Mancy, paper presented at the 41st Annual Conference of the Water Pollution Control Federation, Chicago, September, 1968.

7. A. A. Rosen, R. T. Skeel, and M. B. Ettinger, *J. Water Pollution Control Federation*, **35**, 777 (1963).

8. L. M. Jeffrey and D. W. Hood, *J. Marine Res.*, **17**, 247 (1958).

9. J. P. Riley, in *Chemical Oceanography* (J. P. Riley and G. Skirrow, eds.), Vol. 2, Academic, New York, 1965, Chap. 21.

10. *1968 Book of ASTM Standards, Part 23, Water; Atmospheric Analysis*, American Society for Testing and Materials, Philadelphia, 1968.

11. T. Joyner, M. L. Healy, D. Chakravarti, and T. Koyanagi, *Environ. Sci. Tech.*, **1**, 417 (1967).

12. H. A. Laitinen, *Chemical Analysis*, McGraw-Hill, New York, 1960, Chap. 10.

13. H. V. Weiss and M. G. Lai, *Anal. Chem.*, **32**, 475 (1960).

14. K. M. Chan and J. P. Riley, *Anal. Chim. Acta*, **34**, 337 (1966).

15. *Standard Methods for the Examination of Water and Wastewater*, 12th ed., American Public Health Association, New York, 1966, p. 349.

16. J. P. Riley and G. Topping, *Anal. Chim. Acta*, **44**, 234 (1969).

17. W. D. Silvey and R. Brennan, *Anal. Chem.*, **34**, 784 (1962).

18. W. Nernst, *Z. Physik. Chem.*, **8**, 110 (1891).

19. F. Kutscher and H. Stendel, *Z. Physiol. Chem.*, **39**, 474 (1903).

20. S. Wehrli, *Helv. Chim. Acta*, **20**, 927 (1937).

21. L. C. Craig and D. Craig, in *Technique of Organic Chemistry* (A. Weissberger, ed.), 2nd ed., Vol. III, Part I, Wiley (Interscience), New York, 1956, Chap. II.

22. L. C. Craig and O. Post, *Anal. Chem.*, **21**, 500 (1949).

23. J. J. Kolfenbach, E. R. Kooi, E. I. Fulmer, and L. A. Underkoffer, *Anal. Chem.*, **16**, 473 (1944).

24. R. F. Gould (ed.), *Organic Pesticides in the Environment, Advances in Chemistry Series No. 60*, American Chemical Society, Washington, D.C., 1966.

25. W. L., Lamar, D. F. Goerlitz, and L. M. Low, *U.S. Geol. Surv. Water Supply Paper 1817B*, Washington, D.C., 1965.

26. F. K. Kawahara, J. J. Lichtenberg, and J. W. Eichelberger, *J. Water Pollution Control Federation*, **39**, 446 (1967).

27. A. V. Holden and K. Marsden, *Inst. Sewage Purif. J. Proc.*, 295 (1966).

28. K. Y. Vengershaya and R. A. Yakubova, *Gig. Sanit.*, **31**, 43 (1966).
29. R. D. Hoak, *Intern. J. Air Water Pollution*, **6**, 521 (1962).
30. E. G. Scheibel, *Chem. Eng. Progr.*, **44**, 681 (1948).
31. R. L. Bunch and M. B. Ettinger, *Purdue Univ. Eng. Bull., Ext. Ser. No. 118,* 1965, p. 93.
32. S. C. Caruso, H. C. Bramer, and R. D. Hoak, in *Developments in Applied Spectroscopy,* (W. K. Bair and E. L. Grove, eds.), Vol. 6, Plenum, New York, 1968, pp. 323–338.
33. J. F. Slowey, L. M. Jeffrey, and D. W. Hood, *Geochim. Cosmochim. Acta,* **26**, 607 (1962).
34. P. M. Williams, *Nature,* **189**, 219 (1961).
35. J. T. Cronin, II, Ph.D. Thesis, Oregon State Univ., Corvallis, 1967.
36. S. M. Stoller and R. B. Richards, *Reactor Handbook,* Vol. II, *Fuel Reprocessing,* 2nd ed., Wiley (Interscience), New York, 1961.
37. J. F. Kopp, R. C. Kroner, and D. L. Barnett, paper presented at 18th Pittsburgh Conference on Analytical Chemistry and Applied Spectroscopy, Pittsburgh, Pa., March, 1967.
38. B. G. Stephans and H. A. Suddeth, *Anal. Chem.,* **39**, 1478 (1967).
39. N. Ishiwatari, *Burseki Kagaku,* **14**, 305 (1965); through *Chem. Abstr.,* **63**, 6378g (1965).
40. H. Irving and J. P. Williams, in *Treatise on Analytical Chemistry* (I. M. Kolthoff and P. J. Elving, eds.), Part I, Vol. 3, Wiley (Interscience), New York, 1961, Chap. 31.
41. J. W. Wells and D. P. Hunter, *Analyst,* **73**, 671 (1948).
42. N. A. Gibson and R. A. White, *Anal. Chim. Acta,* **12**, 115 (1955).
43. E. L. Smith and J. E. Page, *J. Soc. Chem. Ind. (London),* **67**, 48 (1948).
44. C. P. Ogden, H. L. Webster, and J. Halliday, *Analyst,* **86**, 22 (1961).
45. F. L. Moore, *Anal. Chem.,* **29**, 1660 (1957).
46. T. H. Gouw, in *Progress in Separation and Purification* (E. S. Perry, ed.), Vol. 1, Wiley (Interscience), New York, 1968, pp. 57–82.
47. J. S. Mathews and N. D. Coggeshall, *Anal. Chem.,* **31**, 1124 (1959).
48. J. Shapiro, *Science,* **133**, 2063 (1961).
49. R. A. Baker, *Water Res.,* **1**, 61 (1967).
50. P. Sue, J. Pauly, and A. Nouaille, *Bull. Soc. Chim. France,* **5**, 593 (1968).
51. H. Schildknecht and A. Mannl, *Angew. Chem.,* **69**, 634 (1957).
52. H. Schildknecht and U. Hopf, *Chem. Ing. Tech.,* **33**, 352 (1961).
53. A. P. Black and R. F. Christman, *J. Am. Water Works Assoc.,* **55**, 897 (1963).
54. S. Kobayashi and G. F. Lee, *Anal. Chem.,* **36**, 2197 (1964).
55. J. Shapiro, *Anal. Chem.,* **39**, 280 (1967).
56. P. A. Kammerer and G. F. Lee, *Environ. Sci. Tech.,* **3**, 276 (1969).
57. R. A. Baker, *J. Water Pollution Control Federation* **37**, 1164 (1965).
58. R. A. Baker, *Water Res.,* **1**, 97 (1967).
59. B. L. Karger, R. B. Grieves, R. Lemlich, A. J. Rubin, and F. Sebba, *Separation Sci.,* **2**, 401 (1967).
60. A. J. Rubin, *J. Am. Water Works Assoc.,* **60**, 832 (1968).
61. H. Kishimoto, *Kolloid Z.,* **192**, 66 (1963).
62. E. Rubin and E. L. Gaden, in *New Chemical Engineering Separation Techniques,* (H. M. Schoen, ed.), Wiley (Interscience), New York, 1962, Chap. 5.
63. R. Lemlich, *Ind. Eng. Chem.,* **60**(10), 17 (1968).
64. C. A. Brunner and R. Lemlich, *Ind. Eng. Chem. Fundamentals,* **2**, 297 (1963).
65. R. B. Grieves and R. C. Aronica, *Intern. J. Air Water Pollution,* **10**, 31 (1966).

66. R. P. Poncha and B. L. Karger, *Anal. Chem.*, **37**, 422 (1965).

67. N. Takemura, T. Akiyama, and C. Nakajima, *Intern. J. Air Water Pollution*, **9**, 665 (1965).

68. B. L. Karger, R. P. Poncha, and M. M. Miller, *Anal. Chem.*, **38**, 764 (1966).

69. R. B. Grieves, C. J. Crandall, and R. K. Wood, *Intern. J. Air Water Pollution*, **8**, 501 (1964).

70. F. Sebba, *Nature*, **184**, 1062 (1959).

71. F. Sebba, *Ion Flotation*, Elsevier, Amsterdam, 1962.

72. V. M. Lovell and F. Sebba, *Anal. Chem.*, **13**, 1926 (1966).

73. B. M. Davis and F. Sebba, *J. Appl. Chem.*, **16**, 297 (1966).

74. R. B. Grieves and D. Bhattacharyya, *Separation Sci.*, **3**, 185 (1968).

75. A. J. Rubin, J. D. Johnson, and J. C. Lamb, *Ind. Eng. Chem. Process Design Develop.*, **5**, 368 (1966).

76. A. J. Rubin and J. D. Johnson, *Anal. Chem.*, **39**, 298 (1967).

77. J. A. Lusker and F. Sebba, *J. Appl. Chem.*, **16**, 129 (1966).

78. B. Dobias and V. Vinter, *Folia Microbiol.*, **11**, 314 (1966).

79. A. J. Rubin, E. A. Cassel, O. Henderson, J. D. Johnson, and J. C. Lamb, *Biotechn. Bioeng.*, **8**, 135 (1966).

80. A. J. Rubin, *Biotech. Bioeng.*, **10**, 89 (1968).

81. M. Tswett, *Ber. Deut. Botan. Ges.*, **24**, 316 (1906).

82. R. Kuhn and E. Lederer, *Naturwissenschaften*, **19**, 306 (1931).

83. R. Kuhn and E. Lederer, *Ber.*, **64B**, 1349 (1931).

84. J. C. Giddings, in *Dynamics of Chromatography*, Chromatographic Science Series (J. C. Giddings and R. A. Keller, eds.), Part 1, Vol. I, Dekker, New York, 1965.

85. J. C. Giddings, *Theory of Chromatography* (E. Heftmann, ed.), 2nd ed., Reinhold, New York, 1967, Chap. 3.

86. S. P. Brunauer, P. H. Emmett, and E. Teller, *J. Am. Chem. Soc.*, **60**, 309 (1938).

87. A. Tiselius, *Endeavour*, **11**, 5 (1952).

88. A. J. P. Martin and R. L. M. Synge, *Biochem. J.*, **35**, 1358 (1941).

88a. S. Dal Nogare and R. S. Juvet, Jr., *Gas–Liquid Chromatography*, Wiley, New York, 1962, p. 67.

89. L. C. Craig, *J. Biol. Chem.*, **155**, 519 (1944).

90. R. Stock and C. B. F. Rice, *Chromatographic Methods*, 2nd ed., Chapman and Hall, London, 1967, Chap. 1.

91. A. L. LeRosen, *J. Am. Chem. Soc.*, **64**, 1905 (1942).

92. A. Tiselius and S. Claesson, *Arkiv. Kemi Mineral. Geol.*, **B15(18)**, 1 (1942); through *Chem. Abstr.*, **38**, 35 (1944).

93. A. Tiselius, *Arkiv. Kemi Mineral. Geol.*, **A16**(18), 1 (1943); through *Chem. Abstr.*, **38**, 2895 (1944).

94. R. S. Alm, R. J. P. Williams, and A. Tiselius, *Acta Chem. Scand.*, **6**, 826 (1952).

95. D. M. Young and A. D. Crowell, *Physical Adsorption of Gases*, Butterworths, Washington, D.C., 1962, Chap. 2.

96. D. O. Hayward and B. M. V. Trapnell, *Chemisorption*, Butterworths, Washington, D.C., 1964, Chap. 1.

97. B. J. Mair, in *Treatise on Analytical Chemistry* (I. M. Kolthoff and P. J. Elving, eds.). Part 1. Vol. III. Wiley (Interscience), New York, 1961. Chap 34.

98. L. R. Snyder, *J. Chromatog.*, **6**, 22 (1961).

99. E. Stahl, *Thin-Layer Chromatography. A Laboratory Handbook*, Academic, New York, 1965, p. 31.

100. J. J. Wren, *Chromatog. Rev.*, **3**, 111 (1960).

101. L. R. Snyder, in *Advances in Analytical Chemistry and Instrumentation* (C. N. Reilley, ed.), Vol. 3, Wiley (Interscience), New York, 1963, p. 251.

102. L. R. Snyder, *J. Chromatog.,* **11**, 195 (1963).

103. L. R. Snyder, *Separation Sci.,* **1**, 191 (1966).

104. R. K. Iler, *The Colloid Chemistry of Silica and Silicates,* Cornell University Press, Ithaca, N.Y., 1955, Chap. 8.

105. A. V. Kiselev, in *The Structure and Properties of Porous Materials,* (D. H. Everett and F. S. Stone, eds.), Academic, New York, 1958, pp. 195–226.

106. V. Y. Davydor, A. V. Kiselev, and L. T. Zhuravlev, *Trans. Faraday Soc.,* **60**, 2254 (1964).

107. L. R. Snyder and J. W. Wood, *J. Phys. Chem.,* **70**, 3941 (1966).

108. C. H. Giles, in *Chromatography* (E. Heftman, ed.), 1st ed., Reinhold, New York, 1961, Chap. 4.

109. J. B. Peri, *J. Phys. Chem.,* **69**, 211, 220 (1965).

110. S. E. Tung and E. Meininch, *J. Catalysis,* **3**, 229 (1964).

111. J. W. Newsome, H. W. Heiser, A. S. Russell, and H. C. Stumpf, *Alumina Properties,* 2nd rev. ed., Aluminum Company of America, Pittsburgh, Pa., 1960.

112. C. G. Scott, *J. Inst. Petrol.,* **45**, 118 (1959).

113. E. P. Parry, *J. Catalysis,* **2**, 371 (1963).

114. L. R. Snyder, *J. Phys. Chem.,* **67**, 2622 (1963).

115. L. R. Snyder, *J. Chromatog.,* **20**, 463 (1965).

116. W. Trappe, *Biochem. Z.,* **305**, 150 (1940).

117. A. V. Kiselev and V. I. Lygin, *Russ. Chem. Rev.,* **31**, 175 (1962).

118. E. Lederer and M. Lederer, *Chromatography,* 2nd ed., Elsevier, New York, 1957, Chap. 4.

119. R. A. Woods and C. D. Lantz, paper presented at 17th Pittsburgh Conference on Analytical Chemistry and Applied Spectroscopy, Pittsburgh, Pa., 1966.

120. N. A. Izmailov and M. S. Schraiber, *Farmatsiva,* **1938** (3), 1.

121. J. E. Meinhard and N. F. Hall, *Anal. Chem.* **21**, 185 (1949).

122. J. G. Kirchner, J. M. Miller, and J. G. Keller, *Anal. Chem.,* **23**, 420 (1951).

123. E. Stahl, *Chemiker-Ztg.,* **82**, 323 (1958).

124. K. H. Mueller and H. Honerlagen, *Arch. Pharm.,* **293/65**, 202 (1960).

125. L. Hoerhammer, H. Wagner, and G. Bittner, *Deut. Apotheker,* **14**, 148 (1962).

126. E. Stahl, in *Thin Layer Chromatography* (E. Stahl, ed.), Springer-Verlag-Academic, New York, 1965, pp. 5–29.

127. A. F. Hofman, *J. Lipid Res.,* **3**, 391 (1962).

128. T. Roessel, *Z. Anal. Chem.,* **197**, 333 (1963).

129. R. G. Coffey and R. W. Newburgh, *J. Chromatog.,* **11**, 376 (1963).

130. K. Egger, *Z. Anal. Chem.,* **182**, 161 (1961).

131. J. Matis, O. Adamec, and M. Galvanek, *Nature,* **194**, 477 (1962).

132. H. K. Mangold, *J. Am. Oil Chemists' Soc.,* **38**, 708 (1961).

133. H. Determan, *Experientia,* **18**, 430 (1962).

134. E. Stahl, G. Schraeter, G. Kraft, and R. Reny, *Pharmazie,* **11**, 633 (1956).

135. M. Mottier and M. Potterat, *Anal. Chim. Acta,* **13**, 46 (1955).

136. J. Vaedtke and A. Gajewska, *J. Chromatog.,* **9**, 345 (1962).

137. E. Knappe and D. Peteri, *Z. Anal. Chem.,* **190**, 380 (1962).

138. H. P. Kaufmann and Y. Su Ko, *Fette, Seifen, Anstrichmittel,* **63**, 828 (1961).

139. S. J. Purdy and E. V. Truter, *Analyst,* **87**, 802 (1962).

140. R. D. Bennett and E. Heftmann, *J. Chromatog.,* **9**, 353 (1962).

141. K. Randerath, *Angew. Chem.,* **73**, 436 (1964).

142. H. H. O. Schmid, W. J. Baumann, J. M. Cubero, and H. K. Mangold, *Biochim. Biophys. Acta,* **125**, 189 (1966).

143. E. Stahl, *Angew. Chem., Intern. Ed. Engl.,* **3**, 784 (1964).

144. R. D. Bennett and E. Heftman, *J. Chromatog.,* **12**, 245 (1963).

145. E. Stahl, *Arch. Pharm.,* **293**, 531 (1960).

146. E. Stahl and V. Kaltenbach, *J. Chromatog.,* **5**, 458 (1961).

147. J. G. Kirchner, J. M. Miller, and G. J. Kelley, *Anal. Chem.,* **23**, 420 (1951).

148. L. D. Bergel'son, E. V. Dyatlovitskaya, and V. V. Voronkova, *Izv. Akad. Nauk SSSR, Otd. Khim. Nauk,* **1963**, 954.

149. B. G. Johansson and L. Rymo, *Biochem. J.,* **92**, 5P (1964).

150. J. G. Kirchner, in *Techniques of Organic Chemistry* (A. Weissberger, ed.), Vol. XII, Wiley, New York, 1967, pp. 120–121.

151. M. Brenner and A. Niederwieser, *Experientia (Basle),* **17**, 237 (1961).

152. E. Ehrhardt and E. Cramer, *J. Chromatog.,* **7**, 405 (1962).

153. H. Ertel and L. Horner, *J. Chromatog.,* **7**, 268 (1962).

154. M. Brenner, A. Niederwieser, G. Potaki, and A. R. Fahrny, *Experientia (Basle),* **18**, 101 (1962).

155. A. Seher, *Nahrung,* **4**, 466 (1960).

156. J. J. Wise, in *Analytical Methods for Pesticides, Plant Growth Regulators and Food Additives* (Gunter Zweig, ed.), Vol. V, Academic, New York, 1967, pp. 57–59.

157. H. Gaenshirt and K. Morianz, *Arch. Pharm.,* **293**, 1066 (1960).

158. E. H. Habermann, G. Bandtloro, and B. Krusche, *Klin. Wochschr.,* **39**, 816 (1961).

159. S. H. Vannier and W. L. Stanley, *J. Assoc. Offic. Agr. Chemists,* **41**, 432 (1958).

160. H. K. Mangold, R. Kammereck, and D. C. Malins, *Microchem. J., Symp. Ser.,* **2**, 697 (1961).

161. R. Guerra-Garcia, S. C. Chattoraj, L. J. Gabrilove, and H. H. Wotiz, *Steroids,* **2**, 605 (1963).

162. A. Vacikova, V. Felt and J. Malikova, *J. Chromatog.,* **9**, 301 (1962).

163. J. Kovac, *J. Chromatog.,* **11**, 412 (1963).

164. T. F. Bradasky, *Anal. Chem.,* **35**, 343 (1963).

165. R. L. Scheig, R. Annunziata, and L. A. Pesch, *Anal. Biochem.,* **5**, 291 (1963).

166. J. C. Giddings, *Anal. Chem.,* **40**, 2143 (1968).

167. Pharmacia Fine Chemicals, Inc., *Sephadex—gel filtration in Theory and Practice,* Piscataway, N.J., 1966.

168. A. J. P. Martin and R. L. M. Synge, *Biochem. J.,* **35** 91 (1941).

169. A. J. P. Martin, *Ann. N.Y. Acad. Sci.,* **49**, 249 (1948).

170. H. G. Cassidy, in *Technique of Organic Chemistry* (A. Weissberger, ed.), Vol. X, Wiley (Interscience), New York, 1957, p. 373.

171. J. F. K. Huber and Y. A. R. J. Hulsman, *Anal. Chim. Acta,* **38**, 305 (1967).

172. J. J. Kirkland, *Anal. Chem.,* **40**, 391 (1968).

173. K. J. Bombaugh, W. A. Dark, and R. N. King, *Res. Develop.,* **19**, 28 (1968).

174. I. Halasz, A. Kroneisen, H. O. Gerlach, and P. Walkling, *Z. Anal. Chem.,* **234**, 81 (1968).

175. L. R. Snyder, *Anal. Chem.,* **39**, 705 (1967).

176. C. Horvath, B. Preiss, and S. R. Lipsky, *Anal. Chem.* **39**, 1422 (1967).

177. C. Horvath and S. R. Lipsky, *J. Chromatog. Sci.,* **7**, 109 (1969).

178. J. C. Giddings, *Anal. Chem.,* **35**, 2215 (1963).

179. J. C. Giddings, *Anal. Chem.,* **37**, 61 (1965).

180. D. C. Locke, *Anal. Chem.* **39**, 921 (1967).

181. J. F. K. Huber, *J. Chromatog. Sci.,* **7**, 85 (1969).

182. R. P. W. Scott, D. W. J. Blackburn, and T. Wilkins, *J. Chromatog. Sci.,* **5**, 183 (1967).

183. S. M. Lambert, *Anal. Chem.,* **37**, 959 (1965).

184. J. E. Stouffer, P. L. Oakes, and J. E. Schlatter, *J. Gas Chromatog.,* **4**, 89 (1966).

185. R. E. Jentoft and T. H. Gouw, *Anal. Chem.,* **40**, 923 (1968).

186. H. Felton, *J. Chromatog. Sci.,* **7**, 13 (1969).

187. J. J. Kirkland, *J. Chromatog. Sci.,* **7**, 7 (1969).

188. J. F. K. Huber, *J. Chromatog. Sci.,* **7**, 172 (1969).

189. K. J. Bombaugh, W. A. Dark, and R. F. Levangie, *J. Chromatog. Sci.,* **7**, 42 (1969).

190. F. Schönbein, *Ann. Chem. Liebigs,* **114**, 275 (1861).

191. F. Goppelsroeder, *Verhandl, Naturforsch. Ges. Basel,* **3**, 268 (1861).

192. H. Flood, *Z. Anal. Chem.,* **120**, 327 (1940).

193. R. Liesegang, *Z. Anal. Chem.,* **126**, 172 (1943).

194. R. Consden, A. H. Gordon, and A. J. P. Martin, *Biochem. J.,* **38**, 224 (1944).

195. D. P. Burma, *Anal. Chem.,* **25**, 549 (1953).

196. J. B. Roberts, *Anal. Chem.* **29**, 1443 (1957).

197. F. Franks, *Analyst,* **81**, 384 (1956).

198. J. Gruen and S. Marcinkiewicz, *J. Chromatog.,* **10**, 35 (1963).

199. L. Rutter, *Nature,* **161**, 435 (1948).

200. H. J. McDonald, E. W. Bermes, and H. G. Shepard, *Chromatog. Methods,* **2**, 1 (1957).

201. J. A. Riddick and E. E. Toops, Jr., in *Technique of Organic Chemistry* (A. Weissberger, ed.), 2nd ed., Vol. 7, Wiley (Interscience), New York, 1957, Chap. V.

202. A. M. Kressfield and F. W. Allen, *Chromatog. Methods,* **2**, 9 (1957).

203. K. Macek, in *Chromatography* (E. Heftmann, ed.), 2nd ed., Rheinhold, New York, 1967, pp. 145–146.

204. H. J. Pazdera, W. H. McMullen, L. L. Ciaccio, S. R. Missan, and T. C. Grenfell, *Anal. Chem.,* **29**, 1649 (1957).

205. A. T. James and A. J. P. Martin, *Biochem. J.,* **50**, 679 (1952).

206. A. W. Breidenbach, J. J. Lichtenberg, C. F. Henke, D. J. Smith, J. W. Eichelberger, Jr., and H. Stieri, *Federal Water Pollution Control Admin. Publ. No. WP-22,* U.S. Dept. Interior, 1966.

207. W. L. Lamar, D. F. Goerlitz, and M. L. Law, *U.S. Geol. Surv. Water Supply Paper, 1817-B,* 1965.

208. S. E. Katz, *J. Assoc. Offic. Anal. Chemists,* **49**, 452 (1966).

209. E. J. Bonelli, *Pesticides Residue Analysis Handbook,* Wilkins Instrument and Research, Inc., Walnut Creek, Calif., 1965.

210. D. Smith and J. Eichelberger, *J. Water Pollution Control Federation,* **37**, 77 (1965).

211. A. Irudayasamy and A. R. Natarajan, *Analyst,* **90**, 503 (1965).

212. A. Goodenkauf and J. Erdei, *J. Am. Water Works Assoc.,* **56**, 600 (1964).

213. K. J. Meulemans and E. T. Upton, *J. Assoc. Offic. Anal. Chemists,* **49**, 976 (1966).

214. F. K. Kawahara, J. J. Lichtenberg, and J. W. Eichelberger, *J. Water Pollution Control Federation,* **39**, 446 (1967).

215. H. B. Pionke, J. G. Konrad, G. Chesters, and D. E. Armstrong, *Analyst,* **93**, 363 (1968).

216. E. Edgerly, Jr., R. T. Skrinde, and D. W. Ryckman, in *Principles and Applications of Water Chemistry* (S. D. Faust and J. V. Hunter, eds.). Wiley, New York, 1967, p. 405

217. S. K. Goren-Struhl and A. E. Mostaert, *Anal. Chim. Acta,* **34**, 322 (1966).

218. Y. Y. Lure and Z. V. Nikolaeva, *Zavodakaya Lab.,* **30**, 937 (1964): through *Chem Abstr.,* **60**, 13035 (1964).

219. R. F. Christman, *Trend in Eng. (Univ. Washington),* **16**, 10 (1964).

220. R. A. Baker and B. A. Malo, *Environ. Sci. Tech.,* **1**, 997 (1967).

221. R. J. Argauer, *Anal. Chem.*, **40**, 122 (1968).
222. M. D. Gebott, *Solutions (Ann Arbor)*, **6**, 8 (1967).
223. M. G. Zigler and W. F. Phillips, *Environ. Sci. Tech.*, **1**, 65 (1967).
224. H. Schaefer, *Helgoländer wiss. Meeres. (Germany)*, **12**, 239 (1965); through *Water Pollution Abstr.*, **39**, 404 (1966).
225. L. Wood, *Proc. Technicon Symp., 2nd, New York, London, 1965*, 1966, p. 652; through *Chem. Abstr.*, **67**, 36290 (1967).
226. Y. K. Chau and J. P. Riley, *Deep-Sea Res. Oceanog. Abstr.*, **13**, 1115 (1966); *Chem. Abstr.*, **66**, 108127 (1967).
227. S. J. Patterson, K. B. E. Tucker, and C. C. Scot, *J. Water Pollution Control Federation*, **38**, 350 (1966).
228. J. Drewry, *Analyst*, **88**, 225 (1963).
229. L. I. Nemtseva, T. S. Kishkinova, and A. D. Semenov, *Gidrokhim, Materialy*, **41**, 129 (1966); through *Chem. Abstr.*, **67**, 93851 (1967).
230. A. G. Stradomskaya and I. A. Goncharova, *Gidrokhim. Materialy*, **41**, 62 (1967); through *Chem. Abstr.*, **68**, 72107 (1968).
231. R. A. Baker, *J. Gas Chromatog.*, **4**, 418 (1966).
232. A. Golden, G. Ungefug, C. Hoffman, G. L. Baker, and E. W. Anacker, *J. Am. Water Works Assoc.*, **56**, 784 (1964).
233. E. Hindin, D. S. May, and G. H. Dunstan, *Water Sewage Works*, **112**, 346 (1965).
234. L. Lively, A. A. Rosen, and C. I. Mashni, *Purdue Univ. Eng. Bull., Ext. Ser. No. 118*, 1965, p. 657.
235. R. Navone and W. D. Fenninger, *J. Am. Water Works Assoc.*, **59**, 757 (1967).
236. J. W. Swinnerton and V. J. Linnenbom, *J. Gas Chromatog.*, **5**, 570 (1967).
237. I. A. Goncharova, A. N. Khomenko, and A. D. Semenev, *Gidrokhim. Materialy*, **41**, 116 (1966); through *Chem. Abstr.*, **67**, 68772 (1967).
238. E. T. Gjessing, *Nature*, **208**, 1091 (1965).
239. E. T. Gjessing and G. F. Lee, *Environ. Sci. Tech.*, **1**, 631 (1967).
240. W. S. Matthews and L. L. Smith, *Lipids*, **3**, 239 (1968).
241. J. J. Murtaugh and R. L. Bunch, *J. Water Pollution Control Federation*, **39**, 404 (1967).
242. K. W. Daisley, *Nature*, **191**, 868 (1961).
243. J. B. Andelman, M. A. Shapiro, and T. C. Ruppel, *Purdue Univ. Eng. Bull., Ext. Ser. No. 118* 1965, p. 220.
244. L. Jakubowska, *Gaz. Woda Tech. Sanit.*, **41**, 234 (1968); through *Chem. Abstr.*, **68**, 15997 (1968).
245. O. Samuelson, *Ion exchange Separations in Analytical Chemistry*, Wiley, New York, 1963, p. 18.
246. O. Samuelson, *Z. Anal. Chem.*, **116**, 329 (1939).
247. C. B. Amphlett, *Inorganic Ion Exchangers*, Elsevier, New York, 1964.
248. G. J. Moody and J. D. R. Thomas, *Analyst*, **93**, 557 (1968).
248a. O. Samuelson, *Ion Exchange Separations in Analytical Chemistry*, Wiley, New York, 1963, Chap. 3.
248b. O. Samuelson, *Ion Exchange Separations in Analytical Chemistry*, Wiley, New York, 1963 p. 87.
249. F. Helfferich, *Ion Exchange*, McGraw-Hill, New York, 1962, p. 46.
250. J. Inczedy, *Analytical Applications of Ion Exchangers*, Pergamon, New York, 1966, p. 347.
250a. F. Helfferich, *Ion Exchange*, McGraw-Hill, New York, 1962, p. 222.
251. M. J. Hatch, J. A. Dillon, and H. B. Smith, *Ind. Eng. Chem.*, **49**, 1812 (1957).
252. R. M. Wheaton and W. C. Bauman, *Ind. Eng. Chem.*, **45**, 228 (1953).

253. R. Kunin, E. F. Meitzner, and N. Bortnick, *J. Am. Chem. Soc.,* **84**, 305 (1962).

253a. O. Samuelson, *Ion Exchange Separations in Analytical Chemistry,* Wiley, New York, 1963, p. 62.

253b. O. Samuelson, *Ion Exchange Separations in Analytical Chemistry,* Wiley, New York, 1963, p. 70.

253c. O. Samuelson, *Ion Exchange Separations in Analytical Chemistry,* Wiley, New York, 1963 Chap. 3.

254. H. Levin, W. J. Diamond, and B. J. Brown, *Ind. Eng. Chem.,* **51**, 313 (1959).

255. G. E. Boyd, A. W. Adamson, and L. S. Myers, Jr., *J. Am. Chem. Soc.,* **69**, 2836 (1947).

255a. F. Helfferich, *Ion Exchange,* McGraw-Hill, New York, 1962, p. 255.

255b. O. Samuelson, *Ion Exchange Separations in Analytical Chemistry,* Wiley, New York, 1963, p. 93.

255c. O. Samuelson, *Ion Exchange Separations in Analytical Chemistry,* Wiley, New York, 1963, p. 105.

255d. F. Helfferich, *Ion Exchange,* McGraw-Hill, New York, 1962, pp. 447–485.

255e. J. Inczedy, *Analytical Applications of Ion Exchangers,* Pergamon, New York, 1966, pp. 99–113.

255f. F. Helfferich, *Ion Exchange,* McGraw-Hill, New York, 1962, pp. 422–428.

255g. O. Samuelson, *Ion Exchange Separations in Analytical Chemistry,* Wiley, New York, 1963.

255h. J. Inczedy, *Analytical Applications of Ion Exchangers,* Pergamon, New York, 1966.

256. G. S. Douglas, ed., *Radioassay Procedures for Environmental Samples, U.S. Public Health Serv. Publ. No. 999–RH-27,* U.S. Dept. Health, Education, and Welfare, Washington, D.C., 1967.

257. J. H. Harley, ed., *Manual of Standard Procedures,* Health and Safety Laboratory, U.S. Atomic Energy Commission, New York, 1967.

258. C. Calmon, *J. Am. Water Works Assoc.,* **46**, 470 (1954).

259. R. Navone, *J. Am. Water Works Assoc.,* **46**, 449 (1954).

260. M. Blumer, *Experientia,* **4**, 351 (1948).

261. J. W. McCoy, *Anal. Chim. Acta,* **6**, 259 (1952).

262. F. Nydahl, *Proc. Intern. Assoc. Theoret. Appl. Limnol.,* **11**, 276 (1951).

263. R. Greenhalgh, J. P. Riley, and M. Tongudai, *Anal. Chim. Acta,* **36**, 439 (1966).

264. D. G. Biechler, *Anal. Chem.,* **37**, 1054 (1965).

265. M. J. Fishman and E. C. Mallory, Jr., *J. Water Pollution Control Federation,* **40**, R67 (1968).

266. K. D. Linstedt and P. Kruger, *J. Am. Water Works Assoc.,* **61**, 85 (1969).

267. B. J. Szabo and O. Joensuu, *Environ. Sci. Tech.,* **1**, 499 (1967).

268. A. D. Westland and R. R. Langford, *Anal. Chem.,* **28**, 1996 (1956).

269. G. W. Dollman, *Environ. Sci. Tech.,* **2**, 1027 (1968).

270. F. I. Browley, Jr., and C. W. Howle, Jr., *Anal. Chem.,* **32**, 1330 (1960).

271. F. S. Kelso, J. M. Mathews, and H. P. Kramer, *Anal. Chem.,* **36**, 577 (1964).

272. Z. Sulcek, P. Povondra, and R. Stangl, *Chemist-Analyst,* **55**, 36 (1966).

273. J. P. Riley and M. Tangudai, *Chem. Geol.,* **1**, 291 (1966).

274. K. M. Chan and J. P. Riley, *Anal. Chim. Acta,* **34**, 337 (1966).

275. E. C. Potter, *J. Appl. Chem.* (*London*), **9**, 645 (1959).

276. L. P. Gregory, *Health Phys.,* **10**, 483 (1964).

277. A. Calderbank and S. H. Yuen, *Analyst,* **90**, 99 (1965).

278. A. Siegal and E. T. Degens, *Science,* **151**, 1098 (1966).

279. U. Eisner and H. B. Mark, Jr., *Talanta,* **16**, 27 (1969).

280. J. B. Andelman and M. J. Suess, *Anal. Chem.*, **38**, 351 (1966).

281. R. Ironside and S. Sourirajan, *Water Res.*, **1**, 179 (1967).

282. A. S. Michaels, *Ind. Eng. Chem.*, **57**(10), 32 (1965).

283. W. F. Blatt, M. P. Feinberg, and H. B. Hopfenberg, *Science*, **150**, 224 (1965).

284. E. F. Barth and N. H. Acheson, *J. Am. Water Works Assoc.*, **54**, 959 (1962).

285. R. B. Midwood and G. T. Felbeck, Jr., *J. Am. Water Works Assoc.*, **60**, 357 (1968).

286. A. Goetz and N. Tsuneishi, *J. Am. Water Works Assoc.*, **43**, 943 (1951).

287. H. L. Golterman and R. S. Clymo, eds., *Methods for Chemical Analysis of Fresh Waters, International Biological Programme Handbook No. 8*, Blackwell, Oxford, 1969, p. 17.

288. L. R. Setter, A. S. Goldin, and J. S. Nader, *Anal. Chem.*, **26**, 1304 (1954).

289. K. K. Turekian and M. R. Scott, *Environ. Sci. Tech.*, **1**, 940 (1967).

290. D. Jenkins, in *Trace Inorganics in Water* (R. F. Gould, ed.), *Advances in Chemistry Series No. 73*, American Chemical Society, Washington, D.C., 1968, Chap. 16.

291. A. L. Smith and A. E. Greenberg, *J. Water Pollution Control Federation*, **35**, 940 (1963).

292. M. W. Skougstad and G. F. Scarbro, Jr., *Environ. Sci. Tech.*, **2**, 298 (1968).

293. H. F. Clark, E. E. Geldreich, H. L. Jeter, and P. W. Kabler, *Public Health Rept.* (U. S.), **66**, 951 (1951).

294. J. I. W. Anderson and W. P. Hefferman, *J. Bacteriol.*, **90**, 1713 (1965).

295. L. A. Lueschow and K. M. Mackenthum, *J. Am. Water Works Assoc.*, **54**, 751 (1962).

296. L. W. Slanetz and C. H. Bartley, *J. Bacteriol.*, **74**, 591 (1957).

297. H. F. Clark, P. W. Kabler, and E. E. Geldrich, *Water Sewage Works*, **104**, 384 (1957).

298. R. C. Loehr and D. T. Schwegler, *Appl. Microbiol.*, **13**, 1005 (1965).

299. G. Berg, ed., *Transmission of Viruses by the Water Route*, Wiley (Interscience), New York, 1967, pp. 45, 121, 139.

300. D. O. Cliver, in *Transmission of Viruses by the Water Route* (G. Berg, ed.), Wiley (Interscience), New York, 1967, pp. 139–141.

301. H. Shuval, S. Cymbalista, B. Fatal, and N. Goldblum, in *Transmission of Viruses by the Water Route* (G. Berg, ed.), Wiley (Interscience), New York, 1967, pp. 45–55.

302. H. Gartner, *Transmission of Viruses by the Water Route* (G. Berg, ed.), Wiley (Interscience), New York, 1967, pp. 121–127.

303. J. W. Hassler, *Active Carbon*, Chemical Publishing, Brooklyn, N. Y., 1951, p. 252.

304. H. Braus, F. M. Middleton, and G. Walton, *Anal. Chem.*, **23**, 1160 (1951).

305. *Public Health Service Drinking Water Standards 1962, U.S. Public Health Serv. Publ. No. 956*, U.S. Dept. Health, Education, and Welfare, 1963.

306. F. M. Middleton and J. J. Lichtenberg, *Ind. Eng. Chem.*, **52**, 99A (June, 1960).

307. A. A. Rosen, R. T. Skeel, and M. B. Ettinger, *J. Water Pollution Control Federation*, **35**, 777 (1963).

308. A. A. Rosen and F. M. Middleton, *Anal. Chem.*, **31**, 1729 (1959).

308a. J. W. Hassler, *Active Carbon*, Chemical Publishing, Brooklyn, N.Y., 1951, Chap. 2, 11.

309. V. L. Snoeyink and W. J. Weber, Jr., *Environ. Sci. Tech.*, **1**, 228 (1967).

310. R. W. Coughlin, F. S. Ezra, and R. N. Tan, *J. Coll. Interface Sci.*, **28**, 386 (1968).

311. J. T. Cookson, Jr., *J. Am. Water Works Assoc.*, **61**, 52 (1969).

312. V. A. Garten and K. Eppinger, *Australian J. Chem.*, **12**, 394 (1959).

313. W. J. Weber, Jr., and J. C. Morris, *J. Sanit. Eng. Div. Am. Soc. Civil Engrs.*, **90**, SA3, 79 (1964).

314. W. J. Weber, Jr., and J. C. Morris, *J. Am. Water Works Assoc.*, **56**, 447 (1964).

315. R. A. Baker, *J. Am. Water Works Assoc.*, **56**, 92 (1964).

316. G. C. Robeck, K. A. Dostel, J. M. Cohen, and J. F. Kreissl, *J. Am. Water Works Assoc.*, **57**, 181 (1965).
317. W. J. Weber, Jr., and J. C. Morris, *J. Sanit. Eng. Div. Am. Soc. Civil Engrs.*, **89**, SA2, 31 (1963).
318. D. Smith and J. J. Lichtenberg, in *Microorganic Matter in Water, ASTM Spec. Tech. Publ. No. 448*, American Society for Testing and Materials, Philadelphia, 1969, pp. 78–95.
319. C. E. Hamilton, *Water Sewage Works*, **110**, 442 (1963).
320. P. E. Antommaria, M.Sc. Thesis, Graduate School of Public Health, Univ. Pittsburgh, 1961.
320a. *Standard Methods for the Examination of Water and Wastewater*, 12th ed., American Public Health Association, New York, 1966, p. 214.
321. M. B. Ettinger, *J. Am. Water Works Assoc.*, **52**, 689 (1960).
322. H. N. Myrick and D. W. Ryckman, *J. Am. Water Works Assoc.*, **55**, 783 (1963).
323. G. F. Lee, G. W. Kumke, and S. L. Becker, *Intern. J. Air Water Pollution*, **9**, 69 (1965).
324. C. A. Rambow, *J. Am. Water Works Assoc.*, **55**, 1037 (1963).
325. R. L. Booth, J. N. English, and G. N. McDermott, *J. Am. Water Works Assoc.*, **57**, 215 (1965).
326. A. E. Greenberg, C. Z. Maehler, and J. Cornelius, *J. Am. Water Works Assoc.*, **57**, 791 (1965).
327. C. C. Ruchhoft, F. M. Middleton, H. Braus, and A. A. Rosen, *Ind. Eng. Chem.*, **46**, 284 (1954).
328. H. P. Nicholson, A. R. Grzenda, G. L. Lauer, W. S. Cox, and J. I. Teasley, *Limnol. Oceanog.*, **9**, 310 (1964).
329. H. F. Mueller, T. E. Larson, and M. Ferretti, *Anal. Chem.*, **32**, 687 (1960).
330. W. W. Ullmann, B. H. Pfeil, and W. W. Sanderson, *Anal. Chem.*, **34**, 213 (1962).
331. J. F. Kopp and R. C. Kroner, *Appl. Spectry.*, **19**(5), 155 (1965).
331a. *Standard Methods for the Examination of Water and Wastewater*, 12th ed., American Public Health Association, New York, 1966, p. 242.
332. A. R. Slonim and F. F. Crawley, *J. Water Pollution Control Federation*, **38**, 1609 (1966).
333. P. M. Baker and B. R. Farrant, *Analyst*, **93**, 732 (1968).
334. D. F. Schutz and K. K. Turekian, *Geochim. Cosmochim. Acta*, **29**, 259 (1965).
334a. *Standard Methods for the Examination of Water and Wastewater*, 12th ed., American Public Health Association, New York, 1966, pp. 137, 187, 229.
334b. *Standard Methods for the Examination of Water and Wastewater*, 12th ed., American Public Health Association, New York, 1966, p. 229.
334c. *Standard Methods for the Examination of Water and Wastewater*, 12th ed., American Public Health Association, New York, 1966, p. 137.
335. S. Megregian and I. Solet, *J. Am. Water Works Assoc.*, **45**, 1110 (1953).
336. S. D. Faust and N. E. Hunter, *J. Am. Water Works Assoc.*, **57**, 1028 (1965).
337. N. T. Crosby, A. L. Dennis, and J. G. Stevens, *Analyst*, **93**, 643 (1968).
338. W. T. Lammers, *Environ. Sci. Tech.*, **1**, 52 (1967).
339. N. G. Anderson, G. B. Cline, W. W. Harris, and J. G. Green, in *Transmission of Viruses by the Water Route* (G. Berg, ed.), Wiley (Interscience), New York, 1967, pp. 75–88.
340. M. Bier, G. C. Bruckner, F. C. Cooper, and H. E. Roy, in *Transmission of Viruses by the Water Route* (G. Berg, ed.), Wiley (Interscience), New York, 1967, pp. 57–73.
341. Beckman Instruments, Inc., *CPE System for Continuous Particle Electrophoresis*, *Bull. No. 7096-B*, Fullerton, Calif., 1967.

Chapter 12 Insoluble Material in Natural Water

William Tuthill Lammers
DEPARTMENT OF BIOLOGY
DAVIDSON COLLEGE
DAVIDSON, NORTH CAROLINA

I. Introduction

Insoluble material, for the purposes of this chapter, is defined as any particle from 0.01 up to 200 μ in size and includes both suspended and colloidal particles. Particles smaller than 0.01 μ are classified as dissolved; they exhibit colligative effects and dialyze through a differentially permeable membrane. Both organic and inorganic dissolved substances exist in natural water, but they are discussed in other chapters (see Chaps. 19 through 24). Particles larger than 200 μ will be found suspended in water only with a high velocity current or when they are free-swimming or buoyant bio-organic particles. These larger particles generally are not found in significant numbers within the relatively small volume (20–40 liters) samples collected. The term bio-organic is used to cover biological organisms, detritus of biological organisms, nonbiological detritus such as organic polymers, and other particles with a density less than 1.9 g/cm^3. The terms inorganic or clay-mineral are used to describe particles with a density greater than 2 g/cm^3 and a noncarbon structure.

This chapter is confined to the physical, chemical, and biological aspects of suspended and colloidal particles which bear on the separation, concentration, and analysis of such particles. Instruments, methods, and calculations used in these fractionations and analyses are also discussed. It is not the intent of this chapter to critically discuss the detailed studies of all particles found in natural water. Such studies, which have an important bearing on the material covered in this chapter, have been adequately reviewed elsewhere. Review articles and articles on special topics are cited at appropriate points in the text.

II. Particle Characteristics

A. Classification

The first step in designing a fractionation scheme is to classify the particles of a water sample by their physical, chemical, and biological characteristics. Once these characteristics are known, systems can be designed to obtain the best analytical results. For this purpose the most useful physical characteristics are particle size, morphology, and density (g/cm^3). The chemical composition, crystal structure, and surface activity, or bioactivity, are also useful. The size and density of the particle can be used to calculate its sedimentation coefficient or rate of

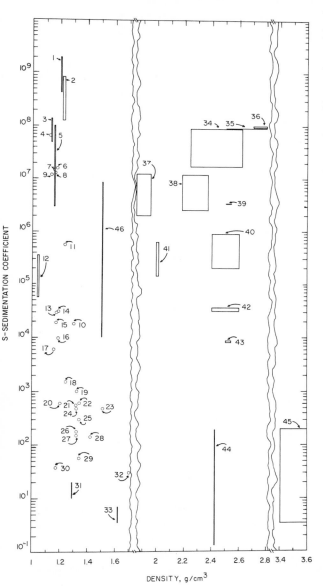

Fig. 1. Semilogarithmic plot of the buoyant density and sedimentation coefficient of selected bio-organic and inorganic particles found in natural water. The data for the particles 1–17, 19, 21, 23, 26, and 33–46 were obtained from the author's laboratory; the remainder of particles from literature sources(20, 103–105).

1-Rotifers (mixed), 2-*Euglena gracilis*, 3-*Daphnia* (mixed), 4-*Chlamydomonas* sp., 5-*Plectonema boryanum*, 6-*Scenesdesmus* sp., 7-*Spongiochloris excentrica*, 8-*Saccharamyces cerevisiae*, 9-*Chlorella vulgaris*, 10-colloidal cellulose, 11-ragweed pollen (*Ambrosia* sp.), 12-*Tetrahymena pyriformis*, 13-*Escherichia freundii*, 14-*Serratia marcescens*, 15-*Escherichia coli*, 16-*Proteus vulgaris*, 17-*Aerobacter aerogenes*, 18-Newcastle virus, 19-T-2 phage, 20-rabes virus, 21-blue-green algae virus, 22-reo-3 virus, 23-T-3 phage, 24-adeno-2 virus, 25-Shope papilloma virus, 26-T-1 phage, 27-polio virus, 28-foot and mouth virus, 29-adeno-3 virus, 30-α-keto-glutarate, 31-Bovine serum albumin, 32-Ribose nucleic acid, 33-sodium humate, 34-metabentonite, 35-dickite, 36-pyrophillite, 37-montmorillonite, 38-halloysite, 39-illite, 40-kaolinite, 41-attapulgite, 42-kaolinite (minimum size), 43-illite (minimum size), 44-Al(OH)₃ (colloidal), 45-Fe(OH)₃ (colloidal), 46-bentonite (colloidal to maximum size).

movement in a given gravitational field [see Eq. (1)]. In Fig. 1, typical particles are plotted by their density on the abscissa and by their sedimentation coefficient in Svedberg units (S) on the ordinate. From the information in Fig. 1, it is evident that the particles, representative of those usually found in natural water, fall into several clusters with relatively large particle-free areas separating the major clusters. The particles in each of these major clusters are relatively homogeneous for density and sedimentation coefficient and are generally rather closely related. The bacteria all fall into one major cluster, the virus particles into another, and the clay-minerals into still another. Within a cluster, the particles of a specific type or species fall into a compact area which is distinct from other species in density or sedimentation coefficient or both. The optimum system for water fractionation would take advantage of these natural groupings.

Suspended particles in the size range $0.2-200\,\mu$ settle in still water under the force of $1\,g(1)$. Their sedimentation coefficients range from a minimum of about $10^4\,S$ to a maximum of about $10^{10}\,S$. For these particles the range of surface area-to-volume ratios (A/V) is from 0.032 for a 200-μ particle to 32 for a 0.2-μ particle. This threefold change in order of magnitude is reflected in an increased surface activity for the smaller suspended particles. As the surface activity increases, the quantity of material accumulated from the environment shows a generally parallel increase.

B. Bio-Organic Particles

Bio-organic particles in the suspended size range are mostly various members of the subkingdom Thallophyta including the phyla Cyanophyta (blue-green algae), Euglenophyta (euglenoids), Chlorophyta (green algae), chrysophyta (yellow-green algae), Pyrrophyta (dinoflagellates), Schizo-mycophyta (bacteria), and Eumycophyta (true fungi). Some of these may be present as dormant spores, a similar type of particle is the pollen of various embryophytes. The animal kingdom is represented by the phyla Protozoa, Rotifera (rotifers), Arthropoda (crustacea), and some larval forms, but these animals are generally not so numerous as the plants. Many of these bio-organic particles are either motile or have a positive buoyancy, or both, and these may not settle in still water at 1 g. Both living and nonliving bio-organic particles are affected by temperature changes. The rates of growth, death, and decay change at approximately an exponential rate ($Q_{10} = 2$) with decreasing water temperature down to an optimum at about 10°C for temperate region samples. Because of this, the best approximations of actual conditions are obtained when a sample is cooled at once to 10°C, rapidly processed, and kept at 10°C until the analysis is finished. Other factors which may increase the death rate are rapid changes in tonicity of the media or introduction of a toxic material. Changes in tonicity may be lessened by transferring the bio-organic particles to an isotonic buffer solution and by gradual addition or removal of solute or solvent molecules to allow the organisms to adjust to the change (2). Bio-organic particles supported by a thick membrane or cell wall will tolerate large changes in tonicity, but those with thin membranes, such as protozoa, are not tolerant and usually rupture with changes. Live particles may accumulate dialyzable material from their environment by active uptake, so some materials may be concentrated several orders of magnitude in the organisms. For this reason it is important to have estimates of the total amount of bio-organic material present, the number of viable particles, and the metabolic rate of the particles. As will be seen later, these data can be used to predict the expected behavior of the bio-organic fraction.

C. Bio-Organic Detritus

Bio-organic detritus ranges in size from the maximum of 200μ down to some of the dissolved humic substances. This includes nonbiological aggregates and cellulose. The detritus ranges in density from that of cell nuclei (1.04 g/cm^3) to that of humate (1.53 g/cm^3). It seems to be generally denser than most live particles but cannot be completely isolated on that basis. This inclusion of bio-organic detritus with live particles is the reason why the estimate of the total amount of bio-organic material must be supported by the number alive and by the metabolic rate. Detritus does not actively accumulate material from the medium but rather depends on surface area and passive exchange.

D. Inorganic Particles

Inorganic particles in the suspended size range include clays, minerals, and aggregates of colloidal-sized clay-mineral particles. These inorganic particles are usually classified as sand if they have an equivalent spherical diameter (esd) of $>20 \mu$, as silt if the esd is $2–20 \mu$, and as clay if the esd is $< 2 \mu$ (3). A 20-μ sand particle with a density of 2 g/cm^3 has a sedimentation coefficient of about $2.2 < 10^8 S$, so most of the inorganic particles considered in this chapter are silt and clay. In most natural water the clays and clay-mineral colloids are aggregated into larger supracolloidal particles due to dissolved electrolytes, and physically these aggregates behave as suspended particles(4,5). Generally, more than 90% (by volume) of the inorganic fraction is in aggregated form with a sedimentation coefficient $>2 \times 10^4 S$. Because of this aggregation, it is important to buffer the sample against ionic changes so the natural level of aggregation is maintained. In addition to causing changes in aggregate size, ionic shifts can cause changes in the quantity of material sorbed from the media by affecting the charge and surface area of the fraction.

E. Colloidal Particles

Colloidal particles range in size from 0.25 μ to 6 mμ and have distinct physical characteristics(1). Their behavior is different from that of suspended particles since colloids do not settle at 1 g but remain in suspension. This is primarily due to mutual repulsion, Brownian movement, and the separate phases of the colloidal system. Unlike dissolved particles in solution, a colloidal sol does not have significant colligative effects(1). The range of A/V ratios of a colloidal particle is from 24 for a 0.25-μ particle to 1003 for a 6-mμ particle, and unlike suspended particles, the surface adsorption capacity is of considerable importance. The bio-organic colloids include detritus and virus particles as well as macromolecules such as proteins and humic acids. Except for infective viruses, these bio-organic colloids are not bioactive and none is capable of active accumulation of material from the environment, although they do accumulate material by surface exchange. These bio-organic colloids may play an important part in cycling materials through the food chain, and their apparent importance seems to increase directly with our increase in knowledge of the fraction(6). There is accumulating evidence that the pathogenic viruses may have a significance out of proportion to the actual size of the viral population in natural water(7). Inorganic colloidal particles are some of the clays and minerals, such as bentonite, iron hydroxide, and aluminium hydroxide(8). These can be shown to be present in a sample, but they vary so much in ionization state, density, and size that it is difficult to obtain accurate physical information about them.

III. Concentration of Particles

A. Sieving

In most natural water samples the quantity of a given type of particle in a 1-liter aliquot is too small for meaningful analysis. Consequently, a larger volume of sample must be collected and the particles of interest concentrated to a higher number per unit volume so that the total quantity lies within the range of sensitivity of the analytical method. For larger inorganic particles this concentration and separation into several size classes can be done with sieves.

Sieving is frequently used to separate inorganic particles into sand, silt, and clay fractions(9, 10). For the larger suspended particles ($>250 \mu$) sieving is better than centrifugation. The particles settle rapidly and are not anomalously retained on the sieves due to surface charge attraction because of the low surface charge of both the larger particles and the >250-μ sieve pores. Indeed, these large clay-mineral particles have a large sedimentation coefficient ($>10^9 S$) and are abrasive, so they are difficult to handle in any but low gravitational fields. For waterborne particles, wet sieving is preferable to dry since the time, effort, and chance of changing the physical nature of the particles are reduced if they are not dried. A $0.2 N$ solution of sodium hexametaphosphate is frequently used to reduce the surface tension and disperse the particles(11). However, if adsorbed materials are of interest, there is danger that this wetting may release surface-adsorbed materials from the particles(12). Once prepared, the sample is generally poured slowly through a stacked series of sieves and the filtrate collected. The sieves are washed with an isotonic buffer solution to flush all particles to their proper sieve plate. Uniform results from sample to sample are obtained by controlled flow rates and number of washes. The particles can be recovered from the sieves by inverting the sieves over a pan and gently washing and brushing the particles from the sieve plate.

Sieving of particles smaller than 200μ should be done under pressure, vacuum, or centrifugal force to increase the rate of particle settling. Cellulose acetate filters of graded pore sizes in conjunction with pressure, vacuum, or a centrifuge may be used to size down to about 0.01μ(13). One difficulty is that the smaller filter pores have an electrical charge. It has been reported that organic colloids such as nucleic acids are adsorbed and retained by the filter(14), and other reports show that radionuclides and colloidal particles in general are adsorbed by the filter(15). Another difficulty is the relatively low flow rate through a small-pored filter if the liquid contains much colloidal material(16). A liter of water from a source such as the Clinch River of Tennessee, with an average silt clay load of about 10^8 particles/ml, can seldom be filtered through a 47-mm, 0.45-μ filter in less than 24 hr. Particles retained on a cellulose acetate filter can be examined directly by mounting the filter on glass and clearing it with microscope immersion oil. This cleared filter can be made into a permanent record slide. A nondestructive analysis, such as biological or radiological analysis, can be made of the particles directly on a filter. The particles can be recovered for other analyses by dissolving the filter in an organic solvent or by ashing. The usefulness of the new filters of hydrous gels of complexed polycations and anions is still not assessed, but the reported flow rate through the filters is too slow for filtration of large volumes [distilled water, 1 liter/4 hr; 1 ppm serum protein, ca. 1 liter/20 hr(*17*)]. In summary, the quality of filter separation and concentration for <200-μ particles is good, but the quantity is restricted to small volumes and there is considerable evidence that many smaller particles in the colloidal range are adsorbed by the filter. The quantity of material that can be filtered is an especially limiting factor when compared to continuous flow centrifugation.

B. Dialysis

If a solvent-solute system of water and sucrose is enclosed in a thin membrane with small pores (<25 Å) and suspended in a larger system with less sucrose per unit volume (hypotonic), a diffusion pressure will be generated. Solvent molecules (water) will rapidly osmose across the membrane with the equilibrium balance from the hypo- to the hypertonic sucrose solution. Solute particles (sucrose) will dialyze across the membrane at a slower rate, but with a net movement from the hyper- to the hypotonic sucrose solution. Solute particles greater than 25 Å are too large to dialyze across the membrane, but they generate a diffusion pressure which affects the equilibrium of the system (Donnan equilibrium). The usual artificial dialysis membrane is a cellulose sheet or tube with a mean pore diameter of 24 Å, which prevents colloidal particles from diffusing across the membrane but allows dissolved particles such as sucrose, ions, and other organic and inorganic monomers to pass through the membrane(*18*). Dialysis can be used to remove these dissolved particles from mixtures with colloidal and suspended particles. Nearly all of the dialyzable material can be removed; however, even with several changes of bath solution some of the dialyzable material will remain in the system due to a Donnan-type equilibrium between the nondialyzable colloidal particles in the system and the dialyzable particles on both sides of the membrane. In most cases, the amount of dissolved material remaining inside the dialysis sac is not troublesome, but it may cause difficulty if the preparation must be very pure. Dialysis tubing comes in several diameters from 0.65 to about 75 cm and is easily used by cutting an appropriate length, wetting one end, and double-knotting it. The next step is to open the other end, which may be done by wetting until it is flexible, and then gently blowing in the open end to inflate and open the entire tube. The sample solution is added, the open end knotted, and the closed system suspended in a dialysis bath of dilute buffer or another suitable medium. The bath volume should be 10- to 100-fold greater than the sac volume, and the rate is speeded by stirring and several bath changes. Dialysis is an excellent means of rapid but gradual removal of density gradient material or desalting an aggregated colloid to redisperse it.

C. Vacuum Evaporation

The suspended and colloidal particles can be concentrated by vacuum evaporation with little damage to inorganic particles or to bio-organic detritus. This method is rapid (2 liters/hr at 35°C, flask vapor temperature) but may result in flocculation as the ionic concentration in the flask increases. This can be kept at a minimum by frequent removal of the concentrate and dialysis of the residue to remove ions. Unstable particles, such as biological organisms and organic macromolecules, may be degraded or destroyed during the evaporation, but many macromolecules, such as proteins, tolerate this process. Vacuum evaporation is a good technique for preparing dilute samples of small colloids for further analysis.

D. Sedimentation

When suspended in distilled water, a nonmotile particle larger than about 0.1 μ and with a negative buoyancy will be affected by the normal gravitational force of 1 g and will settle out of the suspending liquid. If the suspended solution is agitated by a current or by stirring, the sedimentation will be interrupted. Particles smaller than about 0.1 μ, that is, colloidal particles, are small enough that molecular collisions and electrical repulsion by other colloids result in a random movement called Brownian movement. At a normal gravity of 1 g the colloidal particles are kept in suspension by this Brownian movement and do not sediment even when there is no agitation(19).

Suspended particles and colloidal aggregates with a negative buoyancy can be concentrated, and to some extent sized, by allowing them to settle for known lengths of time. A particle with a sedimentation coefficient of $2 \times 10^8 S$ will settle 1 m in water in approximately 6.55 hr, and a $2 \times 10^4 S$ particle will settle 1 m in water in approximately 655 hr. Colloidal particles may be deliberately flocculated for rapid settling by adding a few drops of a heavy salt such as aluminum sulfate or a commercial product such as Rohm and Haas C-7 cationic polymeric flocculant. Once the floc has settled out of solution it can be resuspended by dialysis. Some interesting biological experiments have flocculated antibody particles ($< 10\,S$) into aggregates large enough for density gradient centrifugation. As the aggregates move through the density gradient the salt is gradually diluted by the gradient and the particles are resuspended in their original form by the end of the centrifugation(20).

E. Centrifugation

1. INTRODUCTION

For suspended particles $<10^8\,S$, the physical concentration and separation possible with various centrifugal techniques presents the best approach to the problem of fractionating a water sample. This system can be used to isolate the various classes of particles from a water sample into concentrated homogeneous fractions with enough particles (each carrying their sorbed materials) in each fraction for analysis.

Various types of centrifuges have been designed, but the basic principle of them all is to decrease the time required for a particle to sediment by artificially increasing the gravitational force affecting it. Colloidal-sized particles, which do not sediment at $1\,g$, will sediment if the force of gravity is increased by centrifugation. The increase necessary for settling is inversely proportional to the particle diameter and density and must not only exceed $1\,g$ but also overcome the opposing forces of shear, viscosity, Brownian movement, and mutual repulsion. By subjecting a particle to an appropriate gravitational or centrifugal force, the particle will be made to move or sediment in a centrifugal direction at a predictable rate. The centrifugal force can be increased to the point where even atoms and ions sediment, but a molecular weight of about 10^6 may be taken as the lower practical limit for efficient large volume liquid centrifugation(2).

2. THEORY

The term "force" is appropriate when speaking of a timeless unit such as centrifugal force. When this force is extended over a finite time it is better referred to as an impulse(7,19,21). A waterborne particle will continue to migrate under the influence of centrifugal force until sedimented on the wall of the centrifuge rotor. The important factor in the distance a given particle moves in a centrifugal field is the product of the centrifugal field exerted on the particle and the time that the particle is in the centrifugal field (force in g × time). As long as this product, the centrifugal impulse, is the same, the results will be identical whether a high centrifugal field is used for a short period of time, or a lower field is used for a longer period of time. In both cases force in g × time gives the centrifugal impulse required to move the particle a required distance in the rotor in a given field.

A particle in an aqueous suspension subjected to a centrifugal field will migrate from the centripetal to the centrifugal side of the field at a rate determined by the sedimentation coefficient of the particle. This expresses a relationship between the density of the particle and its diameter as shown in the following simplified statement (22):

$$S = \frac{d^2(\rho_p - \rho_m)}{18_\eta} \times 10^{13} \tag{1}$$

where: S is the sedimentation coefficient, Svedberg units,
  d is the particle diameter, cm,
  ρ_p is the particle density, g/cm³
  ρ_m is the suspending solution density, g/cm³
  η is the viscosity of the solution, poise

For an aqueous suspension this may be simplified to

$$S = \frac{d^2(\rho_p - 1)}{0.18} \times 10^{13} \tag{2}$$

This expression means that both the size and the density of a particle affect its rate of sedimentation, and a dense particle of small diameter will sediment as rapidly as a less dense particle of larger diameter if their S values are the same.

While the sedimentation coefficient expresses the behavior of a sphere under a given centrifugal force, the effect of the impulse is expressed as the precipitation time. This is the time for a particle with a known sedimentation coefficient to move a specific distance in a known centrifugal field. This value must be calculated for each radius, speed, and sedimentation coefficient (22):

$$T_s = \frac{1}{S} \frac{\log_e R_{max} - \log_e R_{min}}{(\text{rpm} \times 2\pi/60)^2} \tag{3}$$

where: $\log_e R_{max}$ is the natural logarithm of the rotor chamber maximum radius
  $\log_e R_{min}$ is the natural logarithm of the rotor chamber minimum radius
  T_s is the precipitation time, sec
  S is the sedimentation coefficient, Svedberg units
  rpm is the revolutions/min of the rotor

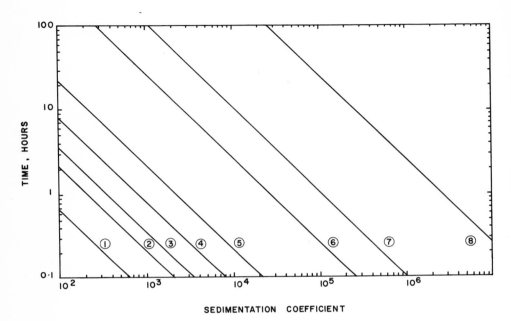

Fig. 2. Logarithmic plot of precipitation time (T_s) and sedimentation coefficient (S). The various rotors are used at the following speeds: (1) Beckman 50 rotor, 50,000 rpm; (2) Beckman 30 rotor, 30,000 rpm; (3) Beckman SW-25 rotor, 25,000 rpm; (4) Zonal B-15 rotor, 24,000 rpm; (5) SW-25 rotor, 10,000 rpm; (6) Zonal A-12 rotor, 4000 rpm; (7) A-12 rotor, 2000 rpm; (8) A-12 rotor, 200 rpm.

The T_s value can be used to plot the sedimentation time for particles under stated conditions. This rate of movement is not uniform because the particle is accelerated as it moves centrifugally in the field. Some sample plots for specific conditions are shown in Fig. 2.

Particle shape complicates the prediction of the expected behavior of a particle in a centrifugal field. While few suspended particles are spheres, their physical behavior closely approximates that of a sphere, although precise measurements will shown differences in their behavior compared to that of a sphere. Studies of the behavior of plate-shaped clay particles and rod-shaped virus particles have been conducted, and corrections have been developed to make the expected results more accurately predict the observed results(23–25). For the separation of particles differing in density and sedimentation coefficient, as in natural water fractionation, these calculations usually need not be used. If, however, the separation of very similar particles is required, the refined calculations, accounting for small differences in shape, should be used to predict the behavior of the particles of interest.

3. MODES OF CENTRIFUGATION

There are several types of centrifugal separation techniques, each using different physical characteristics of the particle as the basis of separation. When an aqueous suspension of particles is subjected to a specific centrifugal impulse, particles with a sedimentation coefficient higher than the critical value will sediment to the rotor wall. Nearly all particles with a sedimentation coefficient lower than that critical value will remain in the solution or supernatant. This is shown diagramatically in Fig. 3. If this supernatant is recentrifuged at a greater total centrifugal impulse, another group of particles will be sedimented to the rotor wall in a similar way. By using a series of such differential centrifugations, fractions representing sedimentation rate classes can be separated from the suspending liquid. The particles in each fraction will be relatively homogeneous with respect to sedimentation coefficient, and the sediment-ed pellet will include all of the types of particles which have the same sedimentation coefficient. In practice, algae and bacteria, which are relatively large ($0.5-40\,\mu$) and have a low density ($1.1-1.2\,g/cm^3$), will sediment at the same rate as clay-minerals, which are smaller ($0.05-5\,\mu$) and denser ($2-3\,g/cm^3$). Further, since a particle with a lower sedimentation coefficient may start at a greater radius of the centrifugal field than a particle with a higher sedimentation coefficient, both may reach the rotor wall at the same time. For this reason, differential centrifugation gives

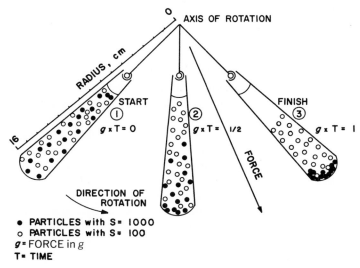

Fig. 3. Diagrammatic representation of differential centrifugation. Note that some of the 100 S particles are in the final pellet along with the bulk of the 1000 S particles.

only a relative separation of particles of different sedimentation rates. For some cases differential centrifugation will give fractions homogeneous enough for the desired analysis.

Most centrifuge rotors fall into either the batch or the continuous flow class of design. The batch-type rotor has a fixed volume, and large volume samples must be processed by centrifugation of aliquots of the original sample until the entire volume has been centrifuged. In the "swinging bucket" rotor the plane of centrifugal force is perpendicular to the axis of rotation. This design has two or more opposed "buckets" for the sample solution. When stopped, the buckets swing down and parallel to the axis of rotation. During acceleration, centrifugal force causes the buckets to swing out perpendicular to the axis. If carefully accelerated and decelerated, this change of orientation has little disruptive effect on the sample. High centrifugal force can be obtained with a swinging bucket rotor.

Another design of batch-type rotor is the "angle head." This is usually machined out of a single block of metal, with holes to contain the sample drilled at a fixed angle around the periphery of the rotor. Although the holes in the angle head rotor do not change their plane during acceleration, the force on the sample does change during acceleration from a force parallel to the axis to one perpendicular to the axis of rotation. The relatively massive amount of metal in this rotor allows high centrifugal force to be used, but the major advantage of the angle head rotor is its large sample volume. A disadvantage of the angle head design is the short distance that the particles in the sample travel before striking the rotor wall. The pellet is often spread over a considerable area of the centrifugal side of the wall.

A particle accelerating from the axis of rotation to the periphery of the centrifugal field follows a course described by the radius of a circle. Because of this, nearly all of the particles strike the parallel walls of a centrifuge tube and slide down the wall from the point of impact(26). Algal, bacterial, and clay-mineral particles have significant "wall effects" since these particles tend to adhere to the tube wall and cohere to one another. If a sector-shaped centrifuge tube is used, the internal walls of the tube are two radii of a circle. In this case, the particles move freely under centrifugal force and no particle strikes a wall until the centrifugal end of the tube (Fig. 4). A number of sector-shaped tubes laid together form a circle. The zonal rotor of the "B" series takes this conformation and is a cylinder with a few internal septa to prevent swirling and convection(27). A detailed description is given by Amburgey(28) and Barringer et al.(29). High centrifugal force and relatively large volume samples are additional advantages of this rotor design.

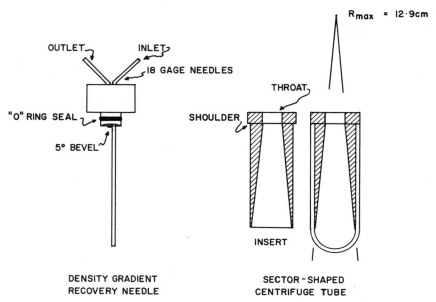

Fig. 4. A sector-shaped centrifuge tube of polycarbonate and a recovery needle used with this tube. The tube shape prevents wall effects, it is autoclavable, and the insert is held in place by a light coat of vacuum grease.

The second major class of centrifuge systems is the continuous flow design. This permits particles to be removed from a large volume of liquid in a single centrifugation. The rotor is a cylinder of the "spinning bucket" design with the rotor spinning about the axis of rotation. There may be internal septa to prevent swirling and convection. A continuous stream of the suspending liquid is introduced into the center of the spinning rotor and accelerated centrifugally to the rotor wall. Particles with a sedimentation coefficient within the range of the applied centrifugal impulse sediment to the rotor wall and are held there by centrifugal force. Particles with a lower sedimentation coefficient than the applied centrifugal impulse do not sediment to the wall but are carried out of the rotor by the flowing liquid stream, and leave the rotor in the effluent. By controlling flow rate, the total impulse ($g \times$ time) is controlled. This complex subject is discussed in detail by Berman(22). However, if the precipitation time of the particle and the rotor volume are known, the flow rate (time in field) at a specific force, giving the required impulse, can be calculated from the statement:

$$F = V/T_s \qquad (4)$$

where: F is the flow rate, ml/min
V is the volume of the rotor, ml
T_s is the precipitation time for the particle at the force used

There are numerous designs based on the continuous flow concept. The major advantage of the continuous flow centrifuge is that rare particles can be concentrated from a large volume of liquid in sufficient numbers for reliable analysis. At present, sample size ranges from 20 to 40 liters for a natural water sample. Advanced rotor designs now under development will permit rapid centrifugation of even larger samples(7,28). Particles existing in numbers far below the level of sensitivity of other isolation systems can be obtained in useful amounts. If the particle under investigation is abundant, as with an algal "bloom," a continuous flow system need not be used since adequate concentration can be obtained with a batch rotor.

If the rotor is not isolated in a vacuum chamber, the sample stream may be introduced and removed at the open center of the rotor. In high speed rotors a vacuum system isolates the exterior of the rotor and requires a seal between the isolated rotor and the influent and effluent lines. This seal is isolated from the vacuum system and leads directly from the influent line to the rotor chamber and from the chamber to the effluent line(29). Most of the seals now in use are subject to slow wear between the static and rotating seal faces and were designed for use with non-abrasive particles. One such static-rotating seal, the "W" seal developed by the Biophysical Limnology Laboratory at Oak Ridge, Tennessee, is especially designed for samples containing abrasive particles such as clay-minerals(30). The abrasiveness of the particles and their abundance will dictate the choice of seals for a particular separation.

IV. Methods of Particle Isolation

A. Ion Exchange

Since the lower limit of practical centrifugation of large volume samples is about molecular weight 10^6, or a sedimentation coefficient of about $50\,S$, some of the smaller colloidal particles of special interest, such as the humic acids and polypeptides, generally require noncentrifugal methods for isolation and concentration(31–34). These particles may be separated and characterized on the basis of their electrical charge(35,36). An extensive literature exists on the use of cationic and anionic exchange resins for this purpose. Ion exchange can be used to selectively adsorb either anionic or cationic charged particles and permit all others to pass through the resin(37). As a first step, the particles are manipulated to the suitable ionic form and introduced to the resin, which usually is uniformly packed in a tube(38–40). The greater the attraction between the resin and the particle, the closer to the point of entry it is adsorbed. In a resin column there is adsorption of particles of different degrees of attraction along the column, with the more readily adsorbed particles at the start of the column and those of less attraction further along. This resolution is improved by using smaller resin beads and higher column pressures but at the cost of the flow rate through the column(41). The adsorbed particles can be recovered from the resin by displacement with a stronger exchanger. It seems likely that mounting concern with smaller bio-organic colloids in water will increase use of the ion exchange technique. Resin columns have been used to recover virus particles from a concentrated solution such as sewage water(42,43), but they are not sensitive enough for use in a stream that is not nearly pure sewage effluent. There are at least three difficulties connected with the use of resin columns for isolation of waterborne particles: (a) A precolumn cleanup is needed to remove the suspended particles ($>0.1\,\mu$) to lessen the chance of blocking the column; (b) the flow rate through a column is generally low (<1 liter/hr), so unstable materials may be lost if a large volume is collected; and (c) once the column becomes saturated the separation process ceases and additional particles are not retained. If the sample volume is large and contains a large number of particles per unit volume, the column rapidly becomes saturated and there will be a low efficiency of recovery and separation.

B. Gel Filtration

The smaller colloidal particles can also be fractionated from their continuous phase water and from each other by gel filtration(44,45). This is not suitable for suspended particles but does an excellent job for many colloids. It has the additional advantage of not requiring chemical manipulation. The gel filtration technique depends on pore size for separation and there is little or no charge in the gel. Larger particles do not get lodged in the pores formed by the cross-linked gel, while smaller particles are delayed in the cross-links. Because of this, the fractionation is based on particle size and shape, but not on charge. By appropriate choice of gel bead size, molecular weight approximations can be based on the rate of passage of a particle through a gel column(46). Gels are generally cross-linked polysaccharides and are available with different bead sizes and degrees of cross-linkage for separating different sizes of particles and for different degrees of resolution. Sephadex G-25 and G-75 have been successfully used to separate concentrated humic acid sols into several fractions each relatively homogeneous for molecular weight, color, and chain length(*33,34,47*). There is a large volume of literature on gel filtration, but little has been published on its use in studies of waterborne particles(*48*). Like ion exchange, gel filtration is a better technique for isolation than for concentration of particles, and generally the particles are diluted several fold in passage and must be reconcentrated on recovery.

C. Electrophoresis

Electrophoresis allows isolation of small colloids on the basis of particle charge and may be used for isolation and, to some degree, for concentration. Silica colloids up to 0.1-μ esd and their aggregates will migrate in an electrophoretic field(*49*). An inert medium, such as agar, starch, filter paper, or alumina powder, serves as the solid phase with little or no charge. The liquid phase is an electrolytic buffer-solvent mixture, and both phases are in contact with the anode and cathode. The particles of interest migrate in the applied electrical field to their isoelectric point in that environment. Knowledge of the isoelectric point, if matched with a known particle isoelectric point, would allow identification of the unknown particles. The particles can be physically recovered after electrophoresis by removal of the solid-phase zone around the particle band and elution of the particles from the solid medium. Electrophoresis is the most rapid of these exchange methods, but it is generally limited to a small sample and is not efficient for preparation of large quantities of particles. The exception is continuous flow electrophoresis, in which the sample is continually added to the liquid phase and the isolated particles are collected in tubes at their isoelectric point(*49a*).

For quantitative isolation by these exchange methods the particles must be preconcentrated by flocculation, vacuum evaporation, freeze drying, or a similar technique so that they can be added to the exchange system in large quantities per unit volume.

D. Density Gradient Centrifugation

1. INTRODUCTION

The weight per unit volume, or density, of a particle is a physical characteristic which does not vary under identical conditions. It is a good character of the particle for identification, although not frequently used, and is the basis of particle isolation by density gradient centrifugation. In this technique, the fluid medium in the centrifuge tube has a density gradient, i.e., the density increases in the tube proceeding from top to bottom (see Fig. 5). Thus, the sedimentation coefficient of the particle decreases as the particle proceeds down the tube [see Eq. (1)]. Intuitively it is evident that particles will move down the tube at different rates, causing banding of those particles with the same S values (rate-zonal centrifugation), or particles of different densities will band with equi-density particles when they reach density equilibrium (isopycnic-zonal centrifugation).

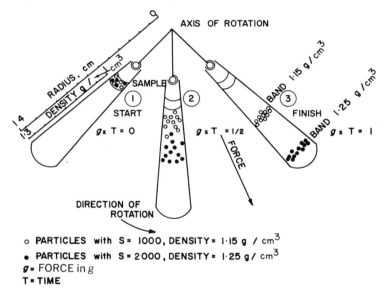

o PARTICLES with S = 1000, DENSITY = 1·15 g / cm^3
• PARTICLES with S = 2000, DENSITY = 1·25 g / cm^3
g = FORCE in g
T = TIME

Fig. 5. Diagrammatic representation of density gradient centrifugation. Note the degree of separation of particles so the isolated particle bands can be easily recovered.

Density is related to the chemical composition and crystal or internal structure of the particle, and any change in either the chemical makeup or the structure will affect the density of the particle. Since different types of particles, by definition, vary from one another in makeup and structure, it follows that, with the exception of some chemical isomers, no two types of particles should have the same density. This means a hydrated particle is usually less dense than the same particle in a dehydrated condition. The density, as mentioned earlier, is one factor which determines the sedimentation coefficient of a particle. The use of density for

identification presents an excellent opportunity for automation of measurement of the quality and quantity of particles present in a sample.

The density of a bio-organic particle varies with the age, nutrition, and
environmental prehistory of the particle. It may also vary between genetic
clones of a single species. These factors, and possibly others, will modify
the chemical composition and structure and therefore the density. A
single species isolated from a natural water sample usually shows a
Gaussian curve of density distribution(19). This represents dense young
individuals with a higher ratio of nucleic acid and protein to water,
middle-aged individuals, and finally old individuals with relatively more
water and less nucleic acid and protein.

Bio-organic detritus and inorganic particles of a single type, but of
significantly different sizes (ca. 100 fold), will often differ in density
within the type(50). While the reason for this discrepancy is not definitely
known, one possibility is that the smaller particle, with its large area-to-
volume ratio, has more water of hydration or ion shells relative to its
volume than the larger particle(23). This relative increase in water or
ions with decreasing size would affect particle density. This hypothesis
would explain the fact that a larger particle appears to be denser than a
smaller particle of the same type. If this hypothesis is correct, then the
true density of the particles does differ with particle size and the observed
differences are not artifacts of the isolation method.

Obtaining the true density of a bio-organic particle is not generally
required for routine investigations. Biological organisms are osmosensitive and gain or lose water in response to the tonicity of their external
environment. If a bacterial cell is transferred from water or medium with
an osmotic pressure of 0.5 atm into a hypertonic medium, water osmoses
from the cell. As water is lost the cell becomes relatively denser as the
proportion of protein and nucleic acid to water increases. If the cell is
transferred into a still more hypertonic medium, this increase in the density of the cell will be repeated until the cell is dehydrated. In addition,
some external ions such as cesium will dialyze into the cell if the internal
and external environments are not in equilibrium for that ion, and the
cell density will further increase. These effects mean that the measured
density of the bacterial cell is greater than the actual density of the cell in
its normal environment. Because of these factors, the measured density
of the cell in a liquid depends, to some extent, on the tonicity of the liquid.
As discussed later, several gradient materials minimize this osmotic
effect and so give a density measurement closer to the actual density of
the particle. Bio-organic detritus and colloids have little free water and
accordingly are less affected by the tonicity of their external environment.

Obtaining the true density of an inorganic particle is not as difficult as for a bio-organic particle since the inorganic particle is not sensitive to changes in tonicity of the external environment(51). However, the distribution of sedimentation coefficients of a single type of clay-mineral is generally a Gaussian curve due to differences in particle size, hydration, and sorbed ions. Many of the colloidal inorganic particles have significant amounts of external and internal water of hydration, and this may be affected in a hyper- or hypotonic environment. As is the case for bio-organic particles, this error is consistent for a particular environment or gradient material and is not a disruptive factor for isolation and concentration of the particles. Generally, the density determinations for clay-minerals in several density gradient materials show good agreement with each other and with dry density determinations(28).

2. PREPARATION OF DENSITY GRADIENTS

The ideal density gradient material has been defined as being physiologically inert and water soluble, with a high density per unit volume and a low viscosity and osmotic pressure(21,52). If a given amount of a substance such as sucrose is dissolved in a given volume of pure water, the resulting solution will have a greater density, or weight per unit volume, than an equal volume of pure water. If the amount of solute (sucrose) relative to solvent (water) is increased, the density of the solution will increase in direct proportion to the amount of solute added until the limit of solubility is reached. Now, if some pure water is carefully layered over this aqueous solution of greater density, there will be a slow diffusion of solvent and solute molecules until an equilibrium is reached and there is no further net movement of molecules. At that point the entire solution has a uniform density. At an earlier point in the diffusion process, there is a relatively linear decrease in density from the bottom of the solution to the top. The resulting density gradient ranges from the density of pure water near the top of the gradient to that of the original dense solution near the bottom. This linearity will last for several days, but the range of density differences will lessen as the solution approaches diffusion equilibrium. By using solution other than sucrose and water, density gradients with a maximum density of about 4.3 g/cm^3 can be made(53). The simplest way to form a density gradient is to layer stock solutions of decreasing density(1.5, 1.4, 1.3 ... 1.01 g/cm^3) on top of one another in a centrifuge tube(54). Twenty-four hr of diffusion will result in a linear gradient. By using a gradient performing device, a gradient can be made in a few minutes with exact control of gradient design and density change. The design of one such device is shown in Fig. 6, and others have been described by Simon(55).

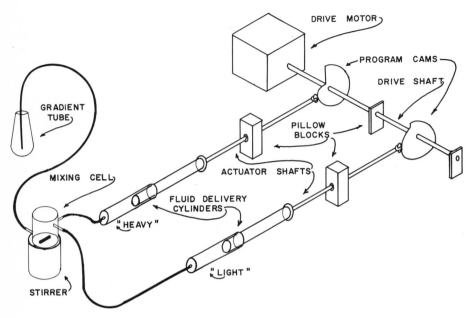

Fig. 6. A simple pump design to preform density gradients. The slope of the gradient is determined by the cam design. The cylinder size can be varied so that either single tubes or zonal rotors can be filled.

Since a zonal rotor must be loaded while spinning, a mechanical device is necessary to deliver a preformed density gradient to that type of rotor.

For most purposes a linear increase in the density of a gradient from the centripetal to the centrifugal side is adequate. In special situations the rate of increase in density may be modified to a sigmoid curve with a dense bottom layer that rapidly decreases in density, then a slow density decrease in the region of expected particle density, followed by a final rapid decrease to buffer at the centripetal side. For maximum resolution and separation of different types of particles which have similar densities, the best gradient design is one with a small overall increase in density from the centripetal to the centrifugal side of the rotor. No single material or design of gradient meets all of the requirements for natural water fractionation, and the type of gradient must be matched to the separation requirement.

3. Density Gradient Materials

The materials used for density gradient separation of bio-organic particles are not dense enough to float inorganic particles, and in general, the materials dense enough to band inorganic particles are toxic and often nonpolar. Due to these factors no gradient is known at present which is suitable for banding both bio-organic and inorganic particles in a single step. The maximum density of gradients suitable for bio-organic particles is 1.9 g/cm³. Excluding the diatoms ($\rho = 1.9$–2.1 g/cm³), the maximum density of bio-organic particles found in natural water is about 1.4 g/cm³. The physical characteristics of selected gradients are given in Table 1. The increase in density in a gradient is due to the increase in the number of solute to solvent molecules. Given this, it is clear why osmotic pressure in the gradient generally shows a parallel increase. The absolute osmotic pressure at a given molar concentration can be minimized by using gradients made of nonelectrolytes, and it is maximized when the gradients are made of electrolytes. The nonelectrolyte sucrose has about half the pressure at a density of 1.176 g/cm³ as CsCl has at a density of 1.174 g/cm³. The behavior of 3,5-DP (methyl glucamine salt of 3,5-diiodo-4-pyridone-N-acetic acid) is more complex since it seems to dissociate as an electrolyte in concentrated solutions (> 0.6 moles/liter), while it behaves as a nonelectrolyte at less than 0.6 moles/liter(2). At a density of 1.16 g/cm³, 3,5-DP has an osmotic pressure of 50 atm, which is less than that of CsCl but somewhat more than that of sucrose, and unlike sucrose and CsCl, 3,5-DP diffuses only slowly into bio-organic particles(2). Since most bio-organic particles fall in the density region 1.1–1.2 g/cm³, the osmotic comparisons are given in that region.

Sucrose density gradients can be used(21), but the viscosity of sucrose increases centrifugal time, and the hypertonicity prevents recovery of osmosensitive particles in a metabolically active condition(2). While CsCl gradients have a low viscosity, they are still not dense enough to band diatoms, and the equidensity osmotic pressure is about double that of sucrose. Because of this, CsCl is unsuitable for all bio-organic particles but viruses and detritus. At present, 3,5-DP is the best material for gradients to separate bio-organic particles from inorganic particles and to isolate major groups of particles. Most bio-organic particles can be banded and recovered in a metabolically active condition in a density gradient of 3,5-DP(2). The gradient more dense than the region of bio-organic particles serves only as a cushion to separate the bio-organic particles from the inorganic particles, and this is the region where 3,5-DP ionizes and has a rapid increase in osmotic pressure. The effect of osmotic pressure is most important when osmosensitive particles are involved. The osmotic shock as the particles enter or leave the hypertonic gradient is so severe that these particles may be destroyed or inactivated(2). Resistant particles with rigid walls and relatively little free water, such as bacteria and viruses, are only slightly osmosensitive,

TABLE 1.
Characteristics of Density Gradients[a]

Sucrose

Molarity	Solute, wt.%	Density, g/cm³	Viscosity, cp	Osmotic pressure, atm
0.29	10	1.038	1.3	1.0
0.59	20	1.081	1.5	14.6
0.88	30	1.127	3.2	21.0
1.17	40	1.176	6.2	28.7
1.46	50	1.230	15.4	36.5
1.75	60	1.289	58.4	48.3
2.19	75	1.375	2323.0	58.0
2.34	80	1.412		

CsCl

Molarity	Solute, wt.%	Density, g/cm³	Viscosity, cp	Osmotic pressure, atm
0.59	10	1.08	1.0	—
1.65	20	1.17	1.0	81.6
1.75	30	1.26	1.0	86.8
2.36	40	1.40	1.0	116.8
2.96	50	1.53	1.0	146.4
3.54	60	1.57	1.0	175.0

3,5-DP[b]

Molarity	Solute, wt.%	Density, g/cm³	Viscosity, cp	Osmotic pressure, atm	Refractive index
0.25	14.6	1.08	1.2	1.0	1.357
0.31		1.10	1.4	13.0	1.365
0.33		1.12	1.5	40.0	1.371
0.50	29.3	1.16	1.8	50.0	1.387
0.59		1.20	2.3	55.0	1.396
0.75	44.0	1.24	2.9		1.414
0.85		1.28	4.0	140.0	1.421
1.00	58.5	1.31	5.4		1.430
1.23	73.0	1.33	8.4		1.347
1.50	88.0	1.51	20.7		1.510

[a]These data are corrected to 20°C.
[b]Methyl glucamine salt of 3,5-diiodo-4-pyridone-N-acetic acid.

and may be centrifuged in CsCl density gradients. Inorganic particles are not osmosensitive, and so far as osmotic effects are concerned, any gradient is satisfactory.

A considerable amount of material has been published about high density liquids and their use in density determination and mineralogical separations. Johannsen(56) has reviewed the early efforts to develop and use heavy liquids. Later contributions have described the use of new liquids, discussed the relative merits of various methods, and presented specific applications(57–59). Amburgey has recently reviewed the application of dense liquids to centrifugal separations and banding of clay-minerals(53). A density gradient formed of tetrabromoethane and ethyl alcohol seems most suitable for separations of clay-minerals from water since the ethanol is polar and thus the concentrated inorganic particles can be introduced to the gradient in a water slurry. If nonpolar materials, such as a methylene iodide–dimethyl sulfoxide mixture, are used, the particles must be dried with ethanol and acetone before layering over the gradient. While thallium formate is polar, its toxicity to humans makes it difficult to use. These gradients can be made in the same design and with the same type of equipment as the gradients for bio-organic particles.

4. INTERFERING PHENOMENA

Both bio-organic and inorganic particles are affected by the gain or loss of molecules exchanged between the gradient and the particle. The particle will tend to reach a diffusion equilibrium with the gradient molecules, and may lose sorbed materials to the surrounding gradient and accumulate dialyzable gradient molecules(60). So far, the sorbed materials investigated have been unavailable for significant amounts of exchange. A loss of sorbed pesticide (DDT) or radionuclide (^{60}Co, ^{106}Ru, ^{137}Cs) from particles in a 3,5-DP gradient was not observed(61,62). Such a loss would be most likely when polyvalent electrolytes or solvents such as 2-bromoethanol are used as gradient materials. An exchange between sorbed materials of unlike particles in close proximity could occur before separation of different types of particles is complete, as in a centrifugal pellet(60). To lessen the chances of this, a fractionation should be planned so separations are complete as soon as possible after the sample is collected. By minimizing the time of contact of particles and gradient, this possible loss of material by exchange is reduced.

Anderson (63) has thoroughly discussed the dangers of particle over-crowding in causing abnormal behavior in a density gradient; generally, the fewer particles in a given volume, the more closely the observed results conform to the expected. As an empirical rule, a suspended particle concentration in the initial water sample of 10^8/ml requires a gradient of 75–100 ml, while an order of magnitude increase in particle concentration to 10^9/ml requires about 750 ml of gradient for nearly normal behavior. If the particles are too concentrated, the bands are mixed and distorted in the gradient and may sediment in large aggregates of mixed particles. On the other hand, if the gradient volume is too large, the particle band may be too dilute for observation and recovery. Spragg and Rankin (64) have recently calculated the capacity of zones in a density gradient and discuss the effects of overcrowding.

5. DETERMINATION OF OPERATING PARAMETERS

The calculation of precipitation time is simple for aqueous solutions, but it is more complex for the situation in a density gradient [see Eqs. (1) and (2)]. The sedimentation coefficient of a particle in a density gradient decreases as the density of the sedimenting particle approaches that of the surrounding medium. This is shown diagrammatically in Fig. 5. Finally a point is reached where $\rho_p = \rho_m$ so that $\rho_p - \rho_m = 0$ and then $S = 0$ [see Eq. (1)]. The particle is then in density equilibrium with the gradient. The particle will come to rest at this point and float there even with continued centrifugation. If more than one particle of the same density is present, a band of these particles will form where they are in density equilibrium with the gradient. As long as the density differences of the gradient are maintained, the particles will remain at the equilibrium point and may be recovered from the gradient without mixing with particles of different density. By proper design of density change in the gradient, it is possible to separate two particles with density differences of as little as 0.005 g/cm^3 (7). This situation is illustrated in Fig. 7 for the bacterium *Escherichia coli* j. This information is needed for accurate separations in both isopycnic and rate-zonal density gradient centrifugation.

If two particles to be separated have nearly the same density, but differ in sedimentation coefficient, they may be separated by rate-zonal density gradient centrifugation (65,66). Although at density equilibrium the particles would be at the same layer in the gradient, the particle with the greater sedimentation coefficient sediments faster. At some time before equilibrium is reached the two particles will have a maximum separation in distance in the gradient. In the case of rate-zonal centrifugation the centrifugation is stopped at the time calculated to have a maximum separation of the particles on the basis of their different sedimentation rates. In the absence of centrifugal force the opposing forces of viscosity, gradient buoyancy, and shear will prevent further movement of the

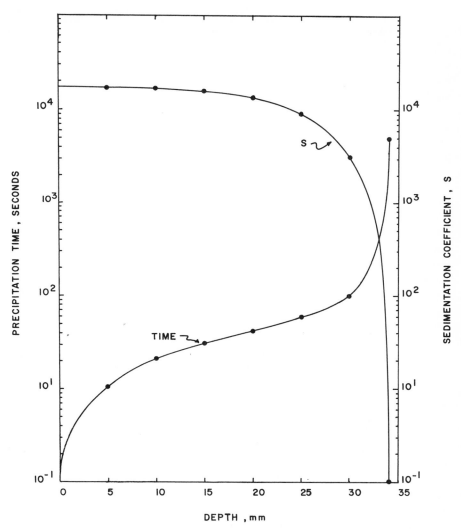

Fig. 7. Semilog plot relating precipitation time (T_s), sedimentation coefficient, and depth in density gradient centrifugation of *E. coli* j. The behavior of the particles from $T = 0$ until approximate density equilibrium at 34-mm depth in the tube is shown. The sedimentation curve is asymptotic.

particles and they may be recovered separately from the gradient. A comparison of precipitation times (T_s) for the two particles in the gradient will allow empirical choice of a time of centrifugation to give the desired separation.

If two particles to be separated differ both in density and in sedimentation coefficient, they may be separated by isopycnic density gradient centrifugation (65,66). In this case, the centrifugal impulse is chosen to cause the particles to reach approximate density equilibrium. At that point the particles are isolated and may be recovered separately from the gradient. Using a combination of differential and density gradient centrifugation, particles can be separated into classes based on sedimentation coefficient and then separated into classes based on density. At completion, the particles are isolated and concentrated into classes homogeneous for both sedimentation coefficient and density.

6. Isolation of Fractions

Metal rotors prevent observation of the particles in the sealed or spinning rotor. If the sample is in a centrifuge tube, then the tube is removed and examined after the rotor has stopped. A camera can be used to record the position and absorbence of a particle band in the centrifuge tube. The isolated particles can be recovered from the tube with a band recovery apparatus such as that shown in Fig. 8. This apparatus allows direct isolation and recovery of specific bands of particles with accuracy and minimum disturbance of the rest of the gradient. The needle is carefully lowered to the bottom of the particle band, and then the syringe plunger is mechanically withdrawn by a 1-rpm motor until the sample is collected. In a simpler system a 1-mm-i.d. glass or stainless steel tube is bent into a 180°, 1-cm-diameter arc to form a "J." This top opening prevents particles from lower, denser layers from being drawn into the tube, so no convection currents are created (54). The "J" tube is lowered into the gradient with a gear drive such as a microscope stand, and the sample is withdrawn into a vacuum flask. A quick clamp on the vacuum line will allow some precision of control, but while fast, this method is not so precise as the band recovery apparatus. The density of the gradient solution at any layer can be determined by measuring the refractive index of a series of drops of the gradient collected at known distances from the axis of rotation. The relation of refractive index to density determined experimentally; Table 1 shows the density, viscosity, and osmotic pressure of molar solutions of sucrose, CsCl, and 3,5-DP and the refractive indices of molar solutions of 3,5-DP.

In a more automated system(19) the density gradient is displaced from the centrifuge tube and forced through the flow cell of an optical densiometer by introducing a still denser liquid into the bottom of the tube. In one system a single 18-gauge needle extends to the bottom of the centrifuge tube to introduce the dense liquid. A similar-sized needle stops just within the tube mouth and receives the displaced gradient. If

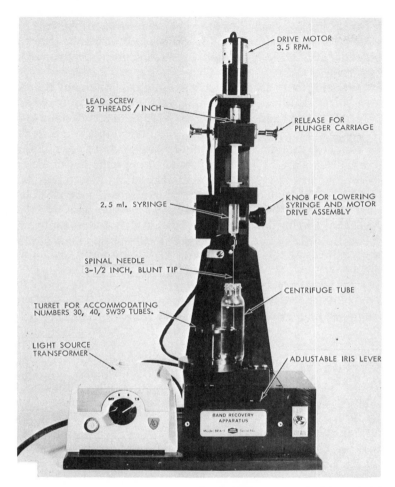

Fig. 8. Band recovery apparatus. A sample of gradient or particulate material can be removed from a specific point in the tube with a minimum of disturbance and contamination.

the cap supporting the needles is introduced into the firmly supported tube with care, there is no significant disturbance of the gradient or of the particle bands (see Fig. 4). An optical densiometer records both the quality and the quantity of the particles in the band by the absorbence at a specific wavelength. If the effluent stream passes through a flow refractometer just before or after the optical flow cell, the density of the gradient can be determined from the refractive index at the same time as the absorbence. Using these data of particle density and sedimentation coefficient, one can tentatively distinguish bands which contain virus particles from bands which contain such nonviral particles as colloidal detritus of cellulose. Similar identifications can be made of other bands. These identifications are supported by microscopic examination of the isolated particles.

When a zonal rotor is used, the density gradient containing the isolated particles is displaced from the spinning rotor by introduction of a dense liquid at the centrifugal side of the rotor. With this exception the displacement of gradient into a densiometer is like that from a single centrifuge tube. In both cases the particles in the density gradient are recovered in a fraction collector after they have passed through the densiometer flow cell. There are existing systems for semiautomating this so that the fraction collector is controlled from the densiometer and each particle band is isolated in a single tube(85). The isolated particles can be separated from the accompanying density gradient material by dialysis or by dilution and recentrifugation. Since the dialysis membrane is cellulose acetate, solvents such as 2-bromoethanol or tetrabromoethanol cannot be dialyzed(52).

V. Methods of Qualitative Characterization

A. Introduction

Following the concentration and isolation of particles is the qualitative identification of the physical, chemical, and biological nature of the isolated fractions. Some data from the concentration and isolation steps, such as density, sedimentation coefficient, and concentration, can be used to characterize the particles, but information about shape, size, morphology, and chemical composition must be derived from secondary analysis of the fractions. Most analyses seem to use certain portions of the electromagnetic spectrum, so they will be taken up in order of increasing wavelength.

B. X-Ray Diffraction

X-ray diffraction is useful in qualitatively identifying certain clay-minerals and some organic crystals. The technique depends on the regular arrangement of atoms in a crystalline compound and the fact that X-ray photons will be scattered or diffracted when they strike an atom. The direction of the diffracted photon beam depends on the repeated distances of the regular pattern, and the strength of the diffracted beam depends on the arrangement of atoms in each crystalline pattern. Each type of crystal should have a distinct pattern, and the more complex or irregular the crystal the more complex the pattern. Once a series of reference diffraction patterns from powder diagrams is collected, unknowns may be identified by comparison(67–70). Usually, high energy photons with a wavelength of about 1.54 Å are used since the short wavelength gives the best resolution, and since it has sufficient energy for good penetration. The use of X-ray diffraction for identification and structural analysis of crystalline bio-organic particles, such as proteins, has been described by Rich and Green(71), but this generally requires elaborate techniques such as heavy atom replacement and Fourier analysis, so it is not suitable for routine identification of large amounts of mixed bio-organic material.

While X-ray diffraction has been developed to a high degree and is probably the most common method of clay-mineral identification, it requires expensive equipment and expert technicians. It is not suitable for noncrystalline materials, and because of this several clay-minerals do not form diffraction patterns. On the other hand, a mixture of clay-minerals need not be separated into single types since both the identification and per cent composition of the types in the mixture can be made without separation. Interpretation of patterns is difficult and can be misleading, with irregular crystals, unusual atom substitutions, and asymmetrical clays. Most clay and some mineral particles do not have universal symmetry and must be precisely oriented in the X-ray beam so that the same angle is exposed each time. This can be done by allowing the clay-mineral particles to settle on a microscope slide or cover slip, since they will settle with their long axis horizontal(8). These considerations mean that positive identification should not rely solely on diffraction patterns but should be supported by other methods.

C. Electron Microscopy

Particle size and surface morphology in the colloidal and suspended particle range can be accurately and directly measured with an electron microscope(71–73). This instrument uses fast electrons, and several new developments have increased its versatility. Except for those with a silica or calcium shell, bio-organic particles are not electron dense enough to stop or diffract electrons. Because of this, the object must be rendered visible by heavy metal staining or shadowing for transmission electron microscopy. The methods of preparation and microscopy are diverse, and each particle of interest seems to have one or more "best" methods. Satisfactory results for viruses, bacteria, and detritus particles from natural water have been obtained with both the phosphotungstate negative stain(*19,74,75*) and with the uranyl formate stain(*7,19*). These stains have the advantage of not requiring vacuum shadowing, but they do not resolve the depth of the object to the extent accomplished by vacuum shadowing. The three-dimensional structure of delicate bio-organic colloids recovered by freeze drying has been resolved by shadowing(*76*). Different stains resolve different morphological features, and the proper stain must be chosen by the investigator to give the best results for his particular purpose(*77–79*). Methods, difficulties, and errors in particle size measurement, population counts, and morphological studies with the electron microscope are discussed in detail by Sachman and Williams(*80*).

Clay-mineral particles are so electron dense that no stain need be used and the particles must be well separated if their size is to be measured with transmission electron microscopy. Patricles $>0.1\,\mu$ are difficult to measure with accuracy(*81*), and unless the particles are well separated, surface details cannot be seen because of the opaqueness of the particles. Two excellent articles give methods and details for clay-minerals(*82,83*). Fischer(*81*) has described the use of transmission electron microscopy of replicas for detailed study of clay-mineral morphology. This technique uses a film of carbon or silica oxide that is translucent to electrons. The film is applied as a vapor and forms a replica of the object surface which can then be shadowed by a heavy metal. After removal from the object, the shadowed film is examined in the microscope. This method renders visible the detailed morphology of the opaque clay-minerals with a good degree of resolution. Another new technique with the electron microscope is the scanning electron microscope, which renders excellent surface detail of bio-organic and inorganic particles. This has a reported magnification range of 10–10,000×, covering from the macroscopic to the submicroscopic resolution. The depth of focus and resolution of the scanning technique are superior to those of optical microscopy, and the morphology is better resolved than with transmission electron microscopy(*81*). Transmission electron microscopy can resolve down to 2–3 Å, while scanning electron microscopy has a lower limit at about 150–300 Å. Bio-organic particles can often be identified on the basis of size and morphology, and a number of clay-minerals also have distinct crystal shapes which are aids in identification.

D. Ultraviolet Spectroscopy

Ultraviolet wavelengths have enough energy to penetrate a short distance into water, so they can be used to monitor particles in thin water columns(84). The flow cell of a UV densiometer usually has a cross section of 0.2–2 cm with a monochromatic UV light beamed through the cell. Since various macromolecules, such as proteins and nucleic acids, have absorption peaks at specific wavelengths, it is possible to identify these compounds and to qualitatively and quantitatively estimate the amount of those present as free molecules in water and as part of larger particles. This is done by a comparison of the ratios of absorption at selected wavelengths (e.g., 254, 260, and 280 nm)(85). Several designs use a wave shift mechanism, such as a stepping switch, so the absorbance of a single particle band is recorded nearly simultaneously at several wavelengths. Particles, such as clay-minerals, which have little or no UV absorbance will scatter the photobeam. The increased turbidity will give a semiquantitative record in terms of per cent transmittance (see Chap. 20).

E. Optical Microscopy

Optical microscopy in the range of 350–750 nm can be used to measure the size and morphology of particles larger than 0.2 μ. Special techniques extend the range well into the colloidal fraction for limited applications. Dark field microscopy resolves colloidal particles as light points in a dark field for proof that particles are present. Fluorescent microscopy will demonstrate the presence of particles smaller than 0.2 μ if they naturally fluoresce, as does calcite, or if they can be marked with a fluorescent dye, as with the fluorescent antibody technique(86). Regular optical microscopy generally requires staining for observation of bio-organic particles and has been largely supplanted by the more versatile phase contrast optics. Since phase contrast will resolve objects which have the same optical absorption as water, but a different refractive index, no staining is required to observe transparent objects. Particle counts, size measurements, and morphological studies can be made directly with raw water samples without further preparation. Clay-minerals are comparatively opaque and refractive and are generally poor subjects for optical microscopy. The size of clay-minerals can be determined accurately, but morphological studies are difficult(87). In all cases photographic recording on high contrast copy film gives a permanent record and a better quality analysis than direct visual measurements with an ocular micrometer.

F. Visible and Infrared Spectroscopy

Visible light spectroscopy (350–750 nm) is used to record the absorbance of particles suspended in a water column or in a UV-opaque solution such as the density gradient material 3,5-DP(2). Absorption in this wavelength region can be used to determine the quantity of particles present and their position in a gradient. A wavelength of 530 nm is used for optimum resolution of 3,5-DP gradients to record the position and quantity of particle bands(2) (see Chap. 20).

Infrared spectroscopy (see Chap. 30) uses the wavelengths from 0.8 μ to about 50 μ, and it is frequently used for identification of bio-organic colloids and for clay-mineral identification. Since water strongly absorbs IR, this region of the spectrum is little used for monitoring waterborne particles. In a concentrated, isolated, and relatively pure sample, the IR absorption spectrum of an unknown material can be compared to that of a known material and an identification may be made. The IR technique is less sensitive than UV spectroscopy, so it requires a larger sample. Furthermore, the IR spectra of inorganic particles usually found in water are not very informative. Identification of isolated clay-minerals does not appear as positive as identification by X-ray diffraction or differential thermal analysis, but it is a good method of conformation (88,89).

G. Differential Thermal Analysis

Differential thermal analysis is another method using infrared radiation for identification of inorganic particles(90–92). The equipment required is simpler than that for X-ray diffraction and can be fabricated and assembled from stock items. The method depends on the change in absorption or emission of infrared radiation by the experimental material when compared with (balanced against) that by a standard block of alundum while both are subjected to a controlled increase in termperature. When the thermal record is compared with that of a known sample, an identification may be made. This and X-ray diffraction can be used to support one another and the two, properly used, will give a high certainty of a correct identification. While X-ray diffraction can be used for the identification of some bio-organic crystals, differential thermal analysis is not applicable to identification of bio-organics. On the other hand, unlike X-ray diffraction, differential thermal analysis can be used successfully with both crystalline and amorphous clay-minerals. Mixtures of different types of clay-minerals can be examined, but the thermal record is more difficult to match with a known than if relatively pure samples are examined.

VI. Methods of Quantitative Characterization

A. Sorbtion Capactiy

It is important to be able to express the results of concentration and isolation in quantitative terms so that a particular fraction, representing a population in the sampled water, can be related to other parameters. If this were successfully done, the estimate of one fraction might be used to predict the expected behavior of another. This has already been done with good initial success (6,61,62). An important measure for both bio-organic and inorganic particles is the ability of the particle to accumulate material from the environment. Since this accumulation may involve both adsorption and absorption, it is conveniently called the sorbtion capacity. Even when the accumulated material is not of central interest, information on the sorbtion capacity of the particle is useful in correlating and comparing results (6,61,62,93).

1. BIO-ORGANIC PARTICLES

The sorbtion capacity of bio-organic particles seems best predicted by relating the total number, or quantity, of particles to the number alive and to the metabolic activity of the particles. The chart record area of the density gradient absorption peak can be measured with a polar planimeter, and this value can be taken as a measure of the total quantity of bio-organic material in the fraction. This measure can be used directly as indicative of the mean surface area of the fraction. The direct count of bio-organic particles made with phase contrast microscopy and a counting chamber is less desirable because it does not generally include rare forms, very small forms, or bio-organic detritus, and it is more a measure of the common, intact, biological organisms. In addition to the quantity and quality of bio-organic material, active uptake of materials due to biological processes must be considered. Part of the sorbtion by the bio-organic fraction will depend on surface exchange between material in the environment and exchange sites on the particle surface. If the fraction is nonliving, this is the only means of sorbtion, but if all or a part of the bio-organic fraction is alive, active transport can occur. In this case the organism uses energy to accumulate material from the environment in greater quantities than would occur by passive exchange. The number of particles alive can be measured by serial dilution and incubation, and the rate of growth can be measured by the turbidity of the first dilution tube (6). These values are used in the calculation:

$$C = V/GA \tag{5}$$

where: V is the number of viable particles
         G is the rate of growth
         A is the quantity of bio-organic material (chart record area)

The number C should reflect both the quantity of total bio-organic material present and the bioactivity of that material(6,61,62). From this, one has a single value which correlates with the sorbtion capacity of the bio-organic fraction. The value is objective and can be compared within and between samples.

2. INORGANIC PARTICLES

For the clay-mineral fraction, the expected magnitude of sorbtion per particle is directly dependent on the number of available exchange sites on the external and/or internal surface of the particle and generally shows a positive correlation with particle surface area. The sorbtion capacity can be measured and expressed as specific surface(93), cation exchange capacity(94), or total exchangeable bases(68,69,95,96). These are related aspects of the same phenomenon, but specific surface seems the method of choice because it is also a measure of the mean particle size. Thus, the required data are the surface area (quality) of the fraction and the dry weight (quantity). The surface area can be measured by gas or liquid displacement. For most accurate results the gas displacement method is used, but the size range of suspended particles in natural water falls between the region of maximum accuracy for the nitrogen and the helium gas methods(93). Since the gas displacement equipment is expensive, it is natural to use the liquid methods, which are less expensive and are sufficiently accurate for this purpose. The glycerol displacement, or its modification with ethylene glycol, can be done in any laboratory with standard equipment. The sample should be freed of bio-organic material either by density gradient centrifugation followed by dialysis or by oxidation in hydrogen peroxide. The sample is then acetone-dried for 24 hr at 105°C and weighed. If only the external surface is wanted, the sample is heated to 600°C to collapse the internal structure. If both the external and internal areas are wanted, the surface area is measured before collapse, then heated to collapse the internal structure, and re-measured(95). Next, the sample is saturated with calcium, wetted with glycerol or ethylene glycol, and then dried to a constant weight over calcium chloride in a vacuum desiccator(93). After a constant weight is reached, the surface area is calculated from the statement:

$$A = W_g/(W_s \times 0.00031) \qquad (6)$$

where: A is the specific surface, m²/g
  W_g is the glycerol retained by the sample, g
  W_s is the dry weight of the sample, g
0.00031 is constant of g of glycerol/m² monolayer(94)

The surface area can be related to the dry weight of the total fraction in the expression:

$$S = A/W \tag{7}$$

where: S is the sorbtion capacity of the sample
  A is the specific surface, m²/g
  W is the dry weight of the clay-mineral fraction, g

This ratio can be compared with the same value from other samples; it expresses the total sorbtion capacity of the fraction. Clay-mineral colloids can be measured in the same way.

B. Other Methods

Except for the virus particles, the colloidal bio-organic fraction is not alive. It may be measured by the chart record area of the densiometer after density gradient centrifugation, as dry weight, or estimated from electron micrographs. The number and identity of virus particles can be determined by a bioassay such as the standard plaque assay(6). Here, one or a few host organisms must be selected and other types of virus particles represented only as "virus-like particles" from electron micrographs. Because of the high degree of host specificity, virus particles mixed with nonhost cells will generally be lost and will give no indication of replicability. Bacteriophages of *Escherichia coli* j, *Aerobacter aerogenes*, and *Proteus vulgaris*, usually present in open water, are reliable for use as marker organisms(6). The same methods should be applicable for human and animal pathogenic viruses, substituting host cells in tissue culture for the bacterial host cells, but so far the only routine assay for animal or human viruses in water has been with samples of grossly polluted water.

Nonliving bio-organic particles or inorganic particles with an initial particle concentration of 10^2 particles/ml can be concentrated and isolated to a final concentration of 2×10^6 particles/ml from a 20-liter water sample. For bio-organic particles in a viable condition, a bioassay for a known virus has a sensitivity of one plaque-forming unit per 10 liters for a 20-liter sample(6). For bacteria and algae, the sensitivity is 5×10^5 cells/10 liters for a 20-liter sample(75). Investigations at the extreme limit of sensitivity may magnify errors and reduce the reliability of the results, so a larger sample (40–100 liters) may be required. In the larger sample, extremely rare particles can be concentrated into useful quantities and the reliability significantly increased (7, 19, 75).

VII. Confidence Limits

A. Sampling

Even the best sample will imperfectly represent the actual water mass. Problems such as patchy distribution of particles, seasonal variations, and short-term cyclic variations with the time of day or week must be circumvented as much as possible. If fractionation is the object, pooled samples collected over a period of time are not suitable due to growth, decay, exchange, and other such degradations. To obtain the same end that the pooled sample is designed for, grab samples must be collected over a long period. As in the case of the pooled sample, this will compensate for patchy distribution, and if collected on a randomized schedule for the hour of the day and day of the week, will also compensate for systematic day and hour bias. Seasonal variation of particles calls for consideration of the results of one or more years as a block, or alternately for consideration of short periods of relatively uniform conditions as blocks (see Chap. 10).

B. Isolation Losses

If one assumes that the original sample arrives in the laboratory in perfect condition and represents a cross section of the sampled water mass, there are certain losses in quality and quantity which result from the laboratory fractionation and analysis. These may be minimized, but not eliminated. Any time a particle comes in close contact with a surface or another particle, there is a chance it will adhere to the surface or cohere to the other particle. This may be especially likely when the particle collides with the surface under high centrifugal force. Clean metal and plastic surfaces, sector-shaped rotors and tubes, and density gradients reduce wall contact and chances of adhesion or cohesion. At present, particle recovery after a centrifugation is about 99%, so if a sample is centrifuged three times during fractionation a 3–5% loss is expected. Another loss is due to failure to sediment all particles from the suspending liquid during centrifugation. The centrifugal impulse used is calculated to give 99% particle cleanout. A certain amount of particle loss is deliberately accepted to reduce the time of centrifugation. The curve of sedimentation in both density gradient and differential centrifugation tends to be asymptotic (Fig. 7), so after about 99% cleanout it takes a large increase in centrifugal time to significantly increase the per cent cleanout. This is the compromise since an extension of the fractionation time results in more loss of particles due to death, disintegration, and deterioration than can be recovered by a 99.99% cleanout(54). The fractionation times and forces are thus set to minimize total particulate losses in numbers and integrity from all causes.

C. Metabolic Losses

Metabolic competence of bio-organic particles is lost with time and the various indignities to which the particles are subjected. To minimize this the fractionation is done quickly and at low temperature (5–10°C) (Fig. 9). For *Chlorella* spp., the loss of metabolic competence due to the effects of the density gradient is about 4%(2). For bacteria and viruses, no significant loss due to the gradient has been noted, and the particles are kept in a phosphate buffer enriched by $0.005\ M\ MgSO_4 \cdot 7H_2O +$ 0.1% gelatin to help maintain the viruses. Death and loss due to aging are reduced by the low temperature, but this factor will vary with both the species and the season. For routinely fractionated natural water samples, the total loss of bio-organic particles, due to physical loss and loss of metabolic competence, is estimated to be $15 \pm 5\%$ of the true value. The recovery will vary with the type of sample, the season, and the end analysis. The total particle recovery for most samples is estimated to be $85 \pm 5\%$ of the amount in the original sample.

VIII. Analysis of Results

The specific statistical analysis must be determined by the requirements of a particular experiment, but the results are especially suited to linear correlations between various combinations of data. Regression lines can then be plotted for expected behavior, and the values of the regression coefficient and of Student's "t" test give an estimate of the degree of correlation and reliability of the experiment(97). If the standard deviation and standard error of the mean are calculated, different sample series can be compared. So far, the linear correlations have proved to be useful methods of expressing the results(6, 61, 62) and to some extent can predict and explain the behavior of one fraction in relation to others(6)

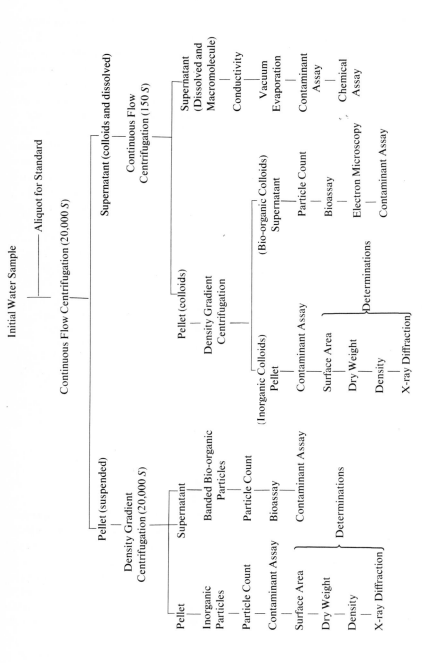

Fig. 9.   Flow diagram for water fractionation.

and in relation to accumulated material such as radionuclides(62) and DDT(61).

Where the regression coefficient is >0.5, four types of behavior may be predicted for accumulated materials: (a) If the X fraction shows a positive correlation with its Y fraction, but not with the total Y for the entire sample, then the X actively accumulated Y but is not efficient in competition with other fractions and so accumulates mostly excess Y. (b) If X is positively correlated with the total Y, but not with the Y in its fraction, then X is active and efficient in accumulation of Y, but not sufficiently so to become saturated at the expense of other fractions. (c) If X shows a positive correlation with both total Y and the Y in its fraction, then it is efficient enough to become saturated, or nearly so, at the expense of other fractions. (d) If X shows no correlations, then either other factors guide its behavior or it is a passive absorber.

Since the gradient media used to band clay-mineral particles could extract pesticides or radionuclides from the particles, the radionuclide accumulation is measured before density gradient centrifugation in these media(62). Pesticides are extracted from the clay-mineral fraction before a similar density gradient centrifugation(61). If the experiment has been designed to determine the pattern of accumulated radionuclides by the isolated fractions, the preparation for radioassay is determined by the particular radionuclide of interest and by the particle fraction involved. For γ-emitting radionuclides there is no need for separation of the radionuclide from the particulate fraction, the γ radiations have enough energy that they are not significantly diminished by the fraction or by the sample container. The fractions are simply reduced to a suitable volume and counted. After radioassay the particles in the fractions are prepared for surface area, dry weight, and similar determinations.

In the case of α and β emitters, the radionuclides must be separated from the particles in order to eliminate absorption of the relatively weak α and β photons by the particle or sample container. Any γ emitters must also be removed because their relatively higher energy will interfere with α and β counting. Detailed techniques have been published dealing with each special case(15, 37, 98, 99). If the extraction method chosen is destructive, some determinations of the quality and quantity of the fraction may have to be made before extraction or on aliquots of the fraction. If there is an initial particle concentration of 10^2 particles/ml and these particles have sorbed radionuclides with an activity of 10^{-3} pCi/ml, the final radionuclide activity concentrated from a 20-liter to 1-ml volume will be 20 pCi, well within the sensitivity of standard instruments (see Chap. 25).

The most sensitive method for pesticide analysis is some form of gas chromatography (see Chaps. 23 and 28). This requires extraction and

cleanup of the pesticide with an organic solvent. DDT has been successfully recovered with a hexane extraction of the isolated, concentrated
particulate fractions(61). However, hexane is not the best solvent for all
hydrocarbons(100–102). Nonpolar organic solvents cause a loss of some
of the sample fraction and generally are toxic to bio-organic forms, so some
determinations must be made before extraction. If a fraction has 10^2
particles/ml in 20 liters and these particles had sorbed $10^{-3}\,\mu g/ml$ of
DDT, the final pesticide quantity would be 20 μg of DDT.

IX. Backup Data

It is important that data from newer methods of water analysis be
integrated with those of older investigations(54). This will increase the
value of the older work and the newer will have, so to speak, a longer
history and hence greater reliability and usefulness. This integration may
be done by continuing in parallel some of the older measurements. At
present, for example, identification and quantitation of bio-organic
particles by density, sedimentation coefficient, and chart record area
are paralleled by microscopical examination and direct population
counts(54). As the relation between the older and newer results becomes
apparent, the older methods can be phased out and replaced by the
newer, more automated methods.

A number of environmental measurements should be made with the
samples collected so that the results may be interpolated to natural
conditions. Unless this is done there is little reason to start with a natural
water sample since one can more easily work with simple laboratory
models. Information on conditions such as temperature, depth, flow, light
intensity, and rainfall at sample time is useful in correlation with natural
conditions(6, 7) and with the results of other series of experiments. These
data also serve as corrections for the laboratory results, accounting for
more or less dilution due to rain, seasonal changes, and similar variables.

X. Summary

A fractionation of the particles in natural water, as described here, can
be used to isolate and characterize one or more fractions from the water
mass, or the entire sample may be fractionated and each fraction analyzed
to present a "balance sheet" of the total numbers, types, and characteristics of waterborne particles. While the quality and quantity of results

from a centrifugal fractionation are at least competitive with those from other methods of fractionation, no other method seems as suitable to the broad spectrum of particle types found suspended in natural water, and no other method has the capacity of rapid, efficient concentration of particles that exist in low numbers per unit volume of water.

REFERENCES

1. *Van Nostrand's Science Encyclopedia*, 3rd. ed., Van Nostrand, Princeton, N.J., 1958, pp. 371, 1528.
2. W. T. Lammers, *Limnol. Oceanog.*, **12** 148 (1967).
3. R. J. W. McLaughlin, *Geochim. Cosmochim. Acta*, **17**, 11 (1959).
4. D. W. Davis, T. G. Rochow, F. G. Rowe, M. L. Fuller, P. F. Kerr and P. Hamilton, in *Clay Mineral Standards Project 49*, Vol. 6, American Petroleum Institute, Columbia Univ. Press, New York, 1950, pp. 1–17.
5. M. A. Glagolera and K. Poznaniyu, *Diageneza Osadkov, Akad. Nauk SSSR Sbornik Statey.*, **5** (1959).
6. W. T. Lammers, *ORGDP K-1760*, Oak-Ridge, Tenn., 1968, pp. 1–20.
7. W. T. Lammers, *ORGDP KL-6131* Oak Ridge, Tenn., 1967, pp. 1–33.
8. T. Tamura, private communication, 1967.
9. R. I. Wigley, *J. Sediment. Petrol.*, **31**, 165 (1961).
10. D. Jenkins, *J. Water Pollution Control Federation*, **39**, 159 (1967).
11. W. D. Reves, *Southeastern Geol.*, **1**, 77 (1959).
12. W. Ryan and W. E. Worrall, *Trans. Brit. Ceram. Soc.*, **58**, 341 (1959).
13. F. G. Bierberly and H. D. Anthony, *Trans. Kansas Acad. Sci.*, **68**, 269 (1965).
14. D. T. Denhardt., *Biochem. Biophys. Res. Commun.*, **23**, 641 (1966).
15. A. Sorathesn, G. Bruscia, T. Tamura, and E. G. Struxness, *ORNL-60-6-93*, Oak Ridge, Tenn., 1960, pp. 1–28.
16. J. B. Andelman and M. Suess, *Anal. Chem.*, **38**, 351 (1966).
17. W. F. Blatt, M. P. Feinberg, H. B. Hopfenberg and C. A. Saravis, *Science*, **150**, 224 (1965).
18. D. W. Hood, *Environ. Sci. Technol.*, **1**, 303 (1967).
19. W. T. Lammers, *Environ. Sci. Technol.*, **1**, 52 (1967).
20. G. Cline, private communication, 1967.
21. W. T. Lammers, *Verhandl. Intern. Verein. Limnol.*, **15**, 1021 (1964).
22. A. S. Berman, in *The Development of Zonal Centrifuges* (N. G. Anderson, ed.), *NCI Monograph 21*, U.S. Govt. Printing Office, 1966, pp. 41–76.
23. C. E. Marshall, *J. Soc. Chem. Ind., Trans.*, **50**, 444 (1931).
24. V. N. Schumaker, *Separation Sci.*, **1**, 409 (1966).
25. R. F. Conley, *J. Am. Ceram. Soc.*, **46**, 1 (1963).
26. M. K. Brakke, *Arch. Biochem. Biophys.*, **93**, 214 (1961).
27. H. P. Barringer, in *The Development of Zonal Centrifuges* (N. G. Anderson, ed.), *NCI Monograph 21*, U.S. Govt. Printing Office, 1966, pp. 77–112.
28. J. W. Amburgey, Jr., *ORGDP KL-6011*, Oak Ridge, Tenn., 1964, pp. 1–18.
29. H. P. Barringer, N. G. Anderson, C. E. Nunley, K. T. Ziehlke, and W. S. Dritt, in *The Development of Zonal Centrifuges* (N. G. Anderson, ed.), *NCI Monograph 21*, U.S. Govt. Printing Office, 1966, pp. 191–198.
30. C. H. Fox, Jr., and J. W. Amburgey, Jr., *ORGDP KL-2709, R-1*, Oak Ridge, Tenn., 1968, pp. 1–22.

31. A. D. Semenov, I. N. Ivleva and V. G. Datska, *Gidrokhim. Materialy,* **33,** 172 (1961).

32. V. G. Datska, A. D. Semenov and I. N. Ivleva, *Izvest. Akad. Nauk SSSR Otdel. Khim. Nauk,* **184** (1961).

33. S. P. Mathur and E. A. Paul, *Nature,* **212,** 5062 (1964).

34. M. Soukup, *Collection Czech. Chem. Commun.,* **29,** 3182 (1964).

35. D. R. Lewis, in *Clay Mineral Standards Project 49,* Vol. 7, Sec. 3, American Petroleum Institute, Columbia Univ. Press, New York, 1950, pp. 91–124.

36. J. G. Green, C. E. Nunley and N. G. Anderson, in *The Development of Zonal Centrifuges,* (N. G. Anderson, ed.), *NCI Monograph 21,* U.S. Govt. Printing Office, 1966, pp. 431–440.

37. V. R. Smit and J. J. Jacobs, *Ind Eng. Chem. Process Design Develop.,* **5,** 117 (1966).

38. V. E. Nash, in *Clays and Clay Minerals* (A. Swineford, ed), Pergamon, New York, 1960, pp. 328–342.

39. C. G. Menke, *J. Am. Water Works Assoc.,* **54,** 303 (1962).

40. J. Shapiro, *J. Am. Water Works Assoc.,* **56,** 1062 (1964).

41. J. G. Green, C. E. Nunley and N. G. Anderson, in *The Development of Zonal Centrifuges* (N. G. Anderson, ed.), *NCI Monograph 21,* U.S. Govt. Printing Office, 1966, pp. 435–438.

42. J. H. Johnson, J. E. Fields and W. A. Darlington, *Nature,* **213,** 665 (1967).

43. S. M. Kelley, *Am. J. Public Health,* **43,** 1532 (1956).

44. P. Flodin, *Dextran Gels and Their Applications in Gel Filtration,* Pharmacia, Uppsala, Sweden, 1962, pp. 1–85.

45. W. H. S. George, *Nature,* **195,** 155 (1962).

46. A. M. Posner, *Nature,* **198,** 1161 (1963).

47. J. W. Amburgey, Jr., *ORGDP KL-2549,* Oak Ridge, Tenn., 1967, pp. 1–15.

48. Literature abstracts are available from Pharmacia, Uppsala, Sweden.

49. H. E. Ries and B. L. Meyers, *Science,* **160,** 1449 (1968).

49a. R. Stock and C. B. F. Rice, *Chromatographic Methods,* Reinhold, New York, 1963, pp. 99–102.

50. W. T. Lammers, unpublished data.

51. A. F. Reid and A. H. Halff, *Science,* **135,** 319 (1962).

52. W. T. Lammers, *Science,* **139,** 1298 (1963).

53. J. W. Amburgey, Jr., *ORGDP KL-2386,* Oak Ridge, Tenn., 1966, pp. 1–18.

54. W. T. Lammers, *Limnol. Oceanog.,* **7,** 224 (1962).

55. W. K. Simon, *ORGDP KL-2378 and KL-2379,* Oak Ridge, Tenn., 1966, pp. 1–10, 1–12.

56. A. Johannsen, *Manual of Petrographic Methods,* McGraw-Hill, New York, 1918, p. 515 et seq.

57. E. A. Zhukovskaya, *Vestn. Leningr. Univ.,* **19,** *Ser. Geol. Geogr.,* **3,** 110 (1964).

58. S. I. Davidovich and G. K. Eremenko, *Razvdeka Okhrana Nedr.,* **30,** 47 (1964).

59. A. H. Beavers, *Soil Sci. Soc. Am. Proc.,* **12** (1958).

60. R. E. Grim, *Science,* **135,** 890 (1962).

61. W. T. Lammers, *ORGDP K-1755,* Oak Ridge, Tenn., 1968, pp. 1–17.

62. W. T. Lammers, *ORGDP K-1758,* Oak Ridge, Tenn., 1968, pp. 1–20.

63. N. G. Anderson, in *Physical Techniques in Biological Research* (G. Oster and A. W. Pollister, eds.), Vol. 3, Academic, New York, 1959, pp. 299–315.

64. S. P. Spragg and C. T. Rankin, Jr., *Biochim. Biophys. Acta,* **141,** 164 (1967).

65. N. G. Anderson, in *The Development of Zonal Centrifuges* (N. G. Anderson, ed.), *NCI Monograph 21,* U.S. Govt. Printing Office, 1966, pp. 9–40.

66. N. G. Anderson, W. W. Harris, A. A. Barber, C. T. Rankin, Jr. and E. L. Chandler, in *The Development of Zonal Centrifuges* (N. G. Anderson, ed.), *NCI Monograph 21*, U.S. Govt. Printing Office, 1966, pp. 253–284.

67. L. S. Birks, J. S. Grosso, R. J. Labrie, J. W. Sandelin and D. J. Nagel, *AD 631–146*, U.S. Govt. Printing Office, 1966, pp. 1–20.

68. P. F. Kerr, P. K. Hamilton, R. J. Pill, G. V. Wheeler, D. R. Lewis, W. Burkhardt, D. Reno, G. L. Taylor, R. C. Mielenz, M. E. King and N. C. Schietlz, in *Clay Mineral Standards Project 49*, Vol. 7, American Petroleum Institute, Columbia Univ. Press, New York, 1950, pp. 1–160.

69. W. F. Bradley, *Am. Mineralogist*, **30**, 704 (1945).

70. L. D. Whittig, in *Methods of Soil Analysis* (C. A. Black, ed.), Part 1, American Society of Agronomy, Madison, Wis., 1965, pp. 671–698.

71. A. Rich and D. W. Green, in *Annu. Rev. Biochem.* (J. M. Luck, ed.), Vol. 30, Annual Reviews, Palo Alto, Calif., 1961, pp. 93–132.

72. J. A. Kittrick, in *Methods of Soil Analysis* (C. A. Black, ed.), Part 1, American Society of Agronomy, Madison, Wis., 1965, pp. 632–652.

73. R. P. Humbert, *Bull. Am. Ceram. Soc.*, **21**, 260 (1942).

74. W. T. Lammers, *ORGDP K-1760*, Oak Ridge, Tenn., 1968, pp. 1–20.

75. W. T. Lammers, *Verhandl. Intern. Verein. Limnol.*, **16**, 452 (1966).

76. R. B. Dean, *Environ. Sci. Technol.*, **1**, 147 (1967).

77. V. E. Cosslett, in *Physical Techniques in Biological Research* (A. W. Pollister and G. Oster, eds,), Vol. 1, Academic, New York, 1955, pp. 463–532.

78. T. F. Anderson, in *Physical Techniques in Biological Research* (A. W. Pollister, ed.), Vol. 3A, 2nd ed., Academic, New York, 1966, pp. 319–388.

79. C. E. Schwerdt., in *Physical Techniques in Biological Research*, (A. W. Pollister and G. Oster, eds.), Vol. 1, Academic, New York, 1955, pp. 329–358.

80. H. K. Schachman and R. C. Williams, in *Physical Techniques in Biological Research* (A. W. Pollister and G. Oster, eds.), Vol. 1, Academic, New York, 1955, pp. 223–328.

81. A. G. Fischer, *Am. Scientist*, **56**, 130 (1968).

82. B. T. Shaw, *J. Phys. Chem.*, **46**, 1032 (1942).

83. J. L. Brown, in *Soil Clay Mineralogy Symposium*, Univ. of North Carolina Press, Chapel Hill, 1964, pp. 148–169.

84. J. F. Scott, in *Physical Techniques in Biological Research* (A. W. Pollister and G. Oster, eds.), Vol. 1, Academic, New York, 1955, pp. 131–205.

85. N. G. Anderson, *Anal. Biochem.*, **4**, 269 (1962).

86. A. H. Coons, in *General Cytochemical Methods* (J. F. Danielli, ed.), Vol. 1, Academic, New York, 1958, pp. 400–422.

87. J. G. Cady, in *Methods of Soil Analysis* (C. A. Black, ed.), Part 1, American Society of Agronomy, Madison, Wis., 1965, pp. 604–631.

88. H. H. Adler, E. E. Bray, N. P. Stevens, J. M. Hunt, W. D. Keller, E. E. Pickett and P. F. Kerr, in *Clay Mineral Standards Project 49*, Vol. 48, American Petroleum Institute, Columbia Univ. Press, New York, 1950, pp. 1–142.

89. J. L. Mortensen, D. M. Anderson and J. L. White, in *Methods of Soil Analysis* (C. A. Black, ed.), Part 1, American Society of Agronomy, Madison, Wisc., 1965, pp. 743–770.

90. P. F. Kerr, in *Clay Mineral Standards Project 49*, Vol. 3, American Petroleum Institute, Columbia Univ. Press, New York, 1949, pp. 1–48.

91. I. Barshad, in *Methods of Soil Analysis* (C. A. Black, ed.), Part 1, American Society of Agronomy, Madison, Wis., 1965, pp. 699–742.

92. R. E. Grim and R. A. Rowland, *Am. Mineralogist*, **27**, 746, 801 (1942).

93. M. M. Mortland and W. D. Kemper, in *Methods of Soil Analysis* (C. A. Black, ed.), American Society of Agronomy, Madison, Wis., 1965, pp. 532–544.

94. H. D. Chapman, in *Methods of Soil Analysis* (C. A. Black, ed.), Part 2, American Society of Agronomy, Madison, Wis., 1965, pp. 891–904.

95. E. B. Kinter and S. Diamond, in *Clays and Clay Minerals* (E. Ingerson, ed.), Pergamon, New York, 1960, pp. 125–134.

96. H. D. Chapman, in *Methods of Soil Analysis* (C. A. Black, ed.), Part 2, American Society of Agronomy, Madison, Wis., 1965, pp. 902–904.

97. A. Goldstein, *Biostatistics*, Macmillan, New York, 1964, pp. 129–134.

98. R. E. Bentley, R. P. Parker, D. M. Taylor and M. P. Taylor, *Nature*, **194**, 736 (1962).

99. Cooperative Studies Unit, Radiological Health Research Activities, *Methods of Preparing Environmental Samples for Gamma Scanning and Strontium 90 Analysis*, Division of Radiological Health, U.S. Public Health Service, Cincinatti, Ohio, pp. 1–7.

100. R. D. Hoak, *Intern. J. Air Water Pollution*, **6**, 521 (1962).

101. R. T. Skrinde and H. D. Tomlinson, *J. Water Pollution Control Federation*, **35**, 1292 (1963).

102. F. A. Voege and H. L. Vanesche, *J. Am. Water Works Assoc.*, **56**, 1351 (1964).

103. N. G. Anderson, *ORNL-3656, Special*, Oak Ridge, Tenn., 1964, pp. 1–128.

104. F. M. Burnet and W. M. Stanley (eds.), *The Viruses*, Vol. 1, Academic, New York, 1959, pp. 1–609.

105. K. M. Smith and M. A. Lauffer (eds), *Advances in Virus Research*, Vol. 9, Academic, New York, 1962, pp. 1–312.

Chapter 13 Bacterial and Viral Analysis of Water and Waste Water

Pasquale V. Scarpino

ENVIRONMENTAL HEALTH ENGINEERING
DEPARTMENT OF CIVIL ENGINEERING
UNIVERSITY OF CINCINNATI
CINCINNATI, OHIO

I. Microbiological Analysis of Water and Waste Water

A. Disease Transmission by Water

Water has always been a medium for the transmission of human microbial diseases—the bacterial-caused diseases of typhoid fever, paratyphoid fevers, bacillary dysentery, and cholera, and nonbacterial diseases such as amoebic dysentery and infectious hepatitis—but we have known definitely for only a century that this is so. Before then, man indicated in his writings and by his public works, customs, and religious practices his suspicions of water as a vehicle of disease transmission(*1*). Anton van Leeuwenhoek was the first to observe and record the presence of bacteria and protozoa in various waters and in his own formed and diarrheic stools, but he did not relate his discoveries to the causation of disease.

As early as 1854, however, without any knowledge of the cause of the disease, John Snow, the English anesthetist, advocated the water-borne nature of cholera. His classical epidemiological investigation conclusively established the role of water in the transmission of the disease. An epidemic of cholera had broken out in London that was most intense on Broad Street near Golden Square, and in neighboring dwellings, Snow found that most of the victims lived near the public water pump located at 40 Broad Street. He noted that in 10 days after the initial outbreak 521 deaths from cholera had occurred within a radius of 250 yards from the pump. Water from this pump was examined and found to contain evidence of sewage pollution from the adjoining house at 40 Broad Street. After the pump was removed from use, the epidemic ceased(*2*).

The specific etiological agents of a number of common infections of the intestinal tract of man were identified toward the end of the 19th century as the "golden age" of bacteriology was drawing to a close. For example, the typhoid bacillus was isolated and described by Eberth in 1880 and was subsequently cultured by Gaffky in 1884. But even earlier, in 1856 and 1873, Budd had pointed out that typhoid fever was transmitted by contaminated water. Although Felix Pouchet in 1849 reported to have seen vibrios in the stools of cholera patients, it was not until 1883 that Koch isolated the cholera vibrio from the feces and intestinal contents of a number of deceased and living victims of the disease. The Hamburg, Germany, cholera epidemic of 1892, which was related to unfiltered river water, confirmed Snow's claim of the waterborne nature of cholera.

The great Japanese bacteriologist Shiga isolated the agent responsible for epidemic dysentery in 1898. His discovery was followed closely by the identification of similar organisms by other investigators. Although pollution of water supplies with the various dysentery bacilli has caused large outbreaks of bacillary dysentery, infection via water transmission is not considered as important a problem as in the case of typhoid fever.

Schottmuller in 1900 used serological methods to differentiate the paratyphoid fevers. Transmission via sewage-contaminated water supplies of the three specific salmonellae that cause paratyphoid fever in humans is not as common as water transmission of typhoid fever, but large waterborne epidemics have occurred. The Riverside, California, waterborne epidemic involving tens of thousands of cases, caused by *Salmonella typhimurium,* an organism usually associated with foodborne diseases, occurred as late as 1965(*3*). Water has also been incriminated as a transmitting vehicle for a number of other bacterial diseases, such as brucellosis, tuberculosis, and tularemia. Thus, evidence has accumulated that irrefutably establishes the waterborne nature of bacterial enteric diseases.

Water has also been considered in the transmission of viral diseases of man(*4*). For example, in a literature survey Mosley(*5*) summarized all the waterborne outbreaks of infectious hepatitis prior to 1967. Coin et al.(*6*) reported polio virus in over 18% of more than 200 drinking water samples taken from the distribution system of Paris. Coin later(*7*) estimated the virus concentration to be not higher than one tissue culture infective dose (TCID$_{50}$) per 250 liters (67 gal) of water. Isolation of viruses was accomplished using the nonquantitative gauze pad technique, leading to the speculation that more would have been isolated if techniques had been quantitative(*8*).

Some parasitic diseases of man can also be contracted through drinking water. Four epidemics of amoebic dysentery caused by *Entamoeba histolytica* have been traced to contamination of the distribution system of water supplies(*9*). Diarrheal disease caused by *Giardia lamblia* (a flagellate) has been endemic in a resort area near Denver, Colorado, and has been linked to contamination of the small water supply obtained from wells(*10*). In endemic regions, schistosomiasis (caused by three blood flukes, *Schistosoma japonicum, S. haematobium,* and *S. mansoni*) is normally contracted by wading or swimming in contaminated water inhabited by appropriate snails which serve as intermediate hosts, but infection can also be acquired through drinking water that contains the infective cercariae(*11*). Hookworm infections of man caused by *Ancylostoma duodenale* and *Necator americanus* are normally contracted by walking barefooted over fecal-polluted soil but can also be acquired by drinking water from ponds or streams that receive surface drainage from contaminated soil(*12*). Guinea worm (*Dracunculus medinensis*) infection is contracted by drinking untreated water, such as that from step wells, containing a suitable infected species of cyclops (a copepod) which serves as intermediate host of the worm. Infections by fish tapeworms (*Diphyllobothrium latum*), liver flukes (*Clonorchis sinensis* and *Fasciola hepatica*), lung flukes (*Paragonimus westermanni*), and intestinal flukes (*Fasciolopsis buski*) are contracted through eating raw vegetation (*Fasciola* and *Fasciolopsis*) or inadequately cooked fish (*Clonorchis*) or crabs and crayfish (*Paragonimus*) (the latter are

not infective if the water from which they came is free of fecal contamination).

Establishment of pure supplies of water was therefore an important
prerequisite for the development and survival of our contemporary
congested, urban civilization. However, increased urbanization and
industrialization and the population expansion have not only aggravated
and created problems of housing, food and milk sanitation, insect and
rodent control, air pollution, and radiological contamination of our
environment, but have also intensified the problems associated with water
pollution. At present in the United States, at least two-thirds of the
population lives on 9% of the land in 212 standard metropolitan statistical areas(13). It has been estimated that by the year 2000 95% of the
expected 280 million Americans will reside in urban areas(14). It is,
and will continue to be, in these urban areas of the United States that
our most pressing water pollution problems exist. In addition, a World
Health Organization (WHO) report(15) noted that the predicted seven-
fold increase in the world's urban population in the second half of the
20th century has made the need for improving the world's urban water
supplies more urgent. WHO reported the growing recognition by the
governments of developing nations of the importance of adequate and
safe water in both rural and urban areas for the economic and social
development of their countries. This is reflected in the increasing number
of requests received by WHO for assistance in programs formulated to
provide the developing countries with more and safer public water
supplies.

A report made in 1967 by an interregional group sponsored by WHO in
New Delhi examined the water pollution problems of 16 developing
countries that were at different stages of urbanization and industrialization but were still predominately agricultural. It noted that eight of the
16 countries reported the occurrence of intestinal disease caused by
waterborne bacteria and viruses(16). For example, the explosive New
Delhi outbreak of infectious hepatitis in 1955–1956, which was responsible for some 30,000 overt cases of the disease before subsiding(17), was
traced to inadequate treatment of the heavily fecal-polluted Jumna
River water used as a raw source of the municipal supply system.
Although it is generally agreed that the United States has few major
outbreaks of disease directly attributable to microbial-contaminated
water supplies, hundreds of recorded outbreaks of microbial-caused
waterborne disease have actually occurred in this country since 1946(18).
The Zermatt, Switzerland, typhoid epidemic in 1963 and the 1965
Riverside, California, epidemic caused by *Salmonella typhimurium* both
involved inadequacies in treatment of piped drinking water supplies.

Thus, well-established water supply systems in highly developed nations are not immune to waterborne disease.

B. Microflora in Natural Waters

The normal microflora of natural waters that are free from gross pollution may consist of blue-green algae, diatoms, phytoflagellates, green algae, bacteria, fungi (both yeasts and molds), protozoa, and such metazoans as nematodes, rotifers, and minute crustacea.

Naturally occurring aquatic bacteria, as an example, may be in the following genera: *Alcaligenes, Caulobacteria, Chromobacterium, Flavobacterium, Leptospira, Micrococcus, Proteus,* and *Pseudomonas.* The sulfur bacteria, i.e., *Beggiatoa alba, Desulfovibrio* spp., and the various thiobacilli, and the iron bacteria, i.e., *Leptothrix ochracea, Gallionella ferruginea,* and *Crenothrix polyspora,* may also be found in surface waters but are more commonly inhabitants of the bottom muds. In addition, members of the genera *Aerobacter* (i.e., *Enterobacter*) and *Bacillus,* the actinomycetes, and nitrogen-fixation bacteria may be present in natural waters, but are soil microbes that have been washed into the water by surface runoffs from the land.

The microflora present in natural waters will vary depending upon a multiplicity of different yet interrelated ecological factors. Physical factors that a microbial individual encounters in its microenvironment include changes in solar radiation, temperature, salinity (and its subsequent effect on osmotic pressure), hydrostatic pressure, turbidity, and surface tension of the water. Essential chemical factors include changes in pH, dissolved oxygen, nitrogen, sulfur, phosphorus, and iron, and organic and inorganic carbon. Radiation, including ultraviolet, visible, and ionizing radiations, has a profound influence on the eventual growth or death of the microbes in a water environment. The density of the organisms in relationship to water, the viscosity of the water, surface tension of the film, and gas retention and release by the organism together with the horizontal and vertical movement of the water will influence the ultimate level at which the organism dwells in water. The presence of organic and inorganic nutrients, growth factors, metabolic regulating substances, poisons, inhibitors, and nutrient analogs, and variations in oxidation-reduction potential profoundly affect the inhabitants of a water environment. Favorable or unfavorable biological interrelationships existing among microscopic and macroscopic organisms determine the number, type, and distribution in water of the microbial flora at any one instant.

C. Bacteriological Analysis of Water and Waste Water

1. PRESENCE OF MICROBIAL POLLUTANTS IN WATER

Water may be described as being potable, i.e., safe to use and aesthetically appealing to the consumer in both appearance and taste. Pollution, on the other hand, refers to the accidental or intentional discharge, directly or indirectly, of any liquid, gaseous, thermal, and/or solid substance into water. These added pollutants may constitute a nuisance or be actually injurious to the health and well-being of man, animals, birds, and aquatic life forms such as fish and plants. Intestinal microorganisms from warm-blooded animals (including man) enter rivers, streams, and large bodies of water, contributing to the pollution of these environments. Among these intestinal microbes are the coliform group, members of the genera *Streptococcus, Lactobacillus, Staphylococcus, Proteus,* and *Pseudomonas,* spore-forming bacteria, and other inhabitants of the gastrointestinal tract of man. Pathogenic forms may be in evidence, but the numbers and types will vary with the geographic area, the state of community health, the nature and degree of sewage treatment, and the physiological state of the organisms. The following pathogenic bacteria may be noted: species of *Salmonella, Shigella, Leptospira, Brucella, Mycobacterium,* and *Vibrio.* Animal viruses may be in evidence, such as those causing infectious hepatitis and polio, and protozoa causing amoebiasis and giardiasis in man.

2. SUGGESTED CRITERIA FOR AN IDEAL BACTERIAL INDICATOR ORGANISM

The question posed by the early water bacteriologists was: "Which bacterium would be most useful to indicate sewage contamination of water and thus the presence or absence of enteric pathogens?" This led to the following definition of criteria for an ideal bacterial indicator organism:

1. The indicator bacterium should be applicable in all types of water, i.e., tap, river, ground, impounded, recreational, estuary, sea, and waste waters.
2. The indicator bacterium should be present whenever enteric pathogens are present.
3. It should have a reasonably longer survival than the hardiest enteric pathogen.
4. It should not reproduce in the contaminated water, i.e., "aftergrowth," thereby leading to an inflated value.

5. The test procedure for the indicator should have high specificity (i.e., other organisms would not give positive results) and high sensitivity, allowing the determination of low levels of the indicator.
6. The testing method should be easy to perform. However, increased sophistication in laboratory technology will result in complex methods becoming simpler to perform. Thus, in the future the complexity of the method should not impose great restrictions on its general usage.
7. The indicator should be harmless to man. However, a pathogen should usually pose no problem to a trained microbiologist. In fact, emphasis today is on direct isolation from water of enteric pathogens such as salmonellae.
8. The density of the indicator bacterium in contaminated water should have some direct relationship to the degree of fecal pollution.

Obviously, it would be desirable to find one bacterium (or microbe) that would indicate the presence or absence in water of not only bacterial enteric pathogens but all enteric disease-producing microbes, including viruses. Alas, the life of a microbiologist is not that simple, and such a happy coincidence has not presented itself as yet. Investigators still attempt to improve upon the bacterial indicators presently used, and suggest new ones that might be superior in certain water environments.

With the exception of the free-living amoeba, *Naegleria gruberi*, which accidentally causes meningoencephalitis among swimmers(*19,20*), the normal microbiota of natural waters are not of sanitary significance since they are not involved in the actual transmission of human or animal diseases and have no known association with human or animal wastes. Since they are also widely distributed in soil and may be carried in air, their presence or absence would not provide any helpful information concerning the presence or absence of pathogens of human or animal origin. Until recently, it was not considered possible or practical to assay directly for human pathogenic bacteria in water. The investigations of Spino(*21*) and others(*22*) may lead to easier detection of pathogenic bacteria in water, and thus to their use in evaluating the potability of water.

3. BACTERIAL PARAMETERS OF POLLUTION

At present, one or more of the following biological determinations are made to assess the bacteriological quality of water and thereby indicate the presence or absence of pathogenic enteric bacteria.

a. The Standard Plate Count

This is a standard quantitative method for the indirect measurement of viable numbers of bacteria in a water environment(23). A flat surface of a given size, covered with a bacterial growth medium solidified with agar, is inoculated with a water sample. The usual procedure is to add a proper aliquot of the water sample or its dilution to the bottom of a sterile glass or plastic container 100 mm wide and 15 mm high. A removable overlapping upper lid ensures the sterility of the contents. Then the liquefied, cooled (43–45°C) growth medium is added, and the plate is rotated to allow for even distribution of the bacteria in the water. Each isolated bacterium fixed in place by the solidification of the agar, contained in the medium, develops into visible spots of growth called colonies. Each colony contains many thousands of cells.

Theoretically, each bacterium present has the opportunity to develop into a visible colony of many thousands of bacteria, where each colony represents the initial presence in the inoculum used of one bacterium. However, a standard plate count gives numbers that are often more apparent than real, since not all viable cells in the water sample may be able to reproduce under the physical, chemical, and biological cultural conditions imposed upon them. The numbers and types of bacteria that will develop are influenced by such environmental cultural conditions as the temperature of incubation, pH of the medium, the presence or absence of oxygen, the presence of specific nutrients in the growth medium, competition among cells for nutrients, antibiosis, and parasitism. Aggregation of organisms in the water sample will also lead to erroneous results, since an aggregate of cells will show up as only one colony on the growth medium. It is seldom possible to use the water sample directly without first diluting out the bacteria in it by passing a known portion of the initial sample through a series of tubes or bottles containing known amounts of sterile dilution water, thus introducing another possibility of error in the final calculation of initial levels of bacteria in the water sample. However, as is discussed later, the standard plate count is still useful in the evaluation of the bacterial quality of water and waste water and in determining the efficiency of various waste treatment processes. In addition, the "differential temperature ratio test," which compares bacterial numbers developing at 20°C to those at 37°C, provides a measure of bacterial origins; i.e., the bacteria indigenous to water and soil grow best at 20°C and perhaps not at all at 37°C, whereas the intestinal forms of warm-blooded animal and human origin develop best near body temperature.

b. The Total Coliform Group Density

The density in water of this group of bacteria indicates the degree of fecal pollution and is therefore a standard test of the sanitary quality of water(23). However, this group includes forms that differ both in biochemical and serological characteristics and in their natural sources and habitats, and also includes organisms of limited sanitary significance. The bacteria placed in the total coliform group can also be divided into "fecal" and "nonfecal" subgroups, although both are found in sewage and in polluted waters(24), and there should not be any coliforms, fecal or nonfecal, present in chlorinated drinking water supplies. The fecal coliform organisms (i.e., *Escherichia coli*) are considered to be indicators of recent fecal pollution, and when present in a finished water they indicate an extremely dangerous situation(24, 25). The presence in untreated waters of the nonfecal coliforms (i.e., the intermediate-aerogenes-cloacal or IAC group) may be due to relatively less recent fecal pollution, soil runoff water, or fecal pollution containing only the IAC group, although the latter is believed to occur infrequently(24).

c. The Fecal Coliform Density

The recent criteria report of the National Technical Advisory Committee(25) established fecal coliforms as the indicator organism for evaluating the microbiological suitability of recreation waters. The differentiation of fecal from nonfecal coliforms in water can now be accurately determined and provides the investigator with a better measure of fecal pollution of water and its possible origin(25,26).

d. The Fecal Streptococcal Density

This group comprises a standard test(23, 26) that is a useful supplement to the total coliform and fecal coliform tests when a more precise assessment of the origin of fecal pollution is required. Although this group should not be used as a primary criterion(25), their presence is indicative of fecal pollution whereas their absence suggests little or no warm-blooded animal pollution(24,25).

e. Presence of Anaerobic Spore-Forming Bacteria (Clostridium perfringens or C. welchii)

Since *C. perfringens* is especially typical of anaerobic bacterial spore formers found in the intestinal tract of man and other warm-blooded animals, and for other reasons discussed later, it has been suggested as a useful indicator of fecal pollution of water, especially in doubtful situations(27,28). A standard test is described in the World Health Organization's *International Standards for Drinking Water*(29).

f. Pathogenic Bacteria

These may be disease-producing enteric forms such as *Salmonella* and *Shigella,* or nonenteric bacteria such as leptospires and the tubercle bacilli. Although the direct measurement of all bacterial pathogens in water is not practical or even possible, interest has increased in the isolation of specific bacterial pathogens from water, such as salmonellae, to supplement primary criteria such as the total coliform and fecal coliform tests. In addition, epidemiological studies are strengthened when the specific pathogen is recovered directly from the suspected source of the human infection. At present no standard tests are available for routine use.

g. Lactobacilli

The anaerobic, non-spore-forming *Lactobacillus bifidus* has been used by only a few investigators as an indicator of very recent fecal pollution of water(29–32). Little direct information has accumulated as to its potential usefulness, and it appears at this time to be more of academic interest than of concern to those responsible for the routine bacteriologic examination of water supplies.

h. Pseudomonas aeruginosa Density

This organism can be accurately determined with available media and techniques, and its presence in water appears to indicate recent and frequent pollution. Since this organism is implicated in human infections and is found in the intestinal tract of man, it has been suggested for use not only as a bacterial index of water and waste water pollution but also to determine the safety of indoor swimming pool water. No standard procedures are presently given in the literature.

i. Staphylococci

These bacteria have been suggested as useful for the evaluation of the bather health hazard in swimming pools. It appears more logical to use such organisms as the staphylococci that indicate oral and nasal pollution from the bathers themselves, than to use the standard total coliform or standard plate count tests.

4. COLLECTION AND STORAGE OF WATER SAMPLES

A representative water sample large enough to accommodate the desired bacteriologic tests and preferably not less than 100 ml should be removed aseptically from the water environment, using procedures and sterilized containers as outlined in *Standard Methods* (23,26). If the water is chlorinated, a dechlorinating agent such as sodium thiosulfate must be added to the container to provide a final level of 100 mg/liter in the sample (23,26). It is recommended in the 12th edition of *Standard Methods* (23) that the water be examined as soon as possible after collection, preferably within 1 hr but in no case exceeding 30 hr. After collection and until examination, the temperature of the sample should be maintained as close to that of the original sample source as possible. The proposed 13th edition of *Standard Methods* (26) suggests the use of ice coolers for transport of water samples to the laboratory, and states that the temperature of all stream pollution samples should be held below 10°C during a maximum transport period of 6 hr. In addition, stream pollution samples should be processed within 2 hr of their arrival at the laboratory. Until the samples are processed they should be refrigerated. The delayed membrane filter technique [described in Sec. I.C.7.b.(5)] or field examination of water samples should be considered when receipt of samples is going to be delayed longer than 6 hr. The time that elapses between collection and examination of potable water samples sent via mail to the laboratory should not exceed 30 hr. Such samples should be refrigerated when sent by mail, but if this is not feasible, it is recommended that sterilizable thermos-type metal insulated sample containers be used (see Chap. 10).

5. FREQUENCY AND LOCATION OF SAMPLING

Frequency of sampling and location of sampling points are of critical importance for the proper evaluation of a sample, whether the water sample is obtained from a raw or finished source used for drinking purposes, recreation, irrigation, industrial use, fish and aquatic life, shellfish culture, or stock and wildlife watering. *Standard Methods* (23) noted that

> ... the inadequacy of the results of the examination of a single sample from a given source must be appreciated. When possible, evaluation of the quality of a water supply must be based on the examination of a series of samples collected over a known and protracted period of time.

In their discussion of public water supplies, the National Technical Advisory Committee (25) emphasized the importance of properly describ-

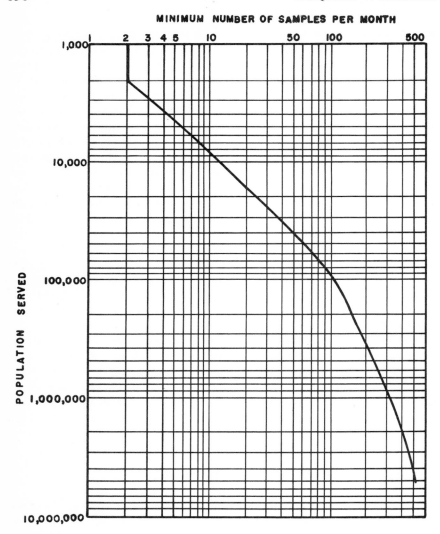

Fig. 1. Frequency of sampling to determine the bacteriological quality of drinking water.

ing the body of water that was being examined by obtaining as frequent and as varied samples as necessary. Although the exact frequency was not stated, it was suggested that samples be obtained, as judged necessary by the investigators, at different times of day, seasons, temperatures, river stages or flows, locations, and depths. The results of the sanitary survey of the water and adjacent environments should be used as guidelines to aid in the selection of the frequency and location of sampling. The important point was made that it is not possible to use water quality criteria, including bacteriological recommendations, as maximum single-sample values, but rather the given criteria should not be exceeded over substantial portions of time using, it was implied, a number of samples.

Public Health Service Drinking Water Standards (24) emphasized the use of samples from representative parts of the water distribution system, and noted that the frequency of sampling and location of sampling points shall be established by mutual agreement of the reporting agency (the state) and the certifying authority (the Surgeon General of the U.S. Public Health Service or his authorized representative) after investigation of the source, method of treatment, and protection of the water. The minimum number of samples that should be examined monthly is based upon the population served by the distribution system, as shown in Fig. 1. For example, for a population of 1000 or 2000, two samples should be taken and evaluated monthly; for a population of 10,000, 12 samples; for a population of 25,000, 30 samples; while for a population of 100,000, a minimum of 100 monthly samples should be examined. The number obtained from the graph should be "rounded off" in accordance with the following: for a population of 25,000 and under, to the nearest 1; 25,001 to 100,000, to the nearest 5; and over 100,000, to the nearest 10.

The World Health Organization's *International Standards for Drinking Water* (29) recommended that treated water entering a distribution system be sampled and bacteriologically examined at each treatment point at least once a day. When water is chemically disinfected before use, bacteriological examination is recommended at least once a week. Maximum intervals between successive routine examinations of untreated water entering the distribution system were proposed, as given in Table 1. The maximum intervals recommended between successive

TABLE 1

Maximum Intervals between Successive Routine Examinations for Untreated Water Entering a Water Distribution System[a]

Population served	Maximum interval between successive samplings
Up to 20,000	1 month
20,001–50,000	2 weeks
50,001–100,000	4 days
More than 100,000	1 day

[a]From Ref. 29.

samples and the minimum numbers of samples to be examined monthly from distribution systems containing treated or untreated water are presented in Table 2.

TABLE 2

Maximum Intervals between Successive Samples and Minimum Numbers of Samples Examined Monthly from Distribution Systems Containing Treated or Untreated Water[a]

Population served	Maximum interval between successive samplings	Minimum number of samples to be taken from entire system
Up to 20,000	1 month	One sample/5,000
20,001–50,000	2 weeks	of population per
50,001–100,000	4 days	month
More than 100,000	1 day	One sample/10,000 of population per month

[a]From Ref. 29.

6. METHODOLOGY

a. Bacteriological Media and the Growth Environment

The culture media used in bacteriologic testing of water and waste water can be formulated to provide for the following:

(1) The enrichment of desired organisms when they may be present originally in small numbers, while inhibiting the unsought ones. Such media may or may not contain inhibitory agents such as antibiotics, dyes, or bile salts. Enrichment media attempt to favor the growth of the desired organisms so that they have the opportunity to outgrow all other forms and become eventually predominant. Final isolation of pure cultures of the desired organisms is now possible by the use of selective or differential media. For example, Standard Methods(23) recommended preenrichment of the bacteria on a membrane filter used in a total coliform procedure for 1.5–2 hr at 35°C on an absorbent pad saturated with lauryl tryptose broth or the equivalent, before using a combination selective and differential medium such as M-Endo broth-MF. Another example of an enrichment medium is tetrathionate broth, which can be used for the selective preliminary enrichment of Salmonella typhosa, the typhoid bacillus, since it favors the rapid growth of this organism but inhibits that of Escherichia coli.

(2) The selection of a particular organism or group of organisms from mixed cultures, while inhibiting others that may be present. The selection media should duplicate as much as possible the natural chemical and physical environments in which the organisms would normally multiply best, and, in addition, should take advantage of the known cultural and biochemical behavior of the organisms being isolated. Selection media can also provide differential ability, as discussed later. Lactose fermentation broth is an example of both a selection and an enrichment medium, and is used to select out members of the total coliform group based upon the latter's ability to ferment lactose with the subsequent production of gas. Evolved gas that collects in an inverted vial in the fermentation tube in any amount constitutes a positive "presumptive test" for members of the total coliform group.

(3) The differentiation or identification, provisional or final, of previously isolated organisms based upon specific reaction or cultural characteristics that separate one bacterium from all others. An example of a differential medium that is also selective in its action is eosin methylene blue (EMB) agar. The morphological appearance of the bacterial colonies on EMB agar indicates the presence or absence of members of the coliform group.

The temperature of incubation, oxygen tension, and pH of the medium can also influence the isolation of a desired organism or group of organisms using enrichment, selective, or differential media. For example, the separation of fecal from nonfecal coliforms is favored by using an elevated temperature of 44.5°C for incubation of the bacteria deposited on the surface of the membrane filter after the water sample is filtered through. The filter is placed upon an absorbent pad saturated with MFC broth. This broth is both a selective and a differential medium, since it contains rosolic acid that aids in the suppression and identification of noncoliforms, bile salts that favor the selecting out of the fecal coliforms, and an aniline blue indicator system that provides differentiation since it imparts a blue color to the fecal coliform colonies.

Other media are used by the water bacteriologist for the enumeration of bacteria, for further characterization of isolates, and for propagation purposes. The exact compositions of these media are given in a number of standard references (23, 29) and trade manuals (33–36); certain aspects of their use are covered throughout this chapter.

b. Multiple-Tube Technique

This technique is used in tests not only for total coliforms and fecal coliforms but also for the fecal streptococci in order to determine their presence and to estimate their most probable number (MPN) in a water or waste water sample(23, 26). For example, the total coliform group determination is based upon the fermentation of the disaccharide lactose followed by the formation of gas, which is collected in an inverted vial in the fermentation tube. A number of fermentation tubes are inoculated with water from a specific source. The presence of gas in any quantity constitutes a positive presumptive test, and the test results may be further used with the MPN tables provided in Standard Methods(23) to estimate the density of the total coliform group in that water. Although the MPN can be computed each time mathematically, based upon the number of positive and negative fermentation tubes and the total number of milliliters used in a given water examination, the aforementioned tables of MPN values are commonly used. These tables can be used for a number of sample volumes and replicates of sample volumes. The numbers of coliform group bacteria in a water sample can be thus determined based upon the observed combination of positive and negative fermentation tube results.

The MPN is a statistical model that uses the theory of probability to estimate the most probable number of total coliforms that may be present in a water sample. The 95% confidence limit is provided for each estimated value in the MPN tables. The precision of the given figure depends upon the number of portions of each sample used per dilution in the presumptive test procedure. However, even when five fermentation tubes are used, the results do not have a high order of precision. The precision will increase, however, as more dilutions of the sample are used along with an increased number of replicates of each sample volume(23).

c. Membrane Filtration

The literature concerned with the membrane filter technique is voluminous, and it is beyond the scope of this chapter to review it completely. However, a few salient facts will be discussed here concerning the origin and usefulness of this technique.

Goetz(37), while working for the American joint Intelligence Objective Agency of the U.S. Armed Services, introduced the membrane filter (or as he referred to it, the molecular filter) to the United States shortly after World War II. He had made a thorough investigation of its use in water bacteriology in Germany during and after the war. The early history of the membrane filter is thus well documented in reports by Goetz (37) and Goetz and Tsuneishi(38). Although collodion versions of the membrane filter for biological use were developed in the 19th century by several investigators, the first practical means of producing membranes on a commercial scale was accomplished by Zsigmondy and Bachmann

(*39*) between 1916 and 1918 at the Institute of Colloid Chemistry of the University of Goettingen, Germany. The Sartorius-Werke Aktiengesellschaft and Company, Goettingen, later manufactured them on a small scale. Improvements in the production of collodion membranes of controlled porosities were made in the 1930's, and several reports were published before World War II concerning their usefulness in determination of the bacterial content of water(*38, 40*). The membrane filter technique was applied extensively in bomb-ravaged Germany during World War II for the bacteriological examination of water supplies, and aroused American interest after the conflict because of its reported accuracy, quickness, and ease of operation, leading to possible reductions in the cost of labor and supplies. Goetz thus reported in 1947 on the nature of the Zsigmondy Membranfilter (membrane filter), its method of manufacture, and known bacteriological applications, and the foundation for subsequent research in the United States by the Public Health Service and others was thereby laid. After extensive investigations, the 10th edition of *Standard Methods for the Examination of Water, Sewage, and Industrial Wastes*(*41*) included the membrane filter technique as a tentative test for determining the presence in water of members of the coliform group. In the 11th and subsequent editions it was designated as a standard method, and it has been widely accepted today as a routine test by many water laboratories(*42*).

The membrane filter technique is presently used for determining other specific bacteria or groups of bacteria that are human pathogens or indicators of fecal pollution in water and waste water. For example, this technique has found application not only for total coliforms but also for fecal coliforms, fecal streptococci, staphylococci, pseudomonads, and salmonellae. [See also Sec. I.C.7.]

Basically, the membrane filter technique can be described as follows: A sterile absorbent pad about 48 mm in diameter is placed in a sterile glass or plastic petri dish 50–60 mm in diameter and about 15 mm in height. Plastic petri dishes with tightly fitting covers can be used to prevent moisture loss during incubation, or loosely fitting glass or plastic petri dishes can be incubated in an incubator with controlled humidity or in a closed container with damp towels to maintain a high humidity (at or near 100%) during the incubation period. The absorbent pad is saturated (e.g., about 1.8–2.2 ml) with a bacterial broth growth medium. The excess medium is drained off. A solid medium can also be used. In this case no absorbent pad is needed; the liquefied medium can be poured in advance directly into the petri dish, allowed to solidify, and stored under refrigeration until required.

A suitable water or waste water sample, or a dilution of the same, is now passed through a membrane filter (preferably grid-marked) composed of cellulose esters with pores having a diameter of $0.45 \pm 0.02 \mu m$. The filter is then placed grid side up on top of the previously broth-saturated pad or the solid medium. All the bacteria in the sample are retained on the membrane surface, and those that find the growth environment hospitable will develop into visible colonies consisting of many individual cells. If the inoculant sample contains the proper range in bacterial density, countable plates will be evident after an incubation period. The constituents of the growth medium and the temperature of incubation will influence the type of bacterium that will develop.

7. Specific Discussions of Bacteriologic Tests Used in the Examination of Water and Waste Water

a. The Standard Plate Count

(1) Introduction and Historical Background. Koch published in 1883 his epic investigation(43) of the poured plate technique for the isolation and quantitation of pure cultures of bacteria from water, soil, and air. He used a 5–10% solution of gelatin combined with meat infusion, 1% peptone, and 0.5% salt. The infusion was prepared beforehand by mixing 1 kg of ground beef with 2 liters of water and allowing the mixture to stand overnight in a cold room or ice chest. Measured aliquots of the water to be investigated were incorporated into portions of the sterile, liquefied "nutrient gelatin" (Nährgelatine), and then the well-mixed combination was poured like a pancake mix onto cold, sterile glass plates — hence the origin of the term "plating" of bacteria. The poured plates were then placed in a bell jar to prevent external contamination during the incubation period. Thus was born, with subsequent slight modification, the method for determining the total bacterial count of water. As Koch stated it(43):

> When the mixture [of nutrient gelatin and water] solidifies, the germs in the water are separated from each other and individual colonies develop, not on the gelatin surface, but rather within it. Each colony, as shown by microscopic examination, is a pure culture; and as each arises from a single germ, the number indicates approximately the number present in the water.

Later, the American-born Fannie Hesse, the wife of one of Koch's pupils, Walther Hesse, suggested the use of agar-agar in place of gelatin for "plating" of bacteria. Agar-agar is a complex carbohydrate, a polygalactoside containing galactose-6-sulfate, obtained from various species of *Gelidium*, especially *G. amansii* and *G. carneum*, which are marine algae belonging to the phylum Rhodophyta (red algae). Agar-agar in the gel state has the advantage of not liquefying until the boiling point of water is reached (about 95°C) and does not form a gel again until about 40°C. Thus, solid medium prepared from agar-agar does not melt at normal incubation temperatures, and because of its temperature peculiarities it can be handled easily in the laboratory. In contrast, solid medium prepared from gelatin has the disadvantage of liquefying at room temperature (about 25°C) and above, thus making it useless for the isolation and quantitation of bacteria requiring higher growth temperatures. Gelatin is also attacked and decomposed by numerous gelatinase-producing bacteria, whereas only a few bacteria and fungi are capable of producing an extracellular agar-agar-digesting enzyme called gelase.

It was therefore not surprising that agar-agar soon replaced gelatin as the principal solidifying agent used in microbiology. Gelatin is today used primarily in the form of gelatin stabs to aid microbiologists in the identification and classification of bacteria based upon the growth appearance of the nonliquefying bacteria and the relative abilities and types of liquefaction produced by gelatinase-producing organisms. Total bacteria developing on nutrient gelatin at 20°C was one of the determinations formerly used in water microbiology to evaluate the quality of a water supply. This method has not been included in the most recent edition of *Standard Methods for the Examination of Water and Wastewater* (23) but is discussed later in this chapter.

The second modification of Koch's plating technique was introduced in 1887 by R. J. Petri, another of Koch's brilliant students. Round glass dishes were used, composed of two interlocking halves, one half serving as a lid and fitting over the second half containing the nutrient agar-agar or gelatin. This resulted in a closed chamber free from external contamination that was ideally suited for the development and observation of bacterial colonies over a long period of time.

Koch recognized early in his work that it was not possible to obtain a universal medium that would provide the ingredients for growth of *all* the bacteria present in a natural environment such as water. Various chemical and biological ingredients were incorporated into solid media by investigators to enhance their chances of recovering as many as possible of the viable organisms present in an inoculum. Physical conditions of incubation were also varied to elicit the best growth response. However, it soon became evident that "the total bacterial count" referred only to those organisms that could develop within the nutritional and physical confines of the plating techniques.

The total bacterial count developing aerobically on nutrient gelatin at 20°C after an incubation period of 72 hr was the original bacterial standard used for determining the potability of water. The first edition of *Standard Methods of Water Analysis* in 1905 (*44*) recommended the use of such nutrient gelatin plates at 20°C, but with a 2-day incubation time. The 1912 second edition of *Standard Methods of Water Analysis* (*45*) advised the use of nutrient agar in place of nutrient gelatin for the determination of total bacteria in a water sample at an incubation temperature corresponding to that of the human body (i.e., 37°C). The colony counts were made after 1 day to obtain quicker results. It was explained that since the 37°C incubation temperature closely corresponded to the optimal required by the human intestinal flora, especially bacterial pathogenic forms, a better indication of the sanitary quality of the water tested would result. The 20°C count on nutrient gelatin was discarded, the rationale probably being that such information indicated numbers of naturally occurring soil and water bacteria that were of no sanitary significance. However, after a meeting of the Laboratory Section of the American Public Health Association in September, 1912, that criticized this action, the fifth edition of *Standard Methods of Water Analysis* (*46*) reinstated the 20°C count along with the continuance of the 37°C determination. Nutrient agar was later recommended for the 20°C determination in the sixth edition of *Standard Methods for the Examination of Water and Sewage* (*47*) as a substitute, when desired by the investigator, for nutrient gelatin.

It came as no real surprise that the proven superiority of agar-agar as a solidifying agent led later to the complete displacement of gelatin as a plating medium in the 20°C determination.

(2) Differential Temperature Ratio Test. Subsequently, scientific evolution led to the use of a so-called "differential temperature ratio test," whereby the 20°C count on nutrient gelatin (or nutrient agar) after 3 days of incubation was compared to the 37°C count on nutrient agar after 2 days. Since the bacteria indigenous to water and soil grow best at 20°C, and perhaps not at all at 37°C, and the intestinal bacteria of warm-blooded animal and human origin develop best near body temperature, comparisons between the two temperature counts aided the investigator in determining bacterial origins. The British report on *The Bacteriological Examination of Water Supplies* (*48*) noted that in unpolluted water the ratio of the plate count at 22°C to the 37°C count is usually 10 or more to 1, whereas in polluted waters it was usually below 10. The higher the ratio the more likely that the bacteria isolated were soil and water forms. However, the ratio had no significance after chlorination. The 22°C count indicated, according to this report, the quantity of organic matter available and the amount of soil, dust, and other substances in the water. It was pointed out that

... on general grounds the greater the number of organisms developing at this temperature [i.e., 22°C], the larger is the amount of available organic matter present, and the
less suitable is the water for human consumption.

(3) Recent Usage and Significance of the Standard Plate Count.
The present 12th edition of *Standard Methods for the Examination of
Water and Wastewater*(*23*) and the proposed 13th edition(*26*) retain
the plate count procedure but make it optional. In addition, the 37°C
incubation temperature was replaced by a 35–37°C range in the ninth
edition(*49*), and 35°C was established in succeeding editions as the
temperature of incubation not only for the standard plate count but
also for total coliform determination. It was noted in the 12th edition
(*23*) that

... experience indicates that an approximate enumeration of total numbers of bacteria
multiplying at a temperature of 35°C and 20°C may yield useful information concerning the quality of the water and may provide supporting data regarding the significance
of the results of the coliform test. The standard plate count is useful in judging the efficiency in operation of various water treatment processes.

The main importance, therefore, of the standard plate count is in warning
the investigator of sudden increases in bacterial numbers over a
previously established base line. This indicates an increase in pollution
and reflects the effectiveness of the treatment process and/or a change
in the quality of the examined water. However, this determination does
not assay for the presence of all bacteria of possible importance in water
(e.g., *Crenothrix, Sphaerotilus,* and actinomycetes), and it ignores the
anaerobes completely.

Although it is recognized that no culture medium known, or growth
conditions devised, can provide for the development at the same time of
all bacteria present in a sample of water, it is recommended by *Standard
Methods for the Examination of Water and Wastewater*(*23*) that tryptone glucose extract agar (or plate count agar) be used. The incubation
temperature for the standard plate count (the term "total bacterial count"
having long since been discarded) using an agar solidified medium is
given as 35 ± 0.5°C for 24 ± 2 hr, or 20 ± 0.5°C for 48 ± 3 hr. Information
regarding the procurement of water samples, exact media and dilution
water specifications, procedures used in the preparation of dilutions and
plating of bacteria, further information concerning the conditions of
incubation, and the counting of colonies are adequately described in
this 12th edition and in the proposed 13th edition(*26*).

(4) The Membrane Filter Technique. The membrane filter technique
also has been used as a method (nonstandard) to determine the number

of bacteria in water and in waste water. Early studies by Clark et al. (40) led to their recommendation of this method for the determination of bacterial counts of relatively clear water with high or low bacterial densities, and of turbid waters with high bacterial numbers. They noted that it had not been used successfully on water samples of extremely high turbidity and very low bacterial populations. They concluded that the membrane filter method was probably more productive than the standard plate count and was, at worst, equal to it in productivity.

The same media recommended in *Standard Methods* (23) for the standard plate count can be employed for the membrane filter technique, except that no agar is added to the medium and the ingredients are used at double the normal strength. Clark et al. (40,50) used as the medium of choice double-strength Albimi M medium with 0.5% lactose added, adjusted to pH 7.0 with potassium hydroxide. The latter was a modification of the medium described by Goetz and Tsuneishi (38). M-enrichment broth prepared by Difco(34) and M-EHC enrichment broth made by Baltimore Biological Laboratory(36) are the commercially produced versions of double-strength Albimi M medium and are both prepared without any added carbohydrates. In addition to tryptone glucose yeast (plate count medium) and the modified Albimi M broths, tryptone glucose extract broth has also been recommended(34,51). Generally, any enriched all-purpose bacterial growth medium can be used. However, regardless of the medium employed, initial parallel studies to ferret out possible differences between the standard plate count and the membrane filter technique should be made. The incubation period is usually 16–20 hr at 35°C. The bacterial colonies that develop should be discrete, not confluent, and no crowding of the membrane surface should be observed. Visual contrast of the developed colonies can be increased for easier counting by staining the filter background with a 0.01% solution of malachite green or by staining the colonies themselves with a 2% solution of 2,3,5-triphenyl tetrazolium chloride, methylene blue, or similar stains (38,51–53).

(5) Recommended Colony Limits on Standard Plates and Membrane Filters. In the case of the previously discussed standard plate count, a minimum of 30 to a maximum of 300 bacterial colonies per standard-sized 100-mm-diameter petri dish (with a side wall at least 15 mm high) is recommended for counting purposes. This allows an effective surface area of 78.54 cm² for colony development. Since bacteria in the standard plate method also develop in the medium as well as on its surface, thereby providing an additional area for colony growth, the selection of plates containing a maximum of 300 colonies is justified. Sometimes plates with

less than 30 colonies are counted since 1.0 ml is set as the maximum amount of water sample that may be used in preparing a standard plate (23). The surface of the filter membrane, on the other hand, represents a total effective surface area of only 9.62 cm², since the effective filter diameter is 35 mm and not the actual 47-mm size. On this surface, Clark et al.(40) recommended the development of not more than 300 colonies, while Kabler(54) noted that the ideal water sample should produce between 50 and 300 colonies on the filter surface. However, in the membrane filter test for the presence of members of the coliform group, it is recommended that an ideal quantity of sample should result in the development of about 50 coliform colonies and not more than 200 colonies of all types(42). Geldreich et al.(42) and the Public Health Service(55) further noted that the range for statistically valid results is 20–80 coliform colonies on a filter surface. Therefore, based on the above information, a strictly arbitrary range of 20–200 bacterial colonies on a membrane surface is proposed, and only those plates within this range should be included in the determination of bacterial numbers.

(6) *Water Quality Criteria.* The maximum number of viable bacteria allowable in treated or untreated waters as determined by standard plate counts is not set in *Standard Methods for the Examination of Water and Wastewater*(23), in the *Public Health Service Drinking Water Standards* (24), or in the World Health Organization's *International Standards for Drinking Water*(29). In regard to recreational water standards, the American Public Health Association recommended the standard plate count as a method for evaluation of the bacterial quality of swimming pools(56,57). The recommended standard was that not more than 15% of the samples covering any considerable period of time shall contain more than 200 bacteria/ml after 24 hr of incubation at 35°C. Samples should be collected only when the pool is being used and the number of bathers is preferably at a peak. A representative cross section of the sanitary quality of the pool should be obtained by varying the hour of the day, the day of the week, the frequency of collection, and the location of the sample points. When facilities permit, it is recommended that one or more samples be collected weekly from swimming pools(56).

b. *The Total Coliform Group Density or Index*

(1) *Introduction and Definition.* The coliform group of bacteria has been used since the early days of sanitary water bacteriology as a basic parameter to assess the bacteriological quality of drinking and bathing waters. By present definition in the 12th edition of *Standard Methods for the Examination of Water and Wastewater*(23), and in the proposed

13th edition(26), the "coliform group" or "total coliforms" includes "all of the aerobic and facultative anaerobic, Gram-negative, nonspore-forming, rod-shaped bacteria which ferment lactose with gas formation within 48 hours at 35°C."

This definition includes all of the following bacteria:

(i)   *Escherichia coli, E. aurescens, E. freundii, E. intermedia.*
(ii) *Aerobacter aerogenes, A. cloacae.* In 1963 the Judicial Commission of the International Committee on Nomenclature of Bacteria adopted the generic name of *Enterobacter* for all motile *Aerobacter* strains as proposed by Hormaeche and Edwards(57a).
(iii) Biochemical intermediates placed between the genera *Escherichia* and *Enterobacter* (i.e., *Aerobacter*). "Atypical" or "aberrant" strains of coliforms are not included under the definition of the coliform group.

The term "coliform group" or "total coliforms" is in reality a casual usage denoting bacteria originally described by Escherich in 1885 as *Bacterium coli-commune* and *Bacterium lactis-aerogenes. Bacterium coli-commune* was subsequently found to consist of two fermentative types, a sucrose fermenter called *Bacterium coli-communior* and a non-sucrose fermenter identified as *Bacterium coli-communis* (or *commune*). The latter *Bacterium coli-commune* corresponds to *Escherichia coli* and was the organism originally isolated by Escherich in 1885 from feces. *E. coli* is placed in the *Shigella-Escherichia* division of the family Enterobacteriaceae by Kauffmann(58), Kauffmann et al.(59), and Edwards and Ewing(60). The alkalescens-dispar (A-D) group of bacteria are anaerogenic, nonmotile, late lactose fermenters or non-lactose fermenters that were formerly classified with the dysentery bacilli but now are considered to be varieties of *E. coli.*

The *Bacterium lactis-aerogenes* of Escherich has been called over the years by various sanitary water bacteriologists *Bacterium aerogenes, Aerobacter aerogenes, Encapsulatus aerogenes, Klebsiella aerogenes,* and *Enterobacter aerogenes.* Edwards and Ewing(60) place this organism, which they call *Aerobacter aerogenes,* in the *Klebsiella-Aerobacter-Serratia* division of the family Enterobacteriaceae, and divide the *Aerobacter* group into subgroups A, B, and C, and the *Hafnia* group. Subgroup A is considered by them to be synonymous with *Aerobacter cloacae,* subgroup B with *Aerobacter aerogenes,* and subgroup C with the *Aerobacter liquefaciens* described by Grimes and Hennerty(61).

The "paracolon group" that is sometimes referred to in the literature can best be described as a heterogeneous group of weak, late, or irregular lactose fermenters, or even non-lactose fermenters, that occupy a position somewhere between *Escherichia-Aerogenes* and *Salmonella.*

Borman et al.(62) placed these "aberrant coliforms" in a separate genus, the *Paracolobactrum*, but this has been deemed unjustified by Edwards and Ewing(60) since this establishment of a genus was based solely upon the delayed fermentation of lactose. In any case, the Enterobacteriaceae Subcommittee in 1958 recommended to the Seventh International Congress of Microbiology at Stockholm that the genus not be recognized. The *Hafnia* group proposed by Moeller(63) does include some of the paracolon group, such as *Paracolobactrum aerogenoides* and *Paracolobactrum intermedium*. Moeller(63) named the type species *Hafnia alvei*. The biochemical reactions and motility of these *Aerobacter aerogenes*-like paracolons are affected by the temperature of incubation. There occurs a delayed fermentation of various carbohydrates, among them lactose, at both 22 and 37°C. At 22°C the Voges-Proskauer test is positive, but it is irregular at 37°C, whereas at 22°C the methyl red test is negative, but it is positive at 37°C.

Escherichia freundii is placed in the *Salmonella-Arizona-Citrobacter* division of the family Enterobacteriaceae by Edwards and Ewing(60), and is renamed *Citrobacter freundii*. The *Citrobacter* group also includes bacteria designated as the Bethesda-Ballerup group, which are late lactose fermenters. *Escherichia intermedia* is now also usually placed in the genus *Citrobacter*(64).

The question of lactose fermentation is an important one to the sanitary microbiologist, although criticism has been directed to this point by Edwards and Ewing(60). In 1893, Theobald Smith had noted that enteric pathogens, such as members of the *Salmonella* and *Shigella* genera, were non-lactose fermenters, whereas the nonpathogenic inhabitants of the intestinal tract of man and other warm-blooded animals, or those "coliform" forms found on plants and in the soil, were mainly lactose fermenters.

The coliform group of bacteria includes, therefore, on the basis of the definition previously quoted from *Standard Methods for the Examination of Water and Wastewater*(23), such diverse forms as the *Escherichia, Enterobacter,* and *Citrobacter* groups that are able to ferment lactose with gas formation within 48 hr at 35°C. All others cannot be considered to be members of the coliform group.

(2) Advantages and Limitations of the Total Coliform Group. The advantages of the coliform group as an indicator of fecal pollution of the water environment may be summarized as follows: The coliforms are ordinarily harmless in the intestinal tract of man, although outside their natural habitat, for example, in the urinary tract, they may occasionally cause infections of man. They are more resistant organisms than the

enteric pathogens, and are present in larger numbers and greater densities in the feces of man than the enteric pathogens. Rosebury(65) reports the average count of coliforms per gram of human feces in the absence of enteric disease as 10^7–10^8, although wide individual variations do exist. Litsky et al.(66) noted that coliforms have been employed for measuring fecal pollution of water because these bacteria are supposedly indicative of sewage contamination and can be easily isolated and confirmed by relatively simple bacteriological techniques. Clark and Kabler(67) have pointed out that whereas the coliform group has represented fecal pollution of potable waters and other water environments, and hence danger potentially exists to the health and well-being of individuals in that environment, no recognition or understanding had been given to the habitat of the coliform group. Coliforms are present not only in the feces of man and other warm-blooded animals but also in the guts of cold-blooded animals, in soils, and on many plants. It is therefore imperative to determine the environmental source of the coliforms. For example, it has been emphasized that the presence of *any* member of the coliform group in a treated potable water supply is not acceptable(24,68,69). Therefore, the absence of the coliform group indicates a safe water. However, an untreated surface water is another problem entirely. Here, the distinction that exists among the members of the coliform group as to native habitat would have profound influence upon subsequent belief that the water presented a hazard to public health.

The value of the coliform group as an index of the degree of original fecal pollution is reduced by the occurrence of aftergrowth (ability to reproduce) in the case of some members that enter polluted waters (48,70,71). Interference with coliform testing may also occur due to the presence of other bacteria. For example, false positive results sometimes occur when two or more noncoliforms synergistically produce gas from lactose. False negative results may occur when species of pseudomonads are present in the testing sample with coliforms(71).

(3) Multiple-Tube Fermentation Technique. The multiple-tube fermentation technique, using lactose broth or lauryl tryptose broth, has been recognized for a number of years as the official standard test for the coliform group in water. The "completed test" most probable number (MPN) procedure is the official test used to determine the sanitary quality of raw or finished waters. The "confirmed test" MPN procedure is an acceptable test that yields results that are equivalent to those of the completed test. It is used in the examination of any water where the "presumptive test" is inapplicable; for routine samples of drinking water, water in process of treatment, and finished waters; for chlorinated sewage

effluents; and for bathing waters. The presumptive test is applied to the examination of "any sample of waste, sewage, sewage effluent (except chlorinated effluent), or water known to be heavily polluted, the fitness of which for use as drinking water is not under consideration" and also "any routine sample of raw water in a treatment plant, provided records indicate the Presumptive Test is not too inclusive for the production of pertinent data" (23).

Thus, to reiterate, one of the standard methods for the presence of the coliform group may consist of three parts: the presumptive test, the confirmed test, and the completed test. The procedures involved have been approved by standard methods committees of the three associations that sponsor the preparation and publication of *Standard Methods for the Examination of Water and Wastewater*. It is not intended here to duplicate in full the test procedures used, but salient features may be summarized as follows:

(a) *The Presumptive Test.* A series of lactose broth or lauryl tryptose broth fermentation tubes are inoculated with graduated quantities of the water to be examined for coliform presence. Dunham fermentation tubes are used that consist of a test tube containing a smaller inverted inner tube, both filled with lactose broth or lauryl tryptose broth. Replicate tubes can be planted with decimal dilutions of 10, 1.0, and 0.1 ml or other multiples and submultiples of 1.0 ml such as 100, 10, and 1.0 ml; 1.0, 0.1, and 0.01 ml; or 0.1, 0.01, and 0.001 ml. The formation of gas in any quantity in the inverted inner tube after incubation at $35 \pm 0.5°C$ for 24 ± 2 hr, or 48 ± 3 hr if no gas has formed earlier, constitutes a positive presumptive test for members of the coliform group and indicates sewage pollution of the examined water. The absence of gas after 48 hr terminates the examination and is reported as a negative presumptive test. Obviously, slow lactose fermenters with gas formation (i.e., beyond 48 ± 3 hr of incubation) that may be members of the coliform group are excluded from consideration. *Standard Methods* (23) recognizes this problem but notes that the exclusion of an occasional slow coliform gas former still conforms to their definition of the coliform group based on an arbitrary limit of 48 ± 3 hr of incubation.

If only coliform bacteria gave positive results, additional tests would be unnecessary. Some noncoliform bacteria, however, form gas during the fermentation of lactose broth. For example, anaerobic *Clostridia* and aerobic *Bacilli* species are spore formers that ferment lactose with the formation of gas. Gas formation may also result from a bacterial association called synergism. For example, synergistic association between two bacteria, such as *Streptococcus faecalis* and *Salmonella schottmuelleri* or *Salmonella paratyphi*(*71*), may produce acid and gas during the fermentation of lactose broth. Neither organism can accomplish this when grown separately, but together they can lead to a false positive presumptive test. In addition, it may be possible for a synergistic association to inhibit the formation of gas by lactose fermenters. Salle(*72*) suggests the incorporation of triphenylmethane stain in the lactose broth, which will inhibit gram-positive organisms involved in synergism or those that produce gas during the fermentation of lactose, but will allow the gram negatives to develop.

(*b*) *The Confirmed Test.* From each lactose broth or lauryl tryptose broth tube showing gas within 48 ± 3 hr at 35°C, a loopful of culture is streaked for colony isolation on eosin methylene blue (EMB) agar or Endo agar poured plates. The plates are incubated at 35 ± 0.5°C for 24 ± 2 hr. Three types of colonies will appear on EMB or Endo agar: (i) typical colonies, that have dark nucleated centers, with or without metallic sheen; (ii) atypical colonies, without dark nucleated centers after 24-hr incubation, which are opaque, mucoid, and pink in coloration; (iii) negative, if different from (i) and (ii).

If typical colonies appear on the plate, the confirmed test may be considered positive. If only atypical colonies appear on the plate, the confirmed test cannot be considered negative, since some coliform organisms fail to produce typical colonies. If only negative colonies appear on the plate, the confirmed test may be considered negative, and no further tests need be made. Regardless of whether typical or atypical colonies are formed, the test will be completed as directed below under (c) Completed Test.

Brilliant green lactose bile (BGLB) broth can also be used as an alternative. One loopful of inoculum is transferred from the lactose tubes showing gas to the BGLB tubes. The tubes are incubated at 35 ± 0.5°C for 48 hr. The formation of any amount of gas in the inverted inner Dunham tube constitutes a positive confirmed test. The test is completed as directed below under Completed Test.

Holt-Harris and Teague(*73*) devised the original EMB agar, but the one that conforms to *Standard Methods*(*23*) specifications was formulated by Levine(*74,75*). According to Wynne, et al.(*76*), the color of colonies of coliforms on EMB agar depended on two factors: (i) the reaction of eosin, which is an acidic dye, with methylene blue, a basic dye, to form a neutral or acidic methylene blue eosinate compound, and (ii) the subsequent formation by lactose fermenters of enough acid to cause the neutral or acidic dye compound to be taken up by the bacterial colony. Colonies of non-lactose fermenters are uncolored, since the compound is not taken up in a basic solution. Thus, colonies of non-lactose fermenters will appear pink or the same color as the medium.

Endo agar medium is an outgrowth of the typhoid organism isolation medium devised by Endo in 1904(77). This latter medium differentiates intestine-dwelling, lactose-fermenting bacteria as the coliforms from lactose nonfermenting ones such as *Salmonella* and *Shigella*. Three basic ingredients of the medium are responsible for this differential ability: lactose, basic fuchsin, and sodium sulfite. The basic fuchsin is initially decolorized with sodium sulfite and acts as a modified Schiff reagent (i.e., fuchsin aldehyde reagent) which traps the acetaldehyde produced by the lactose fermenters (i.e., the coliforms). The acetalde-hydes form addition compounds with the sulfite trapping agent, restoring the color of the basic fuchsin. Non-lactose fermenters are colorless on this medium against a faint pink background, whereas lactose fermenters form red colonies with dark nucleated centers with a metallic sheen. The sheen is due to the precipitation out of the basic fuchsin dye and its subsequent deposition on the colony surface. References that should be consulted for further information are those of Neuberg and Nord(78) and Margolena and Hansen(79).

(c) The Completed Test. This may be performed on the typical or atypical colonies developing on Endo or EMB agar plates, or on the BGLB tubes showing gas in the confirmed test. If BGLB medium is used in the confirmed test, one or more Endo or EMB agar plates are streaked from BGLB tubes showing gas. The plates are then incubated at $35 \pm 0.5°C$ for 24 ± 2 hr. At least one typical colony, or, if no typical colonies are present, at least two atypical colonies are each transferred to lactose fermentation tubes or to lauryl tryptose broth fermentation tubes and to nutrient agar slants. All tubes are incubated at $35 \pm 0.5°C$, for no more than 48 hr for the lactose tubes and for 24 hr for the agar slants. Gram stains are prepared from the cultures on agar slants at the end of 24 hr. The formation of gas in any amount in the fermentation tubes and the demonstration of gram-negative, non-spore-forming rods on the agar slants constitute a positive completed test for members of the coliform group.

The purpose of the completed test is to determine (i) if the colonies developing on Endo or EMB agar plates are again capable of fermenting lactose with the production of gas, and (ii) if the organisms transferred to agar slants show the morphological and tinctorial picture of members of the coliform group.

(d) Estimation of Coliform Count. The MPN tables in *Standard*

Methods(*23*) or in *International Standards for Drinking Water*(*29*) can be used to calculate the coliform density of the examined water. In this statistical estimation of the MPN of coliforms present per 100 ml of water, only the number of presumptive tubes shown to be positive when carried through to the completed test should be used. (See Secs. I.C.5 and I.C.6.b for further discussions of sampling and MPN.)

(4) The IMViC Test. Standard Methods(*23*) also provides tentative methods for the differentiation of the members of the coliform group into genera and species based upon the "IMViC" test. The mnemonic term IMViC refers to four tests, the results of which determine the genus and species of the coliform isolate. The individual letters stand for the following tests: I for indole, M for methyl red, V for Voges-Proskauer, and C for citrate, while i is added solely for pronounciation purposes. The possible reaction combinations indicating the genus and species of the bacterial isolates are given in Table 3.

(a) Production of Indole. The amino acid tryptophan is degraded by such bacteria as *Escherichia coli,* variety I, with the subsequent production of indole in the medium. *Standard Methods*(*23*) recommends tryptophan broth, and *p*-dimethylaminobenzaldehyde in isoamyl (or normal amyl) alcohol and hydrochloric acid as the test reagent for indole.

TABLE 3
Possible IMViC Reaction Combinations[a]

Bacterium	Indole	Methyl red	Voges-Proskaûer	Citrate
Escherichia coli				
Variety I	+	+	−	−
Variety II	−	+	−	−
Escherichia freundii (intermediates)				
Variety I	−	+	−	±
Variety II	+	+	−	+
Enterobacter aerogenes				
Variety I	−	−	+	±
Variety II	±	−	+	+

[a]From Ref. *23*.

[b]+ is positive; − is negative; ± is questionable.

(b) The Methyl Red Test. This is a measure of the amount of acid produced by organisms in a glucose broth medium. Members of the *Escherichia* produce sufficient acid to give a distinct red color upon the addition of the methyl red indicator, whereas the *Enterobacter* strains give a yellow color. In any case, a yellow color with the methyl red indicator is a negative reaction, while intermediate shades are questionable.

(c) The Voges-Proskauer Test. A positive Voges-Proskauer reaction depends upon the presence of acetylmethylcarbinol (acetoin), an intermediate product of carbohydrate metabolism. This compound is produced by strains of *Enterobacter aerogenes* and other organisms but not by the *Escherichia*. The salt peptone glucose broth or the glucose broth medium used for the methyl red test can be used here. The acetylmethylcarbinol, in the presence of potassium hydroxide and air, is oxidized to diacetyl. Then the diacetyl in the presence of α-naphthol and the amino acid, arginine (from the peptone), react to form a crimson to ruby-colored substance.

(d) The Sodium Citrate Test. Typical *Enterobacter aerogenes* and certain *Escherichia* intermediates are generally capable of utilizing sodium citrate when incorporated in a mineral medium as the only source of carbon. Strains of typical *Escherichia coli* are unable to utilize the compound. The result is that the former organisms multiply in the medium whereas the latter fail to grow.

(5) Membrane Filter Technique. A test for members of the coliform group, of more recent vintage and now accepted as a standard test, is the membrane filter technique. The membrane filter technique for total coliform determination has many sound advantages over the multiple-tube fermentation method, but it certainly does possess certain limitations. Positive and negative features of this method have been continuously reported in the literature, and sufficient caution in its use has been recommended in *Standard Methods* (23, 80) and in an excellent article by Geldreich et al. (42).

(a) Advantages and Limitations. One of the great advantages of this technique is the speed of the complete test–definitive results are obtained in 22–24 hr, whereas 48–96 hr are required for the multiple-tube fermentation method. The size of the water sample can also be larger than the customary 55.5 ml of a finished water, thus enhancing the reliability and accuracy of the test. Therefore, in waters of low bacterial densities,

e.g., finished water, a larger sample size can be used. In addition, it has been frequently noted that precision is greater with the membrane filter procedure than can be expected with the multiple-tube fermentation technique. Finally, the method demonstrates definite savings in time, labor, space, supplies, and equipment, besides being portable and therefore useful in field studies(80,81).

Limitations of this technique are several, leading to the statement in *Standard Methods*(23) that "it is still necessary to permit the use of the [membrane filter] technique in drinking water examination only after adequate parallel testing (i.e., using the multiple-tube fermentation technique) to show its applicability." Clark et al.(81) noted that there are samples of water and sewage for which the membrane filter procedure should not or cannot be used. These include samples that:

(1) contain large quantities of colloidal precipitate or suspended solids,
(2) have an excessively high noncoliform bacterial population that can also grow on an Endo-type broth, compared to the presence of a negligible coliform density,
(3) contain at least 1 mg/liter of zinc or copper compounds, or both (82),
(4) contain (rarely) a bacterial strain fermenting lactose with rapid acid production on Endo-type broth, but failing to produce gas in a lactose broth fermentation tube.

Water samples with high densities of colloidal precipitate or suspended solids, such as iron, manganese, or alum flocs, clay, or algae, can clog the filter pores and may lead to the deposition of a film that may cause spreading of colonies over the filter surface and cause poor or no sheen production(81). When the coliform content of such a sample is large, a smaller volume or a higher dilution of the sample can be used, resulting in the deposition of only a small quantity of colloidal and suspended substances which will not interfere with the coliform test(42,81). However, a number of areas, especially in the western United States, are reported to possess waters of high turbidity and low bacterial content(42), thus creating problems when attempts are made to determine coliform density by filtering large volumes of sample. Geldreich et al.(42) noted that, in their experience, attempts at removal of turbidity also resulted in the loss of 20–80% of the organisms originally present in the sample; they stated that there was no practical method of removing turbidity without removing in addition unknown quantities of coliforms. Films of crystalline or silicous materials that may be thicker than those mentioned above may not, however, pose any problems in the recovery of countable, sheen-producing coliform colonies(81).

The presence in the water sample of large numbers of noncoliforms might suppress the coliforms present or cause poor coliform sheen production after the filters are incubated on Endo medium(42,81). It might be pointed out at this time, as repeatedly emphasized by several investigators(42,55,83), that differentiating coliforms from noncoliforms requires experience and proper adjustment of the light source. Diffused, daylight-type light such as that emitted from cool, white fluorescent lamps which are held at an angle of 60–80° above the filter colonies, while using a magnification of 10–15 diameters, will provide the best reflection of the golden metallic luster from coliform colonies on an Endo medium. It has also been recommended that incandescent light bulbs not be used, since they are not adequate for observation of coliform colony sheen(26,42). When in doubt, the best procedure is to verify the doubtful sheen producer by inoculating it into lactose or lauryl tryptose fermentation tubes. No protocol has been provided for such comparative studies, although Geldreich et al.(42) reviewed one established by the State of Ohio Department of Health(84).

Toxic metallic substances in the water may be adsorbed onto the membrane surface and interfere with subsequent coliform development (80,81). It was demonstrated by Shipe and Fields(82) that at least 1 mg/liter of copper and/or zinc sulfates inhibited bacterial development. In previous studies, Shipe and Cameron(85) found that toxic substances in several types of water influenced the coliform count as determined by the multiple-tube and the membrane filtration techniques, with the former providing higher recovery values than the latter. The imprinted grid on the membrane surface was also found to inhibit bacterial growth (42). For example, Gaspar and Leise(86,89) reported that the inhibition of *Brucella melitensis* and *Pasteurella tularensis* was linearly proportional to the intensity of the grid imprint. The Public Health Service's *Evaluation of Water Laboratories*(55) recommended that the ink used to imprint the grid system be nontoxic or restrictive to colony development and, on the other hand, not stimulate colony confluency along the grid lines. Cahn(88) reported that the presence of detergents in membrane filters obtained from several different manufacturers influenced the plating efficiency and differentiation in clonal cultures of various kinds of cells when grown in tissue culture medium filtered through unwashed membrane filters. These detergents are added by the manufacturer to promote the efficiency of filtration and to allow autoclave sterilization of membranes. It was noted that some manufacturers place the detergent not only on the membrane surface but throughout the membrane, thus leading to continuous, slow leaching out of detergents. What effect, if any, these detergents have on recovery efficiencies of bacteria deposited on the membrane surface is unknown.

As previously reported by Clark et al.(*81*), noncoliforms are occasionally able to give false metallic sheens on Endo medium, and will result in higher apparent numbers of total coliforms than are actually present in the water. Geldreich et al.(*42*) noted also that some coliform colonies may fail to develop metallic sheens, and that both types of false reactions are due to the presence of interfering substances in the water or atypical bacterial strains. Their results demonstrated that membrane filtration had a higher rate (78.1%) of coliform verification (using gas production in brilliant green bile broth to indicate coliform presence) than the most probable number confirmed test procedure (70.3%). Besides indicating that different sample sources gave different extents of coliform verification for each method, it was emphasized that membrane filter and most probable number comparisons based on confirmed test data can only be made after adequate studies establish the similarity of confirmed and completed test results. Some of the criticism concerning the validity of certain membrane filter techniques, as reported by Morgan et al.(*89*), might be the result of such use of confirmed and not completed test MPN data(*42*).

After extensive comparative investigations by participating laboratories, Kabler(*90*) concluded that the membrane filter and the MPN procedures did not measure precisely the same group of organisms, and that the sanitary significance of the differences was yet to be determined. The results showed, however, that 1260 (73.8%) of the 1706 water samples that were examined by both methods agreed, while 650 samples with a coliform content in the potable water range had 571 (88%) in agreement. One of the problems that arises in comparisons of membrane filter-MPN data is the misunderstanding that while the membrane filter procedure provides an actual count of coliform presence in a definite volume of sample, the MPN technique is only a statistical estimate of coliform numbers in a given volume, i.e., the "most probable number." Thomas et al.(*91*) emphasized that the most probable number method should only be considered as an index of the number of coliforms present, and that it is biased and overestimates the true coliform density.

(*b*) *Nature of Test Procedure.* As previously described in Sec. I.C. 6.c, this method involves basically the passage of a water sample or its dilution through a membrane filter, composed of cellulose esters of, usually, a pore size of 0.45 ± 0.02 μm, that has been proven to retain bacteria on the filter surface. The bacteria collected on the membrane surface may now be cultured by placing the filter directly on selective media such as M-Endo broth-MF (Difco), M-coliform broth (BBL), or equivalent; or LES Endo agar medium(*23,34,36*). However, the highest numbers of total coliforms may be obtained, according to *Standard Methods*(*23*), only by pre-enrichment of the bacteria on the filter for 1.5–2 hr at $35 \pm 0.5°C$ on an absorbent pad saturated with lauryl tryptose broth or equivalent before using the above selective media. It was noted that(*23*):

> ...This step may be eliminated in the routine examination of drinking water where repeated determinations have shown that sufficiently adequate results are obtained by a single-step technique. Enrichment is generally not necessary in the examination of nonpotable waters or sewages.

Slanetz and Bartley(*92*), on the other hand, using M-enrichment medium, reported that preliminary culturing of their filters on an enrichment medium for 2 hr before subsequent incubation on absorbent pads saturated with M-Endo broth was unnecessary. They found that total coliform counts on the filters directly incubated on absorbent pads containing especially the M-Endo broth were as high, or often higher, than when the bacteria on the filter membranes were first precultured on enrichment medium, and that fewer noncoliforms and spreading colonies developed on such directly cultured membranes. The water samples tested were mainly from river, brook, or reservoir sources. These latter results are at variance with the research of Clark et al.(*40*), who found that preliminary enrichment of the membrane on Albimi M-lactose medium for 2 hr before transfer to the Endo medium improved the growth of coliforms. Included among the common laboratory errors, reported by Clark et al.(*81*), that may result in poor coliform determinations are not only an excessive number of colonies, both coliforms and noncoliforms, on the membrane; errors in basic fuchsin-sodium sulfite ratio; low humidity during incubation; excessive saturation of the membrane with the medium; contamination of the absorbent pads; and air bubbles lodged between the membrane and the absorbent pad preventing uptake of growth medium by the coliforms on the surface of the filter; but also elimination of the enrichment period by the laboratory. Such elimination was cited by Morgan et al.(*89*) as placing the M-Endo broth method in serious jeopardy. Geldreich et al.(*42*) refuted the allegations made by Morgan et al.(*89*) concerning the accuracy of the one-step M-Endo broth method, and noted that:

> ...Many laboratories have found no additional coliform recovery when using a 2-hour enrichment period. However, if parallel tests of methods do show an improvement with enrichment for coliform detection and these sheen colonies verify, then the two-step procedure should be adopted. This difference in enrichment requirement as reported in the literature may reflect the differences in chemical composition, hydrogen ion concentration, electrolyte concentration, protein nitrogen, types of bacterial flora present, and other factors associated with water samples from different geographic areas.

On Endo medium all dark (often purplish-green) colonies with a metallic sheen within 24 hr of incubation are counted and considered to be members of the coliform group. It is believed that this coliform group has the same sanitary significance as the coliform group described in the multiple-tube fermentation technique, although it may not be similar(90). It is suggested that parallel studies be made to determine the relationship in the water being examined between the results obtained with the membrane filter and the multiple-tube tests(23,26,42).

(c) *Acceptable Colony Numbers Per Filter Surface.* The filter surface should not be overcrowded with colonies of either the coliform group or noncoliforms. About 50 coliform colonies and not more than 200 colonies of all types per filter constitute the recommended limits(42). The range for statistically valid results as reported by Geldreich et al.(42) and recommended in the proposed 13th edition of *Standard Methods*(26) was a minimum of 20 to a maximum of 80 coliform colonies per filter, although other reports(81,83) noted that ideal membrane filters should have fewer than 60 coliform colonies. In any case, exceeding the limit of 80 coliform colonies per filter will result in lower coliform counts, due either to a suppression of the sheen or the confluent growth that may result over the membrane surface.

(d) *Verified Membrane Filter Test.* The results of the coliform determination by the membrane filter technique can constitute in themselves the final test; however, a verified membrane filter coliform test may be used when false sheen reactions are suspected(42). Coliform isolates (and also noncoliforms as a control on the techniques used) may be picked off the filters and subjected to additional cultural, biochemical, and staining tests based upon the confirmed test of the multiple-tube fermentation method. This involves inoculation of lactose or lauryl tryptose broth fermentation tubes with the filter isolates, followed by confirmation in brilliant green lactose bile broth(42). A more elaborate verification procedure involves inoculation of the fermentation tubes with an isolate; streaking out the culture on eosin methylene blue agar plates to reisolate the organism; and inoculation into lactose or lauryl tryptose broth fermentation tubes to determine gas formation, and onto nutrient agar slants for later gram staining of the organism(23).

(e) *Delayed Incubation Test.* Since it is not always convenient or practical to analyze water samples immediately after collection, a delayed incubation membrane filter test for coliform bacteria may be used, which has received tentative acceptance in the 12th and proposed 13th editions of *Standard Methods(23,26)*. This involves filtering the water sample at the time of collection or shortly thereafter; placing the membrane on an absorbent pad saturated with a transport preservative medium that may be either M-Endo broth supplemented with sodium benzoate(23,26), or LES MF holding medium(23,26); and removing the filter membrane from the transport medium at the laboratory and placing it on an absorbent pad containing M-Endo broth growth medium in the case of the filter transported on the preservative M-Endo medium, or on LES Endo agar in the case of the filter transported on LES MF holding medium.

(6) *Water Quality Criteria.* The *Public Health Service Drinking Water Standards(24)* sets forth certain limitations in regard to the presence of the coliform group in potable waters. When 10-ml standard portions are examined using the multiple-tube fermentation technique, not more than 10% in any one month should show the presence (*not* the most probable number) of the coliform group. The presence of coliforms in three or more 10-ml portions of a water is not allowable if this happens in two consecutive samples, in more than one water sample per month when fewer than 20 are examined per month, or in more than 5% of the samples when 20 or more are examined per month. When 100-ml standard portions are examined, similar limits are set. Thus, not more than 60% of 100-ml standard portions in any month should show the presence (*not* the most probable number) of the coliform group. The presence of coliforms in all five of the 100-ml portions of a standard sample is not allowable if this occurs in two consecutive samples, in more than one sample per month when fewer than five are examined per month, or in more than 20% of the samples when five or more are examined per month. It should be noted that the above reference to "coliform group" assumes that the multiple-tube fermentation test is carried out to the completed test in each case. Routinely, however, this may be carried out only to the confirmed test, with the understanding that the results obtained with the latter compare beyond any reasonable doubt with those of the completed test.

When the membrane filter technique is used, the limits are set as follows: The arithmetic mean coliform density of all standard samples examined per month must not exceed 1 per 100 ml. Coliform colonies per standard sample should not exceed 3 per 50 ml, 4 per 100 ml, 7 per 200 ml, or 13 per 500 ml in two consecutive samples, or in more than one standard sample when fewer than 20 are examined per month, or in more than 5% of the standard samples when 20 or more samples are examined per month. Verification of the coliform colonies is not required. *International Standards for Drinking-Water(29)* sets forth similar but less strict standards for treated and untreated water supplies.

c. Fecal Coliform Density

(1) *Characteristics and Occurrence.* "Fecal" coliforms are that portion of the total coliform group that are of direct fecal origin, i.e., from warm-blooded animal feces (including man), whereas the "nonfecal" coliforms are more prevalent in soil, vegetation, and other nonfecal habitats. Although "the fecal coliform test is the most accurate bacteriological measurement now available for detecting warm-blooded animal feces in polluted water"(93), "it is not recommended for examination of untreated water supplies being considered for potable water"(23), because there should not be any type of coliforms, fecal or nonfecal, present in chlorinated drinking water supplies. The fecal coliform group is an indication of recent fecal pollution of the raw water supply, whereas the total coliform group may be an indication of recent or remote fecal pollution(24,25,94) and also includes organisms of limited sanitary significance. The use of the total coliform group concept results in an increase in the safety factor regarding the safety of drinking waters and provides a wider margin of safety than the use of the fecal coliform group alone. However, the presence of fecal coliforms in a finished water supply does constitute an extremely dangerous situation that requires immediate remedial action (24,25,94). It is doubtful that the total coliform test will ever be replaced by the fecal coliform test in finished water supplies, but fecal coliform determinations can be an important adjunct test in our surveillance of raw waters entering a water treatment plant and potable waters. In addition, waters obtained from wells and springs used for private water supply might well be examined by the fecal coliform test, especially after heavy rainfalls, because of intrusion into such waters of great numbers of nonfecal coliforms that reside in soils(24, 48). These latter will increase disproportionately the total coliform values in that water system, often without correlating with increased hazard to human health except in areas where fecal pollution of soil exists. Perhaps in this latter case, drinking water standards would not have to be so stringent as in the absolute reliance on total coliforms alone, but could consider the fecal coliform values before deciding on the potable or nonpotable nature of the well or spring water supply.

(2) *Determination of the Fecal Coliform Group in Water.* The World Health Organization(29) defined the fecal coliforms as gram-negative, non-spore-forming rods that are capable of fermenting lactose with the production of acid and gas at 44°C in less than 24 hr. In the United States, the temperature recommended for the elevated temperature test varies, depending on the recommendations in the 12th edition of *Standard Methods*(23), from 44.5 ± 0.5°C with EC broth medium to 43 ± 0.5°C

with boric acid lactose broth. The proposed 13th edition of *Standard Methods* (26) reduces the allowable variation in incubation temperature to ±0.2°C. The procedures available for the elevated temperature separation of fecal from nonfecal coliforms are summarized below. Only the EC broth medium and the boric acid lactose broth procedures are listed in the present and proposed editions of *Standard Methods* (23,26).

(*a*) *EC Broth Medium.* This was developed by Hajna and Perry (95, 96) and was recommended by them for the presumptive detection of the total coliform group when incubated at 37°C, and for the presence of *Escherichia coli* when used at an elevated incubation temperature of 45.5°C. Both the present and proposed editions of *Standard Methods* (23,26), however, recommend a procedure in which the positive lactose or lauryl tryptose broth presumptive test cultures are transferred to EC broth with subsequent incubation in a water bath for 24 hr at 44.5 ± 0.5°C [±0.2°C in the proposed edition of *Standard Methods* (26)]. Gas production in the inverted fermentation vial is considered a positive confirmation test for the presence not of *E. coli* alone but of all the members of the fecal coliform group. The EC test therefore separates fecal from nonfecal coliforms by placing the cultures at an elevated growth temperature which inhibits the development of nonfecal coliforms. The growth of *E. coli* is also not inhibited by the presence of bile salts in the EC medium, while the growth of spore formers and fecal streptococci is inhibited by the presence of bile salts.

(*b*) *Boric Acid Lactose Broth.* This identifies essentially the same group of coliforms as EC medium (23,26). After pre-enrichment in lactose or lauryl tryptose broth fermentation tubes, the positive cultures are inoculated into boric acid lactose broth fermentation tubes and incubated in a water bath at 43 ± 0.5°C [±0.2°C in the proposed 13th edition of *Standard Methods* (26)]. The production of gas from lactose in the presence of boric acid within 48 hr is considered a positive reaction indicating the presence of fecal coliforms in the water sample.

(*c*) *Membrane Filter Procedure Using MFC Medium.* MFC broth is used as an enriched growth medium. It contains the indicator system aniline blue and the sodium salt of rosolic acid. Aniline blue decolorizes almost completely on addition of alkali, and becomes blue as the reaction becomes acidic. Rosolic acid is yellow in an acid solution but can be converted by alkali to form a disodium salt which is red. Since the initial reaction of the MFC medium is 7.4, the aniline blue is decolorized, whereas the rosolic acid becomes red; therefore, the color of the medium at this time is a deep shade of red. As the fecal coliform bacteria develop on the surface of the membrane at an elevated temperature of $44.5 \pm 0.5°C$ for 24 ± 2 hr, organic acids are being produced by them. [A temperature variation of only $\pm 0.2°C$ is recommended in the proposed 13th edition of *Standard Methods* (26)]. These acids lower the pH in the immediate vicinity of the colonies and the colonies develop a blue color as the aniline blue changes from a decolorized to a colored form. Colonies that are blue are considered fecal coliforms. The dual techniques of elevating the temperature of incubation and the use of bile salts in the rich growth medium favor the selection of fecal coliforms. Rosolic acid also contributes to the suppression of noncoliforms and imparts a gray to cream coloration to those that do appear (96a). Based on the studies of Geldreich et al. (96a), the recommended range of fecal coliforms on the surface of a filter is a total of 20–60 colonies (26).

(3) *Water Quality Criteria.* The National Technical Advisory Committee on Water Quality Criteria, in its interim report to the Secretary of the Interior in 1967 and later in the final draft of this report in 1968 (25), recommended fecal coliform criteria for recreation waters. Table 4 summarizes the criteria given for the general recreational use of surface waters suitable for "secondary contact" recreation (i.e., activities that do not involve significant risk of water ingestion); waters specifically designated for "secondary contact" recreation uses; and primary contact recreation waters where significant body contact is involved.

TABLE 4

Fecal Coliform Criteria for Recreation Waters[a]

Water usage	Recommended fecal coliforms/100 ml
General recreation	Average not to exceed 2000, with a maximum of 4000, except in specified mixing zones adjacent to outfalls
Designated for recreation	Not to exceed log mean of 1000, nor equal or exceed 2000 in more than 10% of the samples
Primary contact recreation	Not to exceed log mean of 200, based on minimum of five samples taken over not more than a 30-day period; nor should 10% of total samples in any 30-day period exceed 400

[a]From Ref. 25.

d. Fecal Streptococci Density

(1) Characteristic Species and Occurrence. Since the fecal streptoccoci are found in significant numbers in the feces of man and other warm-blooded animals, their presence is indicative of fecal pollution of water (*23,24,26*). This group cannot yet be rigorously defined, but it has been described as involving three separate but overlapping groups, i.e., the fecal streptococci, Lancefield's Group D streptococci, and the enterococci. *Standard Methods(23)* states that:

> ...it is suggested that the terms 'fecal streptococcus' and Lancefield's Group D streptococcus' be considered as synonymous and that the use of these terms be restricted to denote the following species or their varieties used as indicators of fecal contamination: *Streptococcus fecalis, S. fecalis* var. *liquefaciens, S. fecalis* var. *zymogenes, S. durans, S.faecium, S. bovis,* and *S. equinus.*

The term enterococci, used by some investigators synonymously with fecal streptococci, encompasses the following species of streptococci: *S. durans* and *S. fecalis* with its varieties of *S. liquefaciens, S. zymogenes,* and closely related biotypes. *S. bovis* and *S. equinus* are not included. Thus, the enterococci are considered to be part of the fecal streptococcal group, but the use of the term is not recommended by the proposed 13th edition of *Standard Methods(26)*. Fecal streptococci are considered by Kenner et al.(*107*) to include *S. bovis, S. mitis, S. salivarius,* and *S. equinus,* as well as the enterococci and their biotypes. The reasons given are that *S. mitis* and *S. salivarius* have been frequently isolated from human feces and domestic fecal wastes, *S. bovis* and *S. equinus* have been recovered from domestic animal feces and slaughterhouse wastes, and each of the above has been isolated from combined human and slaughterhouse sewage. The enterococci have been isolated from human feces and domestic fecal wastes, from domestic animal feces and slaughterhouse wastes, and from combined human and slaughterhouse sewage.

The suggestion has been made(*24*) that it may be possible on the basis of species identification to separate fecal pollution caused by humans from that caused by animals for use in identifying pollutional discharges to a stream. For example, certain species of fecal streptococci are indicative of human fecal pollution (e.g., *S. fecalis*), whereas others usually indicate bovine pollution (e.g., *S. bovis* and *S. acidominimus*). The significance and the limitations of the fecal streptococcal group as an indicator of fecal pollution of water and waste water are summarized in Table 5.

(2) Methods for Determination of Fecal Streptococci. Standard tentative tests(*23*) for the fecal streptococcal groups involve the membrane

TABLE 5
Fecal Streptococci as Indicators of Fecal Pollution of
Water and Waste Water[a]

Significance	Limitations
Indicative of warm-blooded animal pollution	Survival studies compared to pathogenic enteric bacteria incomplete
Not normal inhabitants of pure water, virgin soil, or vegetation	Other origins noted besides the intestinal tract of warm-blooded animals
Do not multiply in surface waters	May survive under certain circumstances in various waters and in other habitats
More resistant than total coliforms and fecal coliforms to electrolytes	Low recovery rates compared to total or fecal coliforms

[a]From Refs. *24, 26, 29, 97–104.*

filter method using M-*Enterococcus* agar, and the multiple-tube technique using the azide dextrose-ethyl violet azide procedure. These are described below. Other tests with the membrane filter technique using KF-*Streptococcus* agar, the multiple-tube procedure using KF broth and the pour plate technique using KF-*Streptococcus* agar are also mentioned.

(*a*) *Membrane Filter Techniques.* Slanetz et al.(*105*) described a membrane filter technique using M-*Enterococcus* agar for detection of enterococci in water, sewage, and feces. Their procedure was later modified by the incorporation of 1% agar in the medium and the placing of the membrane filter on the agar surface(*106*). The enterococci colonies appear red and pink on this medium after incubation at $35 \pm 0.5°C$ for 48 hr under normal conditions of humidity. This method is presently tentatively given in the 12th edition of *Standard Methods*(*23*) and is recommended as a standard test in the proposed 13th edition(*26*). Confirmation of the colonies can be made, although it is stated(*23*) that "... practically 100% of the red and pink colonies that grow on filters placed on the M-*Enterococcus* agar are fecal streptococci." What is really meant is that they are enterococci, since M-*Enterococcus* agar does not select out all members of the fecal streptococcal group, as earlier defined.

The use of KF-*Streptococcus* agar(*107*) is not presently listed in *Standard Methods for the Examination of Water and Wastewater*(*23*), but will be listed in the 13th edition(*26*) along with M-*Enterococcus* agar. However, KF-*Streptococcus* agar is not as specific as M-*Enterococcus* agar, since it also favors the development of streptococcal forms common in animals, i.e., *S. bovis* and *S. equinus*, which are not as numerous or are absent in the fecal excreta of humans(*24*). All red and pink colonies visible with a magnification of 15 diameters are counted as streptococci. Orange, yellow, or white colonies or colonies of other colors are not counted since they have not been observed in feces. *S. bovis*, *S. mitis*, *S. salivarius*, *S. equinus*, and the enterococci, including closely related biotypes, produced growth on this medium. No growth was noted by Kenner et al.(*107*) with *S. cremoris*, *S. lactis*, *S. pyogenes*, *S. thermophilus*, and *S. uberis*, or with the nonstreptococcal *Leuconostoc mesenteroides*, *L. lactis*, and *L. acidophilus*. However, in parallel studies *Pediococcus cerevisiae* and *L. plantarum* demonstrated slight growth on the solid KF medium used in the membrane filter procedure, but the characteristic red or pink color reaction in the colony was not present. The data of these authors suggest that a greater number of streptococcal strains develop on KF medium compared to other media tested, such as M-*Enterococcus* agar.

Kenner et al.(*107*) recommended using sample filtration volumes that would give 20–60 streptococcal colonies per filter visible with a magnification of 15 diameters. However, the proposed 13th edition of *Standard Methods*(*26*) recommends counting filters that have 20–100 colonies on the membrane surface. Results are reported per unit volume, usually per 100 or per 1 ml of sample.

(*b*) *Multiple-Tube Techniques.* i. *Azide Dextrose-Ethyl Violet Azide Procedure.* This test is accomplished using azide dextrose broth tubes that have been inoculated with the water samples and incubated at $35 \pm 0.5°C$ for 25 hr and then examined for the presence of turbidity. (The tubes without turbidity are reincubated and read again at the end of 48 ± 3 hr.) The positive tubes are confirmed for the presence of fecal streptococci by inoculation from the positive tubes into tubes of ethyl violet azide broth. After 48 hr at $35 \pm 0.5°C$, the presence of streptococci is noted by the formation of a purple button at the bottom of the tube or by occasional dense turbidity in the broth. The MPN is computed on the basis of the confirmed test results using ethyl violet azide broth.

ii. *KF Broth.* KF broth, recommended by Kenner et al.(*107*), can also be used. However, false positive reactions can occur when species of *Corynebacterium* are present in the water examined. The use of the multiple-tube procedure using KF broth is not recommended over the membrane filter or the agar plate counting procedures using KF-*Streptococcus* agar(*107*).

(*c*) *Fecal Streptococcal Plate Count.* This is a tentative test recommended in the proposed 13th edition of *Standard Methods*(*26*). It is suggested as an alternative to the membrane filter technique and is recommended for use with samples known to contain significant turbidity and few fecal streptococci. The appropriate dilution of the water sample is first placed in the bottom of the petri dish, and then 12–15 ml of cooled (43–45°C) liquefied KF-*Streptococcus* agar are added and thoroughly mixed with the water sample. After incubation at $35 \pm 0.5°C$ for 48 ± 3 hr, the surface and subsurface colonies that are dark red to pink with entire edges are counted as fecal streptococci. Subsurface colonies are frequently lens-shaped.

(*3*) *Water Quality Criteria.* There are presently no official standards for fecal streptococci. The *Public Health Service Drinking Water Standards*(*24*), however, noted that their presence in a water was characteristic of fecal pollution and may be important in interpretation of pollution sources. *International Standards for Drinking Water*(*29*) recommended their use when it was desirable to supplement the total coliform and fecal coliform tests and to confirm the fecal nature of the pollution in doubtful cases. *Water Quality Criteria*(*25*) noted that fecal streptococci, in combination with total coliforms, were being used in sanitary evaluation of water supplies, but that they should only be used as a supplement to the fecal coliform test where more precise determinations of contamination sources were required.

e. Anaerobic Spore-Forming Bacteria

(*1*) *Characteristic Species and Occurrences.* Examination of water for anaerobic spore-forming bacteria to assess the bacteriological quality of a water was first performed by Klein [cited in Ref. (*27*)] at the end of the 19th century. The predominant anaerobic spore former that he identified as *Bacterium enteritides sporogenes* was previously isolated by Welch and Nuttal(*108*) from the foamy organs of a cadaver and named by them *Bacillus aerogenes capsulatus.* Today it is identified as *Clostridium perfringens* by *Bergey's Manual*(*109*), but it is also known as *C. welchii.* It is the most frequent cause of gas gangrene in man and also has been noted in uterine infections and in infections of the gastrointestinal, gastrourinary, and biliary tracts of man. *C. perfringens* is a normal inhabitant of the intestinal tract of man and other warm-blooded animals, is found in small numbers in their feces, and is widely distributed over the earth's surface. Since *C. perfringens* is particularly typical of the other anaerobic spore formers found in feces, it is another bacterium that is indicative of fecal pollution of water.

C. perfringens can be described as a short, plump, encapsulated, nonmotile, gram-positive, strict anaerobic rod of variable length, that occurs singly or in pairs and forms oval, usually central, and rarely subterminal, spores that do not swell the vegetative cell. It ferments the lactose in a skim milk medium to produce sufficient acid to clot the milk, causing the casein to precipitate as an insoluble curd. Strong evolution of hydrogen and carbon dioxide gas occurs that tears the curd to shreds, resulting in a characteristic "stormy fermentation" appearance.

(2) Methods of Testing. The World Health Organization's *International Standards for Drinking Water(29)* recommends the use of an enteritidis test for anaerobic spore formers that is based on the determination of *C. perfringens*. It is pointed out that such a test is of value in confirming the fecal nature of pollution in doubtful cases. Since the spores of *C. perfringens* survive longer in water than coliforms, its presence in a natural water suggests that fecal pollution occurred sometime in the past, and in the absence of coliforms suggests that the contamination occurred in the remote past. The test recommended by the World Health Organization*(29)* for the detection and estimation of the number of *C. perfringens* involves inoculating a freshly boiled litmus-skim milk medium with aliquots of various dilutions of the water to be examined. The tubes are then heated at 80°C for 10–15 min to destroy the vegetative cells present, cooled, and then incubated at 35–37°C for at least 5 days. Incubation may or may not be anaerobic. A positive reaction denoted by stormy fermentation may occur after 24–72 hr. For computation of the MPN index, probability tables used in *International Standards for Drinking Water (29)* for estimation of coliforms are used. However noteworthy the test, it is stated that "a negative reaction is of little value in assessing the purity of the water."

Bonde*(27,28)* recommended the use of a modified Wilson and Blair sulfite-alum medium incubated for 24 hr at 48°C to enumerate and demonstrate the presence of anaerobic spore formers, mainly *C. perfringens,* that reduce sulfite. He compared results with a milk medium (i.e., the enteritidis test) to those using the sulfite-alum method and found that the former procedure gave less precision and resulted in a greater number of false positive and false negative results than the latter procedure.

Bonde based his views*(27,28)* concerning the value of *C. perfringens* as a bacterial indicator of water pollution on the following points: The sulfite-reducing anaerobic spore formers, mainly *C. perfringens,* are a far more homogeneous group than the coliforms; they are ultimately of fecal origin and definitely do not multiply in nature; the spores of these organisms are very resistant to disinfectants and other environmental detrimental effects, and therefore outlive the pathogens and other bacterial indicator groups; and the sulfite-reducers can be enumerated and identified with greater precision and accuracy than the coliforms, based on the development by Bonde and others of an improved *C. perfringens* growth medium.

Bonde(*27*) further noted that *C. perfringens* should be used in preference to *E. coli* in the following cases:

   i. In the examination of waters that may contain toxic substances, such as chlorinated water.

  ii. In the examination of waters that involve a transport period to the laboratory of longer than 12 hr.

 iii. In the examination of such materials as sludge deposits.

Bonde recommended that this test be added to single and all first examinations of untreated and treated waters.

Willis(*110*) examined sand from the filter beds of a city water supply and found anaerobic bacilli, mainly *C. perfringens,* in 50 of 55 samples. Anaerobic vegetative bacilli predominated in the filter and were subsequently destroyed by chlorination of the filter effluent. However, resistant spores of *C. perfringens* passed through the treatment process, and vegetative forms later developed (i.e., "aftergrowth") in the water distribution system. Willis pointed out that the deficiencies of a water treatment filter procedure can be established by examining for *C. perfringens,* using the sulfite reduction test.

(*3*) *Water Quality Criteria.* Standards for the presence of anaerobic spore formers in water are not well established. Neither the *International Standards for Drinking Water* nor the *Public Health Service Drinking Water Standards* lists any standards, although the former discusses the litmus milk test for *C. perfringens.* Bonde(*27*) considered 100 *C. perfringens*/100 ml to be the border line between polluted and pure waters, while good quality drinking water should not have any *C. perfringens* present in a 100-ml sample.

f. Determination of Pathogens in Water and Waste Water

   (*1*) *Pathogenic Enteric Bacteria*

   (*a*) *Introduction.* Interest in direct measurement of the bacterial hazard in water supplies has increased in recent years, although previous attempts by early bacteriologists to use bacterial pathogens as an index of pollution were deemed impractical. An advantage of such isolation is that demonstration of the presence of a known bacterial pathogen in a water supply is conclusive evidence establishing the water's hazard to the human user. However, there is no reasonably rapid, specific test available at this time that could be used routinely to detect all the pathogenic bacterial species of intestinal origin in a water. In addition, since such bacterial pathogens are released intermittently from the human carrier's intestinal tract, their absence does not guarantee safety to the user. Valuable information, however, can be obtained by the isolation of specific pathogens, such as in tracing the source of a bacterial pathogen in epidemiological investigations and in enforcement actions where the isolation of pathogens would complement the demonstrated presence of fecal contamination as measured by bacterial indicators of pollution such as total or fecal coliforms. In addition, as pointed out by Spino[21]: "Isolation of pathogenic organisms, specifically *Salmonella*, in conjunction with the coliform group enhances the importance and validity of the coliform test as an indicator of fecal pollution detrimental to health." A disadvantage of such usage is that pathogens present a health hazard to the careless or uninformed laboratory worker.

The proposed 13th edition of *Standard Methods*[26] includes a section on the isolation and identification of enteric and nonenteric bacterial and other microbial pathogens from water and waste water. Primarily, however, detailed qualitative and quantitative procedures are provided only for the isolation and identification of *Salmonella* and *Shigella* organisms. References are cited in the 13th edition[26] to aid the interested researcher in the recovery of enteropathogenic *Escherichia coli* and leptospires from water, but only mention is given to the vibrios of cholera, cysts of the protozoan *Entamoeba histolytica*, and the larvae of hookworms.

(b) *Methods of Detection.* (i) *Salmonella* and *Shigella.* As noted previously in Sec. I.A, *Salmonella* and *Shigella* species are responsible for such potentially water-transmitted diseases as typhoid fever (caused by *Salmonella typhosa*), the less severe paratyphoid fevers (caused by *Salmonella paratyphi, S. schottmuelleri,* or *S. hirschfeldii*), and a common illness of man called bacillary dysentery (caused by *Shigella dysenteriae, S. flexneri, S. sonnei,* or *S. boydii*). Other *Salmonella* species are also pathogenic for man and animals and could be transmitted via contaminated water. For example, the 1965 Riverside, California, waterborne epidemic of salmonellosis was caused by *Salmonella typhimurium,* a species most commonly associated with the consumption of contaminated food.

Prescott et al.(*111*) reviewed the earlier literature concerning the isolation of typhoid, paratyphoid, and dysentery organisms from water by direct isolation, preliminary enrichment, and physical concentration followed by enrichment procedures or direct isolation. Direct isolation was accomplished by using such differential solid agar media as bismuth sulfite, brilliant green, desoxycholate, Endo, eosin methylene blue, MacConkey, or *Salmonella-Shigella(33–36)*. Preliminary enrichment of the sought pathogens in a water sample was accomplished by the use of such selective media as tetrathionate and selenite broths, followed by the use of differential solid agar media. Physical concentration of the bacterial pathogens was accomplished by the use of serological agglutination techniques, filtration employing metered Berkefeld filters, and diatomaceous disks, or by chemical precipitation of the cells. Some of the chemical precipitants used were sodium hyposulfite and lead acetate, ferric sulfate, ferric oxychloride, alum, or ferric sulfate and sodium hydrate.

It is possible to demonstrate the presence of *Salmonella* and *Shigella* in a qualitative fashion in contaminated water by concentration and enrichment techniques. For example, Spino(*21*), using the microbial concentration ability of modified Moore gauze swabs placed just below the water surface for 5 days, recovered *Salmonella* species from the Ohio River near Cincinnati and the Red River of the North in North Dakota and Minnesota. Pieces of recovered gauze pads were inoculated into duplicate sets of enrichment broths of tetrathionate and SBG (selenite brilliant green) sulfa enrichment. Both broths were useful for selective preliminary enrichment for *Salmonella*. After incubation for 24 hr of one set at the elevated temperature of 41.5°C and the second set at 37.0°C, brilliant green agar plates were streaked from each enrichment medium. Suspected *Salmonella* colonies (white with a red background) were later picked off and identified, using the procedures suggested by Hajna(*112*) involving both serological and biochemical tests. Brilliant green agar is a highly selective medium for the isolation of *Salmonella* species other than the typhoid organism. Thus, only nontyphoid *Salmonella* were isolated using the techniques of elevated temperature (41.5°C) selective enrichment followed by the use of a selective medium. No salmonellae were recovered when the enrichment broths were initially incubated at 37.0°C. Four of the six most frequent *Salmonella* species infecting man and animals in the United States in 1963 were recovered by Spino from the Red River of the North using the elevated temperature technique. He pointed out that this method may have practical application in epidemiological studies by providing a greater yield of *Salmonella* species from natural waters. In addition, since these *Salmonella* organisms were isolated even when total and fecal coliform densities were low, the rationale behind the use of such bacterial indicator groups to detect the presence of bacterial pathogens in polluted waters was thereby strengthened. Prior to the above research, examinations of water for the presence of *Salmonella* species had been made by a number of investigators using a variety of media, incubation temperatures, and procedures *(22, 113–117)*. Geldreich *(118)* recently commented that the development of new media for detection of *Salmonella* and *Shigella* in fecal specimens may improve the recovery of such pathogens from polluted waters. For example, quantitative recovery of *Salmonella* in storm water*(102)* was accomplished using a 48-hr selective growth procedure involving membrane filtration and elevated temperature (41°C) incubation. Double-strength SBG sulfa medium was used for preliminary selective enrichment at 41°C, while differentiation for *Salmonella* was made on double-strength xylose lysine brilliant green medium*(119)*.

The methods reported in the proposed 13th edition of *Standard Methods(26)* for the isolation and identification of *Salmonella* and *Shigella* organisms in water and waste water are considered to be research procedures rather than "standard." In fact, it may be necessary to modify them to obtain the best results in a particular situation. It is emphasized that since there are variable numbers of many different strains of *Salmonella* in water (900–1200 now recognized) negative results are not conclusive.

The qualitative procedures reported in the proposed 13th edition of *Standard Methods(26)* for the detection of *Salmonella* and *Shigella* in water first involve concentration of the pathogens by the swab technique, the use of diatomaceous earth, or the membrane filter technique. Swabs are prepared from 9-in.–wide cheesecloth that is folded five times at 14-in. lengths and then cut lengthwise to within 4 in. from the "head" into $1\frac{3}{4}$-in.-wide strips. Maternity pads or gauze pads of approximately the same thickness as the cheesecloth swabs may be used. The swab is then secured at the "head" with 16-gauge wire and immersed just below the water surface for 3–5 days. After the exposure period, during which time bacterial concentration is presumably occurring as the water flows through and around the swab, the swab is placed in a plastic bag that is iced and then returned to the laboratory. No more than 6 hr should elapse between removal of the swab from the water and assay in the laboratory. The expressed liquid from the pad can be added to enrichment media, or the pad or portions of it may be placed directly into enrichment broth. The bacterial filtering action of diatomaceous earth can also be used to concentrate the organisms. Diatomaceous earth is loosely packed on top of an absorbent pad in the funnel of an assembled membrane filter unit. Two liters of a water sample are passed through the diatomaceous earth using a vacuum, and then portions of the diatomaceous earth "plug" are aseptically added to enrichment media. Finally, the membrane filter technique is recommended for the examination of water relatively free of turbidity. After several liters of the sample are passed through a membrane filter, sections of the filter are placed into enrichment media.

The proposed 13th edition of *Standard Methods* (26) recommends a number of selective enrichment broth media that may be useful in the primary enrichment and selection of *Salmonella* and *Shigella* from water. Enrichment is necessary because these organisms are usually present in low numbers in water. Broth enrichment media are also favored over solid selective media since the latter are somewhat toxic even to the pathogens they are supposedly selecting. It is imperative that the investigator be cognizant of the advantages and limitations of each medium to avoid the pitfalls awaiting the uninformed. For example, dulcitol selenite broth inhibits nonpathogenic colon bacilli but allows the maximum recovery of many *Salmonella* strains after 24 hr. However, since some strains multiply slowly, it is advisable to continue incubation to allow for their development (26). Cultures demonstrating turbidity and an orange-red coloration that is due to selenite reduction are then streaked onto selective solid media for further isolation of the salmonellae. Tetrathionate broth is also recommended for the selective enrichment of *Salmonella* (26). Neither of the two above-mentioned selective enrichment media is appropriate for *Shigella* isolation, since they are generally toxic or inhibitory to *Shigella* development. However, GN broth (34, 36, 120) allows the development of various species of *Shigella* and is recommended for detecting their presence in water (26).

Several types of solid media are recommended in the proposed 13th edition of *Standard Methods* (26) for further characterization of the organisms that develop in the selective enrichment media. For example, brilliant green agar is favored for the development and identification of salmonellae other than *S. typhosa* and a few other *Salmonella* strains, whereas bismuth sulfite agar allows the growth of many *Salmonella* types including *S. typhosa*. Xylose lysine desoxycholate (XLD) agar is recommended for the isolation of *Shigella* strains after selective enrichment of the organisms in GN broth.

A very sketchy separation scheme for the identification of *Salmonella* and *Shigella* isolates based on biochemical and serological testing is described in the proposed 13th edition of *Standard Methods* (*26*). The investigator should be thoroughly grounded in such bacterial identification schemes before attempting to follow the suggested testing schedule. The following references should be helpful in such identification work: *Bergey's Manual of Determinative Bacteriology* (*109*), Blair et al. (*121*), Edwards and Ewing (*60*), Gibbs and Skinner (*122*), and Skerman (*123*).

A quantitative *Salmonella typhosa* isolation procedure using the membrane filter technique is also described in the 13th edition (*26*). Water (100-ml, or more, sample) that is low in organic and particulate matter is first passed through a membrane filter. The filter is then placed on an absorbent pad saturated with M-bismuth sulfite broth (see Sec. I.C.6.c for details on the membrane filter technique). After 18–20 hr of incubation at 35°C, the filter is transferred to another broth-saturated pad and incubated until a total of 30 hr are obtained. Suspected *S. typhosa* colonies are then picked off and identified using triple sugar iron (TSI) agar as an initial screen, coupled later with biochemical and serological testing.

(ii) Cholera. Occurrence and importance: *Vibrio comma* (or *V. cholerae*), the causative agent of cholera, was first isolated by Koch in 1883 from the feces and intestinal contents of victims of the disease. Snow in 1854 related the presence of household sewage in a well water supply, presumably containing the cholera vibrios, to an epidemic of cholera. But it was Dunbar (*124, 125*), using the "cholera-red" reaction produced by concentrated H_2SO_4 in Dunham's peptone solution (*126*), who first detected the organisms in water obtained from the Elbe River during the Hamburg cholera epidemic. The occurrence of cholera vibrios in water is of obvious worldwide public health concern. Their mere presence in a water indicates a hazardous situation to humans who drink the water or are in contact with it. A more parochial attitude concerning their isolation and that of other possible waterborne enteric and nonenteric bacterial pathogens, except *Salmonella* and *Shigella* organisms, from water and waste water is evidenced by the following statement by Prescott et al. (*111*):

> From the sanitary point of view *E. Typhose*, and *Salmonella* and *Shigella* organisms are the most important of the pathogens that may infect American supplies, for these are obviously the germs of disease which here are most likely to be disseminated through water.

Isolation from water: The cholera vibrios can be isolated from water in a nonquantitative manner by using the procedure outlined by Felsenfeld (*127*) of passing a 1-liter water sample through a membrane filter to retain the organisms and then culturing the vibrios on the membrane for 16–20 hr at 37°C in a wide-mouthed bottle containing 50–100 ml of alkaline peptone water composed of 10% sodium chloride and peptone at pH 8.6–9.0. The organisms can then be streaked out on selective media. Smears of the suspected vibrio colonies can then be made and stained with fluorescein-labeled, subgroup 1 antiserum, or slide agglutination tests can be used. In addition, organisms from suspected cholera colonies can be subjected to various biochemical tests, especially when biotypes and incomplete and nonagglutinating cholera vibrios are found.

(iii) *Bacteroides*. Nature, Occurrence, and Importance: The members of the genus *Bacteroides* are a heterogenous group of obligate anaerobic, gram-negative, non-spore-forming bacilli that are normal inhabitants of humans, in the mouth, the upper respiratory tract, genital organs, various levels of the intestinal tract, and normal adult feces, but are also associated with disease states in man(*121, 128, 129*) Eggerth and Gagnon(*130*) found members of the genus *Bacteroides* predominating in the majority (91%) of the stools of 60 adults that they examined. Others (*128*) reported that they occurred in high numbers in human feces, often to the extent of dominating the other microflora. Zubrzycki and Spaulding's(*131*) studies revealed that *Bacteroides* (as defined by them) constituted from 78% (on one occasion) to 88–99%, usually, of the total viable count of normal human feces. One group of investigators(*132*) suggested the use of *Bacteroides* as an indicator of fecal pollution of water, and described a growth medium useful in the selective isolation of certain strains of *Bacteroides* and *Sphaerophorus* from feces and from various sewage treatment stages. They found that these organisms survived complete sewage treatment (i.e., aerobic secondary treatment) in low numbers and that their decline during sewage treatment paralleled that of the total coliform group.

Bacteriological Test: The developed medium for determining *Bacteroides* in water was composed of 0.009% sodium azide, 0.07% sodium deoxycholate, and 0.0007% ethyl violet in brain heart infusion agar (Difco)(*132*). Appropriate dilutions of feces, water, and sewage were spread on the surface of previously poured plates, and the plates were placed in an atmosphere of 90%N_2 and 10% CO_2 and incubated at 37°C for 4–5 days. It was suggested that the possibility of using exclusively human strains of *Bacteroides* to measure exclusively human pollution merited further study(*132*).

(iv) Enteropathogenic *Escherichia Coli*. Nature, Occurrence, and Importance: Ordinarily, the pathogenicity to man of *E. coli* in its normal intestinal habitat is very slight. The association, however, of *E. coli* with infant diarrheal disease had been noted for a number of years, but biochemical means were not adequate for distinguishing differences between the *E. coli* isolated from such cases of the disease and those found in normal individuals. It was not until Kauffmann and his co-workers (*60, 133–135*) initiated the development of a serological diagnostic procedure based on the presence of certain antigens in different strains of *E. coli* that a means was provided for identifying those strains that cause infantile diarrhea. The serologic classification of *E. coli* is based on the existence of three highly specific surface antigens, O, K, and H, on different strains. At present 148 O, 91 K, and 49 H antigens have been elucidated(*121*). The O antigens are somatic antigens present on the cell surface proper that are not inactivated by heat at 121°C. The K antigens are somatic antigens that occur as envelope or capsular antigens. They interfere with the agglutination of live bacteria with O antisera, but cellular heat treatment at 100 or 121°C inactivates their previous inhibitory effect. The K antigens themselves contain three antigenic types, L, A, and B. The H antigens are flagellar antigens that are inactivated by heat at 100°C. Detailed discussions of the preparation and use of O, K, and H antisera and a listing of the serotypes of *E. coli* reported in diarrheal disease are found in Edwards and Ewing(*60*) and Blair et al.(*121*). The reason for the pathogenicity of the serotypes involved in diarrheal disease is unclear. One view is that the resistance of enteropathogenic *E. coli* serotypes to phagocytosis may be one of the factors involved in their pathogenicity.

Certain serotypes of *E. coli* associated with infantile diarrhea have been recovered from water(*136–138*). However, the proposed 13th edition of *Standard Methods*(*26*) does not consider that the presence of these enteropathogenic serotypes of *E. coli* in water presents a serious problem to the health of the consumer if the potable water supply is properly treated. Also, since disease caused by the enteropathogenic serotypes or strains of *E. coli* occurs almost exclusively in infants, and infants normally use boiled or sterilized water, transmission via water is deemed highly unlikely(*26*).

Detection: Although isolation procedures are similar to those used for the detection of total coliforms and fecal coliforms in water(*26*), preliminary and final identifications of enteropathogenic serotypes are considerably more involved. Previously cited references(*60, 121*) are excellent sources of information on such identification procedures using serological techniques.

(2) Nonenteric Pathogens

(*a*) *Introduction.* A number of nonenteric bacterial pathogens have been recovered from water and waste water. Several of them have been directly or indirectly implicated in disease outbreaks disseminated via contaminated water, while others are believed to pose a potential threat to the health and well-being of the water user. Transmission of these diseases to man via the water route may occur through the alimentary tract or by bacterial contact with mucous membranes of the eye, nose, and throat, and with abraded body surfaces. The following diseases are caused by nonenteric pathogenic bacteria, and all are potentially transmissible to man via contaminated water: anthrax, brucellosis, leptospirosis, listeriosis, tetanus, tuberculosis, and tularemia. Their isolation from water or waste water does not ensure the presence or absence of other bacterial pathogens, either enteric or nonenteric forms, but does provide useful information for epidemiological studies when a specific organism is under investigation. There are no "standard" methods available, but a number of isolation and identification procedures are reported in the literature and some are reviewed herein.

(b) *Methods of Detection.* (i) Leptospirosis. Nature, Occurrence, and Importance: *Leptospira icterohemorrhagiae* is the causative agent of Weil's disease or hemorrhagic or infectious jaundice in man and can be transmitted to man via contact with water containing the urine of infected rats and sometimes dogs and other mammals. During the course of the disease, spirochetes are discharged more or less continuously into the animal's urine and may eventually pollute water. The resultant contamination may affect not only water consumers or bathers, but also coal miners, rice field and sewer workers, and those whose occupations place them in close and prolonged contact with leptospire-containing water or sewage(*139–141*). The spirochetes do not survive long in acidic environments(*140, 141*), whereas they are favored by an alkaline urine or discharge into waters having a neutral or alkaline reaction(*140, 141*). It is believed that infection takes place through abraded skin, mucous membranes of the eye, nose, or mouth, or possibly from ingestion and subsequent infection via the alimentary tract(*139–141*). The ingestion route is probably rare, however, because of stomach acidity(*139*).

Investigators have implicated other *Leptospira* species in a variety of human illnesses. For example, *L. canicola* may be carried by dogs to humans, while *L. pomona* may be transmitted by swine and cattle to farm workers or to bathers who swim in streams or ponds that drain leptospire-contaminated pasture lands(*139, 140, 142*). The latter species cause disease that is less severe than the leptospirosis caused by *L. icterohemorrhagiae.* Although leptospirosis is low in incidence, it is a widespread and not uncommon disease and is considered endemic in some parts of the world(*140*). It occurs in epidemic proportions in certain occupations and is important in war situations among soldiers(*140, 141*).

All the common leptospires are pathogenic to man except the sapro-phytic *L. biflexa*, an inhabitant of fresh water that closely resembles *L. icterohemorrhagiae*. *L. biflexa* can be differentiated from the patho-genic forms, however, on the basis of growth in simple media such as hay infusion or feces, whereas the parasitic forms will not grow in such systems(*109*). Research by Johnson and Rogers(*143*) demonstrated inhibition of parasitic leptospire serotypes by the purine analog 8-azaguanine, which, however, allowed the growth of saprophytic sero-types. This fact was used in later studies by Braun and McCulloch(*144*) to differentiate between the leptospires isolated from surface waters. Stuart broth without phenol red and enriched with 10% rabbit serum was used as the growth medium.

Studies of pathogenic leptospiral survival in river(*145, 146*), tap(*145*), and sea(*145*) waters and in sewage(*145*), drainage water from infected soil(*147*), and in soil extracts(*148*) have gained some insight into the extent and duration of these forms in the environment. Wilson and Miles (*140*) noted, however, that even under favorable circumstances the pathogenic forms die out fairly rapidly and that human infections are due to frequent contact with leptospires in heavily contaminated water. Information is not available concerning the relationship between the presence of parasitic leptospires in water and the extent of other patho-genic microbial contaminants in the same water.

Isolation Techniques: The presence of *L. icterohemorrhagiae* in water was determined by Appelman and van Thiel(*149*), who scarified the shaved abdomens of guinea pigs, immersed the animals in leptospire-contaminated water for 1 hr, and then evaluated the animals for clinical signs of infection. A simpler and more consistent technique that takes advantage of the relatively small leptospiral width [e.g., 0.25–0.3 μm for *L. icterohemorrhagiae*, 0.2–0.25 μm for *L. biflexa*(*109*)] is based upon the initial separation of leptospires from other microbes, followed by sub-sequent cultivation on a solid or in a liquid medium. Pokorny and Havlik (*150*) and Rittenberg et al.(*151*) proposed the use of membrane filters to separate cultures of leptospires from contaminating microbes. Ritten-berg et al.(*151*) used a filter porosity of 0.45 μm for best retention of these contaminants and passage of leptospires through the filter. Braun(*152*) took note of the fact that leptospires are filterable through Berkefeld V and N candles because of their size, and used membrane filtration with a 0.45-μm filter to separate the organisms in the filtrate. The filtrate then may be inoculated into a leptospire growth medium such as Stuart's broth which may be supplemented with 8-azaguanine(*143, 144*). As noted previously, this medium would separate saprophytic from pathogenic leptospires on the basis of the latter's sensitivity to 8-azaguanine. This separation may also be accomplished by planting on a variety of solid media, such as Cox solid medium(153) or Stuart's medium with 1% agar added(154), or onto artificial solid enrichment media, as noted by Baseman et al.(155).

(ii) Mycobacteria. Nature, Occurrence, and Importance: According to Rosebury(65), mycobacteria are commonly found on healthy human body surfaces and in the feces. They are sometimes found in the upper respiratory and genitourinary tracts of man. Mycobacteria range from those responsible for leprosy and those responsible for tuberculosis or tuberculosis-like diseases such as the human strain of the tubercle bacillus isolated by Koch in 1882, and other pathogenic mammalian, bovine, avian, and "atypical" forms, to the nonpathogenic saprophytic mycobacteria. The leprosy acid-fast bacilli cause leprosy, a severe disfigurement disease in humans that dates back to antiquity. The human tuberculosis organism, *Mycobacterium tuberculosis*, is a strict parasite of man that is pathogenic not only to man but also to other mammals; *M. bovis* can cause disease in both cattle and man. *M. avium* causes tuberculosis in chickens, pigeons, and other birds, and in swine. Atypical (anonymous or unclassified) mycobacteria also produce a pulmonary infection in man that is indistinguishable from tuberculosis, and the atypical *M. balnei* is the cause of skin lesions (granulocytosis) in man. All the mycobacteria possess the staining characteristic called acid fastness, i.e., after being stained by special methods, e.g., by steaming carbol fuchsin for 3–5 min, the stained organisms resist the decolorizing action of acids or alcohols.

Leprosy is not considered to be highly contagious(156, 157), although Cochrane(158) and Badger(159) regard it as "fairly highly" contagious. The route or routes of infectivity are uncertain, although entrance of the bacilli into man has been suggested as occurring via skin abrasions, cuts, and fissures(157, 160). Infected nasal mucous is believed to be the main vehicle of infection in tropical and subtropical areas, with lepromatous patients being the main sources of infectivity. It is also suggested that bloodsucking flies and other insects are involved in transmission of the infection to man(160), but Newell(157) considers this unlikely.

Inhalation of human tubercle bacilli present in dust and droplets can cause pulmonary tuberculosis in man, whereas ingestion of the bovine tubercle forms through the alimentary tract usually results in a non-pulmonary type of human tuberculosis. The bovine type of tuberculosis is acquired by drinking raw milk containing the bacilli, but protection afforded by the pasteurization of milk and the use of extensive tuberculin testing of dairy herds has eliminated to a great degree the problem of tuberculosis in cattle(*160*). *M. balnei* is acquired usually by swimmers with body surface abrasions and results in a granulomatous type of lesion. Saprophytic forms are nonpathogenic and are found distributed in soils, water, and on plant surfaces.

The presence and prolonged survival of human and bovine tubercle bacilli in feces, soil, sewage, food, and water is well documented in the literature; the reader is referred to review articles by Laird et al.(*161*), Jensen(*162*), and Greenberg and Kupka(*163*). The latter authors(*163*) noted after the exhaustive review of the available literature to 1957 that transmission of tuberculosis to man can occur via contaminated water or sewage, and that:

> The danger is most marked with swimming and near-drowning, but the danger associated with other uses should not be minimized nor neglected and, at the very least, it should be kept in mind.

The resistance of human and bovine tubercle bacilli outside the animal host and their longevity in waste water from slaughterhouses, in cows' feces, on pasture lands, in feces of patients with pulmonary tuberculosis, and in tuberculosis sanatoria waste should generate interest in the presence and survival of these organisms in nature. An added incentive for public health concern is the fact that coliform bacteria have been found to be more sensitive than the tubercle bacilli to chlorination (*162–164*), and therefore it would appear that the presence or absence of the coliform indicator group has no direct relationship to that of the tubercle bacilli. This work certainly needs to be elaborated, but it does point out the importance of direct isolation of tubercle organisms from water and waste water under circumstances where contamination might be suspected.

Bacteriological Tests: Early investigators usually made no attempt to determine quantitatively the tubercle bacilli in sewage and in contaminated water, but rather dealt only with the demonstration of their presence or absence. Pramer et al.(*165*) and Pramer and Heukelekian(*166*) tackled the problem of quantitative recovery of tubercle bacilli from highly contaminated systems such as sewage, and devised a method based upon pretreatment of the sample by heating at 50°C for 30 min, followed by surface inoculation upon Dubos agar medium(*165, 166*) supplemented with five units of penicillin and 50 units of grisein per milliliter of medium. The combination of heat pretreatment and addition of antibiotics suppressed the normal saprophytic sewage population 87–94% in one study(*165*) and 89 to more than 97% in another study(*166*) without suppressing to a significant degree the tubercle bacilli present. An aliquot of the sample after heat pretreatment was passed through dilution blanks of liquefied diluted Dubos agar medium. One milliliter of the appropriate dilution was placed onto the surface of previously poured plates of modified Dubos agar medium, the inoculum was rotated over the surface, and the completely solidified plates were incubated at 37°C. The sewage organisms that survived heat pretreatment and antibiotic inhibition were counted after 48 hr, while the test mycobacterium used in initial studies, i.e., *M. avium,* was counted after 7 days. In later studies dealing with the isolation of mycobacteria from various parts of a sewage treatment plant servicing a sanatorium and the receiving stream, the plates were incubated for a total period of 1 month, after which typical mycobacteria colonies were selected and subcultured in Dubos liquid medium. Acid-fast organisms morphologically identical to *M. tuberculosis* were subsequently found to be present at levels of 1500/ml in the raw sewage, 100,000/ml in fresh solids, 10,000/ml in ripe sludge, and 10/ml in treatment plant effluent.

Two publications by Heukelekian and Albanese (*167, 168*) on enumeration and survival of human tubercle bacilli in sewage, in sewage treatment facilities, and in polluted waters were an extension of earlier studies (*165, 166*) and established a cultural procedure for the quantitative recovery of *M. tuberculosis.* Although heat pretreatment of the sample and the use of antibiotics in the growth medium were found to be not as effective for the suppression of sewage saprophytes without causing reductions of added *M. tuberculosis,* chlorination or Bradosol (a quarternary ammonium compound) pretreatments were found to be suitable. Chlorination pretreatment of the sample to a chlorine residual of 1 ppm for 30 min prior to plating onto Dubos oleic acid agar (*167*) resulted in a 99% suppression of sewage saprophytes but reduced the recovery of *M. tuberculosis* by 50%. The presence of 500 ppm of Bradosol in a sample for 20 min before cultivation completely suppressed the saprophytes and allowed a 70–80% recovery of the human tubercle bacillus.

Kelly et al. (*115*) demonstrated the effectiveness of the nonquantitative Moore gauze pad (swab) technique (*169*) for detecting human tubercle bacilli. This method was favored over the catch (or grab) sample, since the fluid expressed from gauze squares that had been immersed in flowing sewage, usually for 24 hr, was believed to be more indicative of the microbial composition of the sewage during the entire exposure period. In addition, although concentration of the mycobacteria in 1-gal catch samples by centrifugation gave results equivalent to those provided by the gauze pads, the latter method was believed easier and safer to use. The phosphate buffer-neutralized sediments, obtained from expressed swab samples that were first suspended in heated (37°C) 4% NaOH, shaken, and then centrifuged, were inoculated into guinea pigs for identification of human tubercle organisms by the development of tuberculosis lesions. Lactose was later added to the sediment during neutralization to increase the density of the suspending medium. This was found to effect a separation, after shaking and centrifugation, of the tubercle bacilli in the supernatant layer from the suspended solids and bacterial spore formers in the sediment. A portion of the supernatant was subsequently used as the inoculum.

The nonquantitative floating gauze method was used by Coin et al.(6) to detect the presence of mycobacteria in waters receiving wastes from hospitals, sanatoria, and children preventoria. This method used gauze ribbons tied together at one end to form a tuft, the head of which was anchored in the water about 1 m below the surface. The gauze strips or ribbons at the other end were allowed to float free horizontally in the current. After 24–48 hr the fluid was expressed from the ribbons and inoculated into guinea pigs for detection of tubercle bacilli.

A promising method for the quantitative detection of tubercle bacilli in water and waste water is the membrane filter technique(34, 36, 170, 171). A known quantity of water can be filtered through a standard $0.45\text{-}\mu\text{m}$ filter, a disinfectant can be added to suppress the nontubercle population present on the filter surface, and then the filter can be placed on mycobacterium growth medium. A procedure using Zephiran as the disinfectant for a 10-min contact time, and Tarshis blood agar to detect mycobacteria, has been reported(172) but appears to have been devised mainly for clinical materials. Kelly et al.(115) had previously used membrane filtration to concentrate tubercle bacilli in sewage, but found that the material collected on the filter along with the tubercle bacilli resulted in a greater mortality and less evidence of tuberculous infection in guinea pigs than with other methods. However, further research could prove to be instructive in establishing a relatively simple procedure for the quantitation of human and bovine tubercle bacilli in water and waste water.

g. Lactobacilli

(1) *Nature and Occurrence.* Certain species of the strict anaerobic lactobacilli (i.e., *Lactobacillus bifidus* or bifid bacteria) have been suggested as suitable indicators of fecal pollution of water(30–32). Other synonyms for this bacterium are *Actinomyces bifidus*(65) and *Bifidobacterium bifidum*(173). *L. bifidus* organisms are anaerobic gram-positive, nonmotile, non-spore-forming bacilli that form characteristic bifurcated and pointed ends, and are sometimes club-shaped or doubly bifid(109, 123). They are nonpathogenic to man and are even in vivo and

in vitro antagonists of the pathogenic enteric bacteria(*173*). According to *Bergey's Manual of Determinative Bacteriology*(*109*), they are normally found in the feces of infants to the extent of constituting almost the entire intestinal flora of breast-fed infants, and to a lesser degree in bottle-fed infants. It was noted(*109*), however, that this organism is possibly more widely distributed in the intestines of warm-blooded animals than is reported. Prévot's manual(*173*) on the classification and determination of the anaerobic bacteria listed as the prime habitat of *L. bifidus* the intestinal tract of the nursling infant, while a secondary habitat was in the intestines of adults. In addition, it is reported to be present in the mouth, vagina, and intestinal tract of animals. Haenel (*174*) and Haenel and Müller-Beuthow(*175*), as cited by Gyllenberg et al.(*32*), found that the feces of man and certain animals contained high levels of these bacteria. Gyllenberg et al.(*32*) noted that the numbers of *L. bifidus* in examined human feces were 10–100 times greater than the numbers of coliforms and enterococci. Four different subtypes of the bifid bacteria, A, B_1, B_2, and C, were described by Dehnert(*176*) and distinguished from each other on the basis of characteristic sugar fermentation reactions and basic nutritional demands of the organisms (*32, 176*). Since subtype B_1 occurred regularly in the feces of human adults, it was selected as an indicator of fecal contamination of food and water(*31, 32*).

(*2*) *Significance of the Bifid Bacteria in Water.* It was demonstrated(*32*) that *L. bifidus* organisms, as found in the feces of healthy human adults, do not multiply in natural waters (well and lake waters) and actually survived as well as the coliforms in these environments. The numbers of enterococci, however, were reduced at a lesser rate than both the bifid bacteria and the coliforms after storage in natural waters held either at room temperature or in the refrigerator. Bifid bacteria are found in adult feces in higher numbers than the coliforms or enterococci, and their numbers decrease rapidly with time in warm waters (18–20°C) or in cold waters (4–6°C). Thus, when these organisms are recovered from waters in high numbers they may be indicative of fecal pollution as recent as a few days or even a few hours(*32*).

(*3*) *Bacteriological Test Procedure.* Gyllenberg et al.(*31, 32*) used a selective synthetic solid medium in conjunction with the membrane filter technique to isolate and enumerate the presence of the B_1 subtype of *L. bifidus* in water. After the filters were placed on previously prepared plates, they were incubated at 37°C under a carbon dioxide atmosphere. The subtype B_1 developed on the medium as an almost colorless, smooth, circular, convex colony 0.2–2 mm in diameter. The incorporation of 0.01% of 2,3,5-triphenyl tetrazolium chloride (TTC) in the medium aided in the final identification of B_1 subtype colonies by causing the appearance in them of flakes of a red precipitate. Gyllenberg et al. reported that on their selective synthetic medium less than 1% of the developed colonies were not bifid bacteria, as determined by microscopic examination of the cells.

h. Pseudomonads

(1) *Species, Nature, and Occurrence.* The pseudomonads, one of the most widely distributed bacterial groups, are found in fresh and marine waters, soils, on plants, and in decaying organic matter. These organisms are placed in the genus *Pseudomonas* and are described (109) as aerobic, gram-negative rods, without flagella or with polar flagella found either singly or in tufts; they do not produce spores. They may develop water-soluble or -insoluble pigments which may be fluorescent and which diffuse through the growth medium. Oxidative metabolism of carbohydrates with the production of little acid and no gas is characteristic of this group. These bacteria often oxidize glucose, but not lactose. Many members of this genus are plant pathogens, while a few cause disease in cold- and warm-blooded vertebrates. One of the pseudomonads, *Pseudomonas aeruginosa,* is of particular interest since it is pathogenic to man and has been suggested as a bacterial index of water pollution. This organism is associated with, among others, suppurative infections, endocarditis, meningitis, otitis, and pneumonia. It has also been implicated in diarrhea of adults and newborn children apparently caused by *P. aeruginosa*-contaminated drinking water (177). Rosebury (65) extensively reviewed the distribution and pathogenicity of *P. aeruginosa* in man. Since Ringen and Drake (178) found this microbe to be present in 90% of sewage samples, in 11% of fecal samples, and in 2–3% of soil and manure samples, they concluded that its natural habitats are human feces and sewage. Sutter et al. (179) reported that although *P. aeruginosa* was found in the intestinal tract of some individuals, it appeared to be transient in others and thus was not considered to be a common inhabitant of the human intestine. *P. aeruginosa* was found (179) in fecal specimens of 28 (11.9%) of 235 healthy adults, while specimens from 23 of these subjects indicated that 10 had less than 1000 *P. aeruginosa* per gram of fecal material, five had less that 10,000/g, and eight had between 1×10^4 and 2×10^5/g. The numbers of *P. aeruginosa* in individuals and in the environment have evidently increased in recent years because of the increased use of anti-biotics; according to Hussar and Holley (180) this is apparently the reason for increased incidence of *P. aeruginosa* in secondary infections.

Selenka(*181*), Potel(*182*), and Kleinmaier and Quincke(*183*) have also noted the increase in *P. aeruginosa* in surface and drinking waters. Bonde(*27*) reported the presence of *P. aeruginosa* in all sewage samples examined and often in heavily polluted fresh water, but only in a few seawater samples and only when the wind and current carried the pollution to the sampling sites.

(*2*) *Significance in Water and Waste Water*. Although *P. aeruginosa* was first described by Houston in 1902(*184*) as an indicator of sewage pollution, the organism was not widely accepted by the early water bacteriologists, and it is only in recent years that investigators have proposed once again its inclusion as an indicator of recent and serious pollution of water(*27, 185–187*). Although Buttiaux(*185*) generally found this organism accompanied by numerous strains of the Enterbacteriaceae, which includes total and fecal coliforms, Reitler and Seligman(*186*) often found *P. aeruginosa* alone or accompanied by a few coliforms in the 1000 samples of drinking water that they examined from northern Israel. Drake(*188*) stated that *P. aeruginosa* was always accompanied by other fecal bacteria in polluted water, whereas it was never found in unpolluted water. The *P. aeruginosa* levels in sewage ranged from 760/ml in a raw sewage and 17/ml in a final clarifier effluent, observed by Ringen and Drake(*178*), to 33,000/ml in sewage from the city of Überlingen in Germany, reported by Selenka and Ruschke(*189*). In the previously cited 1000 samples of drinking water examined by Reitler and Seligman(*186*), 58% had MPN values of one or more *P. aeruginosa*/ 100 ml, and 3.3% had MPN values of greater than 38 per 100 ml. Studies by Selenka in surface waters, using a direct plating method on a selective medium, gave levels of two to seven *P. aeruginosa*/ml, whereas subsequent membrane filtration studies(*189*) with Selenka's medium demonstrated five organisms/liter of surface water and 2.7 organisms/ liter of water taken at a depth of 60 m. Hoadley(*190, 191*) found that *P. aeruginosa* base line densities in rivers generally fell below 100 organisms/100 ml of water and originated on a continuous basis from both urban and rural storm drainage. He stated that the presence of *P. aeruginosa* in surface waters in excess of 1000 per 100 ml indicated very recent contamination by waste water. Lanyi et al.(*192*) felt that the presence of *P. aeruginosa* in natural waters was due to fecal contamination of the water, and they noted that 0.4–3.3% of all potable water supplies that met the coliform standard contained these organisms. Drake (*188*) noted that *P. aeruginosa* are constantly present in raw sewage and in polluted waters, but their numbers are far lower than those of coliforms. Also, in rivers with definite *P. aeruginosa* levels the number of such bacteria ranges from 1 to 10 per 100 ml.

(a) *Significance and Limits in Swimming Pool Water.* Considerable effort has gone into the study of the significance of *P. aeruginosa* in swimming pool water, starting with such investigations as those by Taylor(*193*), who identified this organism as one of the principal causes of otitis externa (inflammation of the external auditory canal) among swimmers. Cothran and Hatlen(*194*) isolated *P. aeruginosa* of the same phage type from a swimming pool and from bathers using the pool who were suffering from otitis externa. They considered the presence of *P. aeruginosa* a definite public health hazard, and it was suggested that swimming pool waters be analyzed for this organism using the membrane filter technique, although the critical level that indicated dangerous pollution was not stated. Favero et al.(*195*) reported that *P. aeruginosa* did not usually occur in well-chlorinated pools unless the chlorine residuals were low, and that at a free available chlorine residual of more than 0.5 mg/liter this organism was rarely present. A high incidence of *P. aeruginosa* was noted, however, in private pools dosed with sodium dichloroisocyanurate. Favero et al.(*195*) suggested periodic qualitative or quantitative testing for *P. aeruginosa* during periods of obviously heavy microbial contamination or at times when ear infections were occurring. Closure of a pool was in order when *P. aeruginosa* was isolated in 100 ml or less of swimming pool water. Favero and Drake (*196*) pointed out that the presence of *P. aeruginosa* in swimming pools was undesirable since it is a common but frequently overlooked cause of otitis externa and other infections. These investigators observed the presence of this organism whenever the chlorine level dropped below an unstated "critical level."

(b) *Significance of Green-Fluorescent Pseudomonads in Water.* Although other pseudomonads are not considered to be pathogenic to man or other warm-blooded animals, and therefore do not constitute a health hazard in themselves, it has been suggested(*27, 28*) that the green-fluorescent pseudomonads exclusive of *P. aeruginosa*, i.e., strains of the *fluorescens-intermedia* group according to Bonde(*27*), might also signify pollution. For example, it was found that with increasing levels in the water examined of "thermotolerant" coliforms, i.e., those able to develop in glucose-peptone medium at 43°C, the green-fluorescent pseudomonads were recoverable with a corresponding increase in frequency. In excess of 1000 coliforms/100 ml of water the green-fluorescent pseudomonads were found in 90% of the samples, and *P. aeruginosa* appeared in a significant percentage of samples.

(3) *Test Procedures.* Drake(*188*) extensively reviewed the literature concerning liquid and solid media that have been suggested for the

isolation and cultivation of *P. aeruginosa*. In addition, media devised primarily for the enhancement of pigment production or other characteristics were also investigated. Three different media considered superior to the ones previously known were developed by Drake for primary isolation of *P. aeruginosa* from water and waste water using multiple-tube, membrane filtration, and pour plate methods. Both sewage and contaminated water were used as the source of the organism in up to 4-day growth studies. The results indicated that growth was slower on the modified media, but the total recovery of *P. aeruginosa* was consistently higher. In addition, ultraviolet light used to determine fluorescence gave an earlier indication of the presence of *P. aeruginosa* in all of the growth media. A basal mineral salts medium was initially devised based on one proposed by Georgia and Poe(*197*), with the additions of potassium sulfate as recommended by King et al.(*198*) and proline to enhance pigment development as suggested by Chmura and Pelczar(*199*). The multiple-tube procedure used the basal mineral medium with supplements as noted above. However, ethyl alcohol was used in place of glycerol, since fewer non-*P. aeruginosa* organisms appeared able to utilize alcohol than glycerol and *P. aeruginosa* recovery was greater. The innoculated tubes were incubated at 38–39°C, to prevent the growth of *P. fluorescens* and other saprophytes, and were examined every 24 hr for 4 days. Growth of isolates on acetamide confirmatory medium(*188*) provided final verification for the presence of *P. aeruginosa*. *P. aeruginosa* numbers were determined by the most probable number method. Clark(*200*) used Drake's basal medium, but streaked organisms from tubes showing fluorescence onto the surface of MacConkey agar, where blue-green, strong grape-like, odoriferous colonies characteristic of *P. aeruginosa* developed.

The pour plate medium is prepared using the multiple-tube medium, with the addition of agar and cadmium chloride as recommended by Shklair et al.(*201*). The plates are incubated at 38–39°C for 72 to preferably 96 hr for best results. The count of *P. aeruginosa* colonies is increased by the use of ultraviolet light to detect fluorescence.

After water passage through a 0.45-μm membrane filter, the filter was incubated either on a solid agar medium or a pad previously saturated with the liquid medium. The medium finally used by Drake was a modification of medium A of King et al.(*198*), in which glycerol was replaced by ethyl alcohol, and hexa-decyltrimethyl ammonium bromide was added as a selective inhibitor. The dirty grayish to brownish *P. aeruginosa* colonies surrounded by a diffusing greenish pigment were best counted after 48 hr at 38–39°C.

Hoadley and McCoy(*187*) isolated *P. aeruginosa* and other pseudomonads from surface waters using two primary selective media; one was similar to that of Selenka(202) and the second was King's B medium (198). Selenka's medium gave P. aeruginosa recoveries that were approximately 25% of those found when King's B medium was used. However, Selenka used a different strain of P. aeruginosa that gave him almost complete recovery on his medium(202). To eliminate colonies of nonpseudomonads that developed after 48 hr at 30°C on Selenka's medium, Hoadley and McCoy used the replica plate technique of Lederberg and Lederberg(203) to transfer the colonies from Selenka's medium onto plates of Masurovsky's selective medium for further differentiation. Colonies belonging to the genus Pseudomonas turned Masurovsky's medium alkaline and red, due to the action of arginine dihydrolase produced by most Pseudomonas species on the arginine contained in the medium(204–206). Using the above methodology, pseudomonads including P. aeruginosa were isolated in surface waters from Lake Mendota in Wisconsin and along Six Mile Creek, a tributary to Lake Mendota.

Bonde(27) used a penicillin-citrate liquid medium that was held for 24 hr after inoculation at a temperature of 42°C, and found it to be selective for the growth of P. aeruginosa. The 42°C temperature, which is more selective for the development of P. aeruginosa, limits the growth of other bacteria and pseudomonads, except P. pseudomallei. The penicillin-citrate medium was supperior to King's A and B solid media when recovery of P. aeruginosa was examined in the presence of Klebsiella organisms. Further research established the following protocol for the recovery of P. aeruginosa for use with mixed cultures and when natural waters, both fresh and ocean, and drinking water were examined: After "presumptive" appearance of P. aeruginosa in the selective penicillin-citrate medium, demonstrated by fluorescein production in the broth, the organisms were subcultured on King's A solid medium to demonstrate pyocyanine production. Using this methodology, Bonde(27) was able to demonstrate the presence of P. aeruginosa in locations where previously this organism had not been found by cultivations on King's B agar only.

In summary, methods are available for the determination of P. aeruginosa in water, but certainly none can be looked upon as "standard." Although there are some indications that P. aeruginosa exhibited die-away in a stream environment, or at least did not increase in numbers, considerably more information will have to be obtained before we can effectively evaluate its presence and survival in water as compared to other microbes, especially total and fecal coliforms and the enteric pathogens. These organisms, however, have been found to occur in numbers far below those of coliforms in the same environments. It appears that the presence of *P. aeruginosa* does indicate, because of its presence in human feces, raw sewage, and polluted water, recent and frequent pollution of water.

i. Staphylococci

(1) *Species, Nature, and Occurrence.* Although staphylococci have been investigated only recently as possible indicators of pollution of swimming pool waters, the literature is already of a fair size. Two species of staphylococci can be recognized on the basis of their colonial pigmentation, i.e., *Staphylococcus aureus* produces golden-yellow colonies, whereas *S. epidermidis* (or *S. albus* according to older usage) forms chalky white colonies. *S. aureus* is considered to be the pathogenic strain for man that is the cause of a wide variety of suppurative (pus-forming) diseases, such as furuncles, carbuncles, deep internal tissue abscesses, wound infections, osteomyelitis, pneumonia, etc., and food poisoning due to an intoxication after the ingestion of preformed staphylococcal enterotoxin. Enteritis (inflammation of the intestine) caused by pathogenic staphylococci has assumed increasing importance due to the general increased usage of antibiotics, especially the broad spectrum oral antibiotics(64, 129) that may favor the subsequent development of drug-resistant staphylococcal mutants. These mutants can develop to enormous numbers in the bowel and can be found along with pus cells in fecal smears. The most severe state of this infection can lead to an almost complete lack of gram-negative bacteria in the gut. The second species of staphylococci, *S. epidermidis*, is spoken of as being relatively low in pathogenicity for man, and *Bergey's Manual of Determinative Bacteriology*(109) notes that it is parasitic rather than pathogenic. An indication of the virulance of a staphylococcus culture is its ability to clot plasma by elaboration of an enzyme called coagulase. Thus, this forms the basis of a simple test for differentiation of these two species, i.e., coagulase-positive staphylococci are members of the usually pigmented *aureus* strain, whereas coagulase-negative ones are *epidermidis*. Both species of staphylococci are found on healthy skin and mucous membranes of man, especially of the nose and mouth. In addition, staphylococci appear infrequently or in relatively small numbers in feces(64).

(2) *Present Bacteriological Standards for Swimming Pool Water.* In reports published by the American Public Health Association(56, 57) standard tests for the bacterial quality of swimming pool waters were recommended. Not more than 15% of the water samples obtained from a

pool over any considerable period of time were to show positive tests (confirmed tests) for coliform organisms in any of five 10-ml portions of a sample, contain more than 1.0 coliform organism/50 ml when the membrane filter test was used, or contain more than 200 bacteria/ml on standard nutrient agar after incubation of the plates for 24 hr at 35–37°C.

(3) *Proposed Staphylococcal Standards for Swimming Pool Water.* Horwood et al.(207) pointed out that the coliform group, which has long been used as an indicator of fecal pollution in water, was unsatisfactory in demonstrating the presence of nonfecal pathogens in swimming pool water. They suggested that an indicator was needed that would effectively demonstrate the degree of pollution arising from the bathers' eyes, ears, nose, and throat. Bacterial indicator species subsequently recommended by various investigators were the previously discussed fecal streptococci, and the staphylococci.

Several investigators(196, 208) found that staphylococci had higher resistance to the chlorine levels in pool waters than the coliforms and streptococci and were still being isolated when streptococci and coliforms were absent. Robinton et al.(209) also noted that high chlorine residuals were needed to destroy the staphylococci present (*S. aureus* and *S. epidermidis*) and found that *S. epidermidis* was the more chlorine-resistant species. Seligmann(210) proposed a "coccus" index for swimming pool waters as determined by the multiple-tube dilution method for the detection of gram-positive cocci using azide dextrose broth; it was recommended that the number of cocci should be less than 15 per 100 ml. Isolates from positive tubes of azide dextrose broth that were examined consisted of 43% staphylococci (*S. epidermidis*) commonly present on the skin and mucous membranes of man. The remaining isolates were divided among streptococci (*S. mitis*, 27%; *S. salivarius*, 15%; *S. fecalis*, 10%) and unidentified micrococci (5%). It was found that streptococcal numbers paralleled increases in coccal pollution; however, *Staphylococcus epidermidis* was found to be more resistant than the streptococci to chlorine.

Investigations by Favero et al.(195) led to their recommendation that staphylococci be adopted as indicators of pollution in swimming pools. The numbers of staphylococci isolated followed the number of bathers present in the pool—the higher the bathing load, the higher the staphylococcal count. When coliform bacteria were present the numbers of staphylococci as well as streptococci were very high, but the absence of coliforms did not indicate a corresponding lack of staphylococci. In addition, when large numbers of staphylococci were present in pool waters, no coliforms or enterococci were found, and the "total" bacterial counts were low. Because the staphylococci have a higher resistance to chlorine than do coliforms, the absence of staphylococci in numbers implied the absence of coliforms and, therefore, enteric pathogens in the swimming pool water being tested. Favero et al.(195) maintained that the staphylococci were valid indicators of microbial pollution from the mouth, nose, throat, and skin surface of bathers and, being pathogens themselves, were the best pollution indicator organisms in swimming pool waters. It was suggested that they be adopted as the pollution indicator in swimming pool waters; Favero et al. proposed an allowable maximum of less than 100 staphylococci/100 ml of water.

(4) Methods of Detection. Favero et al.(195) recommended the membrane filter procedure with selective media as the method of choice for the quantitative isolation of staphylococci in swimming pool waters. They determined numbers of staphylococci on Chapman-Stone agar, phenol red mannitol salt agar, and Vogel-Johnson agar(33–36), but finally recommended Chapman-Stone medium since it was somewhat superior to either of the others. However, Vogel-Johnson agar was definitely superior in the selecting out of coagulase-positive, mannitol-fermenting S. aureus. Their data showed that whereas 98.1% of the staphylococci isolated from membrane filters on Vogel-Johnson agar were S. aureus, only 54.6% of the Chapman-Stone isolates and 0.36% of the phenol red mannitol salt agar isolates were S. aureus. Staphylococci that neither fermented mannitol nor produced coagulase were classified as S. epidermidis. The proposed 13th edition of Standard Methods(26) added on a tentative basis a membrane filter test for S. aureus that could be used for the bacteriological evaluation of swimming pool and bathing place waters. The medium suggested for use was M-Staphylococcus broth, which is patterned after the formulation of Staphylococcus Medium No. 110 with the gelatin and agar omitted(34). It was recommended that sample quantities be used that produced membrane filter counts of 40–100 colonies. All yellow-golden colonies were counted as S. aureus. Typical ones were then subjected to gram staining and coagulase testing. A positive confirmed test required the presence of both gram-positive staphylococci and a positive coagulase test.

Other media might well be examined for their relative efficiency in selection and enumeration of staphylococci from swimming pool waters. Additional research and epidemiological studies with freshwater pools would also be helpful, correlating staphylococcal content and other indicator bacterial levels, such as the total coliforms, fecal coliforms, and fecal streptococci, with incidence of illness among the bathers. Previous studies by Stevenson(*211*) investigated the relationship between bathing water quality and the health of the bather, using beaches on Lake Michigan at Chicago; the Ohio River at Dayton, Kentucky, and a nearby swimming pool; and municipal beaches on Long Island Sound at New Rochelle and Mamaroneck, New York. It is significant in regard to the proposed staphylococcal standard that Stevenson found that eye, ear, nose, and throat ailments represented more than half of the overall illness incidence observed among the bathers, whereas gastrointestinal disturbances comprised up to one-fifth. Skin irritations and other ailments made up the balance of the recorded illnesses. The pool swimmers, in particular, showed an incidence for all types of illnesses of 13.8 per 1000 person-days, where person-days referred to the number of days of participation by subjects in the study. Sixty-eight per cent of this incidence involved illnesses of the eye, ear, nose, and throat, 15% involved gastrointestinal disturbances, and other ailments comprised the balance. Pool bathers had a higher rise in overall illness incidence, reaching 32 per 1000 person-days, for a bather group that swam 10–19 days during the study period. This was due primarily to a higher incidence of eye, ear, nose, and throat ailments which, according to Stevenson(*211*), may be attributed to diving and bathing in close proximity in a body of water that has a low dilution effect on the microbial population. During the pool study the water quality as reflected by most probable number of total coliforms was less than 3.0. Thus, the use of a staphylococcal standard might have been more indicative of the true quality of the pool water.

(*5*) *The Future of Staphylococci as Indicator Organisms.* It appears more logical to use an indicator like staphylococci in indoor and outdoor artificial pools that indicates specific oral nasal, and skin pollution from the bathers themselves, than to use the presently accepted coliform or total bacterial count tests. Normally, outright fecal pollution is not a problem in artificial pools, and the water used is always of a high and consistent quality. Although many investigators have suggested over the years the discarding of the coliform and total bacterial count tests in evaluating the bacteriologic quality of artificial swimming pools, new proposed bacteriologic standards have been accepted by health departments with more distain than acclaim. The problems inherent in the reeducating of their staffs, an unfamiliarity with the suggested new procedures, and conservatism in the acceptance of new ideas have resulted in a distinct lag between development and use of proposed standards and methods for evaluating the pollution of swimming pool waters.

II. Viral Analysis of Water and Waste Water

A. The Nature and Kinds of Viruses

Viruses can be defined as ultramicroscopic, obligate intracellular parasites, which are dependent for multiplication upon an intimate association with living host cells. They have no metabolic activities extracellularly. Viruses may live in animal cells (animal viruses), in plant cells (plant viruses), in insect cells (insect viruses), or in bacterial cells (bacterial viruses or bacteriophages). Most viruses are under 300 nm in size, with a size range from about 10 to 300 nm. Viruses are composed of a nucleic acid core contained in a protein coat called a capsid. The nucleic acid core is composed of either deoxyribonucleic acid (DNA) or ribonucleic acid (RNA), but never both. The capsid is itself divisible into subunits called capsomeres. The larger viruses may also be surrounded by an outer membrane. There is a diversity in shapes among the viruses, depending on the symmetry of the capsid; cubic, helical, or binal symmetries are possible. The complete virus particle is called a virion.

B. Cultivation and Quantitation of Animal Viruses

Animal viruses can only be cultivated in the laboratory within susceptible living cells. The following techniques have been used: chick embryos, tissues in plasma clots, cell or tissue cultures, and animal inoculations.

The chick embryo technique of animal virus cultivation was introduced by Woodruff and Goodpasture(212) in 1931. Fertile hens' eggs are first incubated at about 37.5°C for various time periods depending upon the future desired site of virus injection and subsequent multiplication in the embryonated egg. Thus, the recommended days of incubation for the following stated injection sites are 3–5 days for yolk sac inoculation, 9–11 days for allantoic and amniotic inoculation, and 12–13 days for chorioallantoic membrane studies. After inoculation of the desired site and sealing of the injection incision on the shell surface with paraffin, cellophane tape, or nail polish, the eggs are reincubated for several days at 37.5°C and then opened and examined. The multiplied virus is recovered in the embryonated egg from the site of the original inoculation. Thus, the virus is recovered from the yolk sac membrane when the yolk sac is inoculated, in the allantoic fluid when the allantoic cavity is inoculated, in the amniotic fluid when the amniotic cavity is inoculated, and in the chorioallantoic membrane when the chorioallantoic membrane is inoculated. Cultivation of certain animal viruses in fertile hens' eggs is useful in the following cases: the primary isolation of viruses, propagation of stock viral strains and large quantities of viruses for vaccine production or chemical analysis, titration of viruses and antiviral sera, chemotherapeutic studies, and studies on the manner of viral multiplication.

The plasma clot technique is representative of organ culture methods that have been used for animal virus cultivation. In this technique pieces of tissue (explants) are added to the clot surface, and tissue establishment occurs. Subcultures can be made from these explants. The explants are then inoculated with the desired virus, and the multiplied virus is later harvested.

The cell or tissue culture technique has revolutionized virology. As pointed out by Berg(*213*), "...the development of the cell culture technic (often called tissue culture) in the late 1940's has resulted in the discovery and characterization of more new viruses since that time than had been discovered previously." Both primary and continuous cell cultures are used in viral research. Primary cell cultures originate from the cells of living tissue taken directly from an animal, while continuous cell cultures are obtained from previously established cell lines that are being grown in the laboratory. The latter were originally prepared from primary cell systems.

Primary cell cultures are prepared from minced living embryonic, adult, or tumor tissues that may be treated enzymatically with the proteolytic enzyme trypsin to liberate cells from the tissue. After the trypsin treatment the extracted cells are collected by low speed centrifugation and are washed. A viable cell count is made at this time in a hemocytometer, and the volume of the cell suspension is adjusted with an appropriate nutrient medium to obtain the final desired cell concentration. Cell concentrations for planting may vary from 150,000 to 500,000 cells/ml, depending upon the tissue used. The suspension is now planted into appropriate glass or plastic containers and is incubated at 35–37°C for about a week. During this time the cells attach to the surface of the vessel and develop into a confluent single layer (monolayer) of cells. This monolayer sheet of cells is usually very susceptible to viral infection, and such infection may result in the appearance of degenerative changes in the cells (cytopathic effect or CPE).

The CPE is often characteristic for the virus infecting the cells. Cytopathic changes can be restricted and localized by overlaying the inoculated monolayer with a medium containing cell nutrients, agar as the solidifying agent, and a vital dye such as neutral red. The viruses released by the initially infected cells are restricted in their spread to contiguous cells by the overlay, thus resulting in localized circular areas of degenerating cells. The pink color imparted to the cells by the neutral red stain disappears as the cells are destroyed, leaving macroscopically visible clear areas called plaques. Each plaque was originally started by one virion or perhaps by a clump of virions. If the dilution of the original sample and the size of the inoculum used are known, the number of plaques formed per cell sheet is proportional to the amount of virus present in the original suspension. By convention, the number of virus particles present in the original sample is reported in terms of plaque-forming units (PFU).

The advantage of primary cultures lies in their great degree and range of susceptibility to viruses, which often exceeds that found with continuous cell lines. However, primary cultures may harbor latent "passenger" viruses from the animal donor, may not contain one cell type but rather many of varying susceptibility to the virus being examined, are expensive to produce, may not always be readily available, and can be propagated only over a short period of time. Continuous cultures or established cell lines, on the other hand, are either prepared from primary cultures by repeated in vitro serial subculturing of cells for an indefinite time by the investigator, or may be obtained as established cell lines from commercial sources. These are usually of one cell type and may be propagated for long periods of time. Continuous cultures do not harbor latent viruses but may contain contaminating bacteria and mycoplasma.

Inoculation of animals constitutes another test system that may be used for the cultivation, recovery, and thus detection of the presence of specific viruses. A host of different animals have been used depending upon the virus to be cultivated. White mice (suckling to 3 or 4 weeks old), for example, are used mainly in work with the neurotropic, arbovirus, and Coxsackieviruses (214). Hamsters are employed with pneumonitis agents and certain neurotropic viruses, while guinea pigs are used in the study of rabies, herpes, lymphocytic choriomeningitis, and foot and mouth disease viruses. Ferrets, pigeons, psittacine birds, rabbits, and monkeys are also used. After inoculation of the virus through the skin or by instillation onto the nasal or conjunctival membranes, symptoms of infectivity are looked for that may be characteristic for a specific virus. Histological examination of animal tissues with a light or electron microscope or examination of the blood for specific antibodies may serve to identify the virus.

Virus infectivity can be measured not only on the basis of PFU, but also by determining the extent to which the virus must be diluted out before failing to kill susceptible animals or failing to produce signs of virus growth, such as CPE, in tissue cultures. The viral density or strength is expressed as the $TCID_{50}$ (tissue culture infectious dose) or TCD_{50} (tissue culture dose) when tissue cultures are used, and as the LD_{50} (lethal dose) for animal host systems. Thus, the virus titration results are calculated in terms of a 50% end point—the amount (dilution) of the virus required to cause the appearance of CPE in 50% of the inoculated tissue culture containers (usually test tubes) or death of 50% of the inoculated animals. Various methods are available(214) for determination of the dilution (end point) at which 50% of the tissue culture tubes or animals would have been positive (indicated by CPE or death). The figure obtained indicates the strength of the original virus-containing solution.

C. Cultivation and Quantitation of Bacterial Viruses (Bacteriophages)

Bacterial viruses, or bacteriophages, are cultivated by growing them in young, susceptible, actively multiplying bacterial host cells. The density of a bacterial virus population in a solution can be assayed by using the plaque count technique. Dilutions of the bacterial viruses are made in diluent water and then added separately to tubes of cooled, liquefied, semisolid nutrient agar. Each tube was previously inoculated with the host bacterial strain. The mixture is then poured over a hardened nutrient agar surface in a petri dish, and allowed to set. The bacterial viruses have an opportunity to meet the bacterial hosts in the semisolid agar before and after the latter gels. As each infected bacterium lyses, large numbers of bacterial virus progeny are released that infect adjacent bacterial cells. This leads to the eventual creation of a number of macroscopic circular clear areas, or plaques, free of bacterial growth on the plate surface. Since the uninfected bacterial cells are also multiplying, the plaques stand out quite distinctly as clear areas upon a dense lawn of bacterial growth. Since the dilutions used are known, the plaques can be counted as one would count bacterial colonies, and the number of bacterial viruses in the original sample can then be determined. The results are given in terms of plaque-forming units (PFU) present in the original virus suspension.

D. Occurrence and Importance of Enteric Viruses

The animal viruses we concern ourselves with are human viruses that are excreted in feces and are potentially transmissible to man via ingested contaminated water. Chang(222), however, noted that the viruses that we should be most concerned with are those that actually grow in the intestinal wall and are excreted in large numbers in the feces. This thus restricts us to consideration of members of the enteric group only.

Over 100 new human enteric viruses have been described since the investigations of Enders et al. (215) on viral propagation techniques using tissue cultures. Enteric viruses are the most important virus agents of infectivity for man known to be present in water and waste water. This group includes all viruses known to be excreted in quantity in the feces of man; they are listed in Table 6 along with their associated diseases. Thus,

TABLE 6

Human Enteric Viruses and Their Associated Diseases[a]

Major subgroup	Number of types	Associated disease
Poliovirus	3	Paralytic poliomyelitis, aseptic meningitis
Coxsackievirus		
Group A	26	Herpangina, aseptic meningitis, paralytic disease
Group B	6	Pleurodynia, aseptic meningitis, and infantile myocarditis
Echovirus	29[b]	Aseptic meningitis, fever and rash, diarrheal disease, respiratory infections
Infectious hepatitis	1(?)[c]	Infectious hepatitis
Adenovirus	30+	Respiratory and eye infections
Reovirus	3	Fever, respiratory infections, and diarrhea

[a]From Refs. 129, 214, 216, 223.

[b]Echovirus serotype designations were assigned originally to 32 viruses, but serotypes 9, 10, and 28 have now been reclassified and these numbers are now unused (129).

[c]Isolation uncertain.

the enteric viruses consist of the enteroviruses (poliovirus, Coxsackievirus, and echovirus), infectious hepatitis, adenoviruses, and reoviruses. Other viruses may be swallowed by man (e.g., influenza, mumps, and cold or fever sore viruses) and may also be isolated later from his feces. However, these latter are not believed to be particularly significant in disease transfer via contaminated water. Clarke et al (216) pointed out that since enteric viruses are found in the feces of infected individuals and are readily isolated from urban sewage, especially in the late summer or early fall, they may enter water supplies and present a health hazard to humans. However, it was noted that the number of *recognized* waterborne outbreaks of enteric virus disease was not large, which indicated that many may not be reported or understood to be viral in origin.

The enteric virus density of domestic sewage has been estimated at 700 virus units/100 ml of sewage(216). Northington et al.(217), while studying the health aspects of waste water reuse, noted that if such sewage underwent activated sludge treatment with a subsequent virus removal efficiency of 80–90%(216,218–220), the secondary effluent would contain 70 virus units/100 ml. Further flocculation processes would effect a 90–99% virus reduction(221), so that the tertiary effluent would contain about 1–7 virus units/100 ml. A figure of 5 units/100 ml was now assumed to be in the renovated water prior to chlorination. If a 99.99% reduction of virus units occurred after chlorination, the virus density would be reduced to 1 unit/50 gal. Thus, 1×10^6 virus units could be present in a 50 million gpd water supply. If 0.2% of this water is consumed as drinking water, about 2000 virus units could be ingested daily by the consumer.

The importance of such low level transmission to man is evident when consideration is given to what constitutes a minimal virus dose capable of producing infection and disease in man. Plotkin and Katz(224) reviewed the available literature concerning the minimal dose of viruses that would be infective for man via the oral route and concluded that one tissue culture infective dose was sufficient to infect a human if it comes in contact with susceptible cells. Recent experimentation by these workers(225) with the attenuated poliovirus demonstrated that one tissue culture infectious unit (1 $TCID_{50}$) constituted an infectious dose.

E. Occurrence and Importance of Bacterial Viruses

The detection of bacteriophage levels in water and waste water has been recommended by a number of investigators as being a sensitive, convenient, and reliable index of water contamination by pathogenic enteric microbes, and as a useful epidemiological tool in determining the origins of waterborne microbial diseases. Bacteriophages are bacterial viruses, i.e., viruses that infect, reproduce in, and eventually destroy specific bacterial cells. They are widely distributed in nature(226). D'Herelle(226) noted in regard to the ubiquity of the bacteriophage that:

It is everywhere present, one might say. Up to the present time it has been shown to be present not only in the intestinal contents of the normal man and of healthy animals but particularly in those who are convalescent from a bacterial infection, in the urine of these convalescents, in their blood, in pus, in river water, and in cultivated soil. Being in fact, a constant inhabitant of the intestinal tract it may be encountered in everything which may be contaminated by fecal material.

Thus, since bacterial viruses are associated with the intestinal bacteria of man, they are found not only in his feces, but also in his sewage and in sewage-polluted waters(226). The importance of bacteriophages in reducing the microbial flora of polluted waters, thus contributing to the water's self-purification mechanism, has been noted by various researchers. For instance, although he was unaware of the true nature of his discovery, Hankin(227) in 1896 observed that the waters of the fecal-contaminated Jumna and Ganges Rivers in India exerted a bactericidal effect upon bacteria in general and upon the vibrios of cholera in particular. D'Herelle(226) believed that this was the first record of the antiseptic action of bacteriophages on bacterial hosts.

Bacteriophages are infective for a host of bacterial genera that may be found in water and in waste water, viz., *Bacillus, Clostridium, Enterobacter, Escherichia, Mycobacterium, Pseudomonas, Salmonella, Shigella, Streptococcus, Vibrio*, etc. In addition, there exist in nature viruses similar to bacteriophages that attack actinomycetes, blue-green algae, spirochetes, and yeasts(228,229). Some bacteriophages may be quite specific in their action and multiply in only a certain bacterial strain, while others are able to multiply in many different strains of the same genus, or even in closely related genera(226,228).

While numerous reports have stressed the advantages of bacterial viruses in the assessment of fecal contamination of water, there is disagreement as to the ultimate merit of such an indicator model. The following sections investigate the background that influenced scientific evolution leading to present-day recommendations concerning the use of bacteriophage indicators for bacterial and viral pollution of water and waste water. The epidemiologic potential of bacteriophages is also discussed.

1. BACTERIOPHAGES AS INDICATORS OF PATHOGENIC ENTERIC BACTERIAL POLLUTION OF WATER

The literature dealing with this subject is extensive, and only that deemed most pertinent is mentioned in this section. The first references reflect those found in the earlier literature. For instance, Gildemeister and Watanabe(230) studied the presence of bacteriophages active against the coli-dysentry-typhoid-paratyphoid groups in several different types of surface waters. They found in every case a direct correlation between bacteriophage isolation and the degree of fecal contamination. Bacteriophages active against the above organisms were abundant in highly polluted waters, especially after periods of rainfall, but very low in uncontaminated waters. In a later paper the same authors(231) noted that the bacteriophages detected were most active against bacteria of the dysentery group and the Shiga bacillus organisms, but less active against those of the typhoid-paratyphoid-coli groups. Schlossmann(232) arrived at similar conclusions, that direct correlations existed between high bacteriophage content of water and fecal contamination. Surface waters under favorable hygienic conditions contained few or no bacteriophages active against the test bacteria that served as possible host strains. After fecal pollution of the water, bacteriophages active against the dysentery bacillus were first detected, while serious fecal pollution was definite if additional bacteriophages against the coli-typhoid-paratyphoid groups were detected.

The use of bacteriophages to provide information on the quality and origin of a water was recommended by Diénert(233). He was able to demonstrate low levels of bacteriophage active against the typhoid bacillus in water obtained from the Seine River during and after a small epidemic of typhoid fever in Paris during 1933 and 1934. A later publication(234) reported the detection in the Seine River of bacteriophages infective for the typhoid organism in greater quantities immediately below Paris than upstream, whereas bacteriophages active against *Escherichia coli* were only isolated far downstream. In an article dealing with the persistence of bacteriophages in groundwater and in the soil, Etrillard and Lambert(235) reported that a well 40 m deep possessed the chemical characteristics of a polluted water, but no bacterial pathogens or indicators (*E. coli*) could be detected. However, they were able to find in the water bacteriophages active against the typhoid bacillus.

Abdoelrachman(236) pointed out the presence of bacteriophages against the Shiga dysentery bacillus in a considerable percentage of the stools of healthy individuals. This fact, coupled with the persistence of the Shiga bacteriophages in water polluted with human feces, made detection of these bacteriophages indicative of fecal contamination of water.

A number of investigations by Guélin established the public health significance of bacteriophages in water. For example, in one report(237) he noted that bacteriophages infective for *E. coli* were a more sensitive indicator of pollution than isolation of the bacterium *E. coli*. In another study(238) a strain of *E. coli* susceptible to a wide range of bacteriophages was used to determine levels of bacteriophages in Seine River water above and below sewage outfalls. Although the results varied according to seasonal and topographical conditions, bacteriophage numbers correlated roughly with those for coliforms. It was suggested that a quantitative estimate of bacteriophages against *E. coli* might be used as an indication of fecal contamination of water. In investigations dealing with the detection of bacteriophages infective for *Salmonella typhi* in waters, Guélin(239,240) found that the Vi-bacteriophage levels varied directly with the degree of fecal pollution. Vi-bacteriophages are specific for *S. typhi* organisms that possess the Vi antigen. This bacterial virus was practically absent from waters that were slightly polluted. Guélin(*241*) later extended his work to seawater, reporting the presence of bacteriophages from sampling points near Roscoff, France. These bacteriophages were found to be active against the coli-typhoid-paratyphoid-dysentery groups of bacteria. The numbers of bacterial viruses were found to vary directly with the degree of sewage contamination. Bacteriophages were also found to survive in seawater for a longer time than bacteria. Isolation from polluted water of bacteriophages active against *Clostridium welchii* was achieved by Guélin(*242*) in quantities that were proportional to the degree of pollution. However, the numbers of *C. welchii* and its bacteriophage were often lower than the numbers of *E. coli* in the same water.

Diénert's later work(*243,244*) supported the contention that bacteriophages were useful indicators of the degree of pollution of water by pathogenic bacteria. Bacteriophages active against *E. coli* and typhoid and paratyphoid fever organisms were found in polluted surface waters but not in waters unexposed to pollution. Diénert concluded that the bacteriophage test was more reliable for detecting pollution than the determination of *E. coli*. This was especially true when the source of the pollution was several kilometers remote from the bathing area sampled, since bacteriophages, unlike bacteria, are easier to detect when they are present in small numbers. A bathing water was considered satisfactory if no bacteriophages were present in 20 cm³ of water(*244*).

Investigations by Morzycka and Georgiades(*245*) generated data which indicated that pollution of water was more conclusively proved by the presence or absence of the specific or nonspecific anti-Vi-bacteriophage for *Salmonella typhi* bacteria, than by the routine test for *E. coli*. The specific anti-Vi-bacteriophage was reported to be found only in human feces. A high percentage of the feces of typhoid fever patients contained this bacteriophage, but it was rare in healthy persons. The nonspecific anti-Vi-bacteriophage was reported to occur frequently in the feces of humans and pigs, bur rarely in other animals.

Cornelson et al.(*246*) determined the content of *E. coli* and typhoid bacteriophages in 336 water samples collected over a period of 1 year from 14 wells in three villages near Iasi, Rumania. *E. coli* Brx and *S. typhi* Vi A were used as indicator organisms or hosts for the detection of the specific bacteriophages in the water. The level of bacteriophages in well waters that were infective for *E. coli* Brx was higher in summer (385 bacteriophages/liter) than in winter (10 bacteriophages/liter) and increased after periods of rainfall. *E. coli* bacteriophages were found in 115 (82%) of 140 samples collected in the summer, 40 (57%) of 70 collected in the autumn and spring, and 50 (40%) of 126 collected in the winter. Wells that were more liable to contamination by surface waters due to poor construction showed greater numbers of bacteriophages specific for the Brx strain of *E. coli*. The authors found similar results with the typhoid specific bacteriophages. These were found in 39 (11.3%) of the samples, while their frequency of isolation provided some correlation with the local incidence of typhoid fever. Detection of *Salmonella* bacteriophages in water was believed by Lenk and Ackermann(247) to provide a better indication of fecal pollution since agreement was noted between coli titers and *Salmonella* bacteriophage content of the water. However, detection of *Salmonella* bacteriophage only occasionally agreed with actual *Salmonella* detection, thus demonstrating the sensitivity of the bacteriophage method for detecting water pollution from fecal sources.

Carlucci and Pramer(248) described the occurrence, persistence, and activity of bacteriophages active against the coliforms *E. coli* and *Enterobacter aerogenes* and against a marine bacterium, *Serratia marinorubra*, in seawater collected 600 ft offshore at Long Branch, New Jersey. These authors noted no difficulty in isolating bacterial viruses active against the above three genera. Coliphages infective for *E. coli*, however, were inactivated rapidly in natural seawater containing no added organic matter, with less than 2% remaining after 10 days, and 0.01% after 20 days. They concluded that the ability of coliphages to multiply in seawater was dependent upon the presence of sufficient nutrients to support the growth and multiplication of host cells. As noted by Carlucci and Pramer(248), in areas of pollution the organic matter content of seawater may reach levels that support bacterial growth. Multiplication of bacterial viruses may then occur and may be of significance in reducing bacterial levels in seawater. Little dissolved organic matter, on the other hand, is found in seawater free of pollution. Extensive growth or rapid multiplication of bacteria therefore does not occur, and as a consequence bacteriophage multiplication ceases. This research thus raises the possibility of using bacteriophage (coliphage) levels to indicate the degree of bacterial pollution of water.

Research by Kott and Gloyna(249) attempted to correlate coliform bacteria with *E. coli* bacteriophages as found in oysters from polluted waters and those purchased from a market. Oysters collected from a reef located along the Gulf Coast of the United States were placed in a bay at 50, 150, and 250 m from a sewage treatment plant discharge ditch. Although the coliform bacteria and *E. coli* bacteriophages recovered from the oysters paralleled each other in numbers, coliforms were always more numerous. The coliform numbers in oysters from the three sampling stations were 10 times as numerous as *E. coli* bacteriophages. Bacteriophage counts in market oysters (shucked and unshucked) were also low. Later, Buras and Kott(250) observed in raw sewage a ratio of coliforms to coliphages (colibacteriophages) of 100 : 1, whereas in the effluent from the Haifa treatment plant in Israel the ratio was 10 coliform bacteria to 1 bacteriophage. The ratio of *E. coli* bacteriophage to *Enterobacter aerogenes* bacteriophage in the effluent was found to be 100 : 1. It was therefore concluded that the coliphages were rapid and reliable indicators of water pollution. Another report by Kott(251) indicated a definite ratio existing between coliforms and *E. coli* bacteriophages in any polluted system.

Studies by Suñer and Piñol(252) showed a coliform-to-bacteriophage ratio of 1 : 1 in polluted seawater collected along the Barcelona coast of Spain. These authors used a C–5 strain of *E. coli* for the detection of bacteriophages. It was pointed out by them that their most probable number method of coliphage assay was an indirect means of arriving at the *E. coli* pollution level in water and perhaps was not really useful, since *E. coli* could be detected easily anyhow. However, bacteriophage assay might be useful when dealing with pathogens that are more difficult to isolate, such as *Salmonella*. However, as pointed out by Slanetz(253), recent advances dealing with direct isolation of pathogenic microbes such as *Salmonella* from water and waste water have definitely influenced the ultimate worth of this indirect bacteriophage assay approach for *Salmonella*. In fact, he emphasized that since microbiological techniques have been perfected "we no longer need to rely entirely on the use of indicator organisms (coliforms, fecal coliforms, fecal streptococci, or bacteriophages) to establish the health hazard or the safety of seawater."

I might add that the complexity of the bacteriophage methods (to be described later) and the time required before final results are available certainly do not allow for a more convenient, rapid, or reliable view of bacterial pathogens in water when compared with existing methods, such as the membrane filter, for detection of presently accepted bacterial indicator organisms in water. Also, some investigators are at variance with others concerning the potential usefulness of bacteriophages as indicators of bacterial pollution of water. For instance, no correlation could be found by Couture(254) between bacteriophage levels and water potability. Emilianowicz(255) found no relationship between the rates of survival of homologous Vi typhoid bacteria and anti-Vi-bacteriophage. The bacteriophage technique was found by others(256) not to be superior to the usual bacteriological techniques used for evaluating water pollution from fecal sources, since one bacterial culture could not be attacked by all strains of bacteriophages found in polluted waters. Finally, Zieminska(257) compared the levels of *E. coli* in river water over a period of 1 year to the

levels of bacteriophages infective for *Salmonella typhi* Vi, *Shigella flexneri*, and *Salmonella paratyphi* B. He could not find any correlation between the *E. coli* titer and the titers of any of the above bacteriophages.
It was concluded that the determination of bacteriophage levels was not a
suitable procedure for the routine examination of water to detect contamination by enteric bacterial pathogens.

Although this biological criterion for determination of fecal pollution of water should be considered by researchers, it is obvious that
additional studies must be made before it can replace those criteria, such
as the total coliforms, that have provided and continue to provide a considerable measure of safety to our populations.

2. BACTERIOPHAGES AS INDICATORS OF ENTERIC VIRAL POLLUTION OF WATER

Bacterial viruses have also been suggested as indicators for the detection of enteric viral pollution of water, and several bacteriophage models
have been proposed. For instance, *Serratia marcescens* bacteriophages
have been used as indicators for tracing the reduction during sewage
treatment processes of not only pathogenic bacteria but also animal
viruses (258). Preliminary results showed a similarity between the inactivation curve for the bacteriophage infective for *S. marcescens* and for
the bacterium *E. coli*. In addition, the *S. marcescens* bacteriophages are
inactivated at a lower rate than the Mahoney strain of poliovirus, type 1,
thus providing a margin of safety. A later report (259) compared the use of
the bacteriophage infective for *S. marcescens* as an indicator of the
survival of type 1 poliovirus during sewage treatment processes. Comparative data were accumulated on the effects on the bacteriophage and
the animal virus of temperature, freezing and thawing, ultraviolet radiation, direct sunlight, pH values, distilled water, tap water, and filtered
sewage, the presence of algae, synthetic detergents, chlorine, and adsorption on sand. It was found that poliovirus was more resistant than the
bacteriophage at 2°C, as resistant at 20°C, and less resistant at 37 and
56°C, while 20 cycles of freezing and thawing had no effect on either of
the viruses. Ultraviolet radiation had a pronounced effect on both viruses
during the first 30 sec of exposure, although a small proportion of each
virus survived irradiation for 5 min. Direct sunlight affected both viruses,
with the inactivation being more efficient in shallow layers of fluid. At
pH 6.4 the bacteriophage was affected more than the poliovirus, while the
survival of both viruses was almost identical in distilled water, tap water,
or in filtered sewage. Algae did not appear to be an important factor in
removal of the bacteriophage or the animal virus. Synthetic detergents,

however, affected the bacterial virus but not the animal virus. Chlorine doses up to 13 mg/liter for a contact time of 2 hr reduced the levels of both viruses but did not eliminate them. Finally, it was found that both viruses were adsorbed to about the same extent on sand, but not enough to result in a virus-free filtrate. Coetzee's laboratory studies(260) demonstrated that bacteriophages infective for *S. marcescens* could be used as an indicator of poliovirus, while additional studies in a sewage lagoon revealed that the bacterial virus was inactivated less than the animal virus, providing once again a margin of safety.

Coliphage models have also attracted considerable attention in recent years. As pointed out by Metcalf(261), justification for the use of coliphages instead of enteroviruses was based upon alleged similarity in behavior under various environmental influences, the convenience of working with bacteriophages, and the ability to enumerate bacteriophages in a quantitative fashion. However, little information is available comparing the relative survival time of coliphages to that of animal enteric viruses of pathogenic significance to man.

Joyce and Weiser(262) in laboratory studies compared enterovirus (Sabin polio virus 1, Coxsackievirus, and echovirus) survival to coliphage (T2) survival in farm pond waters. Their studies showed that the coliphage did not survive for any significant length of time in the absence of the bacterial hosts, whereas the enteroviruses were capable of survival for long periods of time.

Kott et al.(263) carried out studies concerning the fate of bacterial viruses in a marine environment using a coliphage model that was believed to be similar in behavior to enteroviruses. The model included the T1 to T7 coliphages that were infective for *E. coli* B. From their results these workers assumed that coliphages were as resistant as enteroviruses to the marine environment. A rough, tentative estimation of enterovirus pollution of seawater was made based upon the presence of the following coliphage levels: Less than 10/100 ml of seawater indicated slight and not recent pollution; 100/100 ml indicated recent, medium-sized pollution; and 1000/100 ml indicated recent, heavy pollution. Actual correlations between the coliphage densities and enteroviruses were not made. Berg(264) pointed out that coliphage counts often will not reflect enterovirus levels in water, since the latter will occur in human feces at incidence levels ranging from 0 to 100%, depending upon the season of the year, the sanitary conditions, population age, and other factors that exist in a community. On the other hand, Berg(264) noted that the coliphage levels in water and waste water may reflect the number of coliforms present. However, since coliphages are likely to be present in fresh domestic sewage when enteroviruses are present, and assuming an equal resistance to the marine environment, the absence of coliphages would indicate the absence of enteroviruses (264). A margin of safety would thus be provided when coliphages were present in greater numbers than enteroviruses (264). Nevertheless, it was pointed out (264) that:

> Reasonable proof is now required that coliphage are always present when viruses of human origin are present and in equal or greater numbers; proof is also required that coliphage are at least as resistant as the viruses of man to the marine environment. Such proof can come only from carefully devised experiments in which sufficient numbers of different coliphage and human viruses are tested simultaneously under parallel conditions.

3. EPIDEMIOLOGICAL USE OF BACTERIOPHAGES

Several investigators have noted the use of bacteriophages to trace the origin and the extent of a bacterial disease. D'Herelle (226) commented early on this subject:

> Demonstration of the presence of a bacteriophage active for *B. pestis* in the rats of a locality would in certain cases be very useful, for it would indicate the presence of the bacillus in the exterior world and the possibility of a renewal of the epidemic... Suppose a few suspicious deaths have occurred in a group sometime previously. The presence in the rats of the neighborhood of a bacteriophage showing a virulence for *B. pestis* would eliminate all doubt; the deaths were due to plague.

Gell et al. (265) reported the usefulness of bacteriophages in epidemiological studies, while Peso (266) investigated the origin of waterborne diseases by looking for bacteriophage tracers. The focus of infection can be determined by examination of cases of the disease (as typhoid) and healthy carriers for specific bacteriophages. Although Hruby (267) could not isolate typhoid organisms from the Shusnica River in Slunj, Yugoslavia, bacteriophages infective for *Salmonella typhi*, *S. paratyphi* B, *Shigella dysenteriae* I, and *S. flexneri* were detected. Thus, the water from the river was implicated in a previous disease outbreak. Bacteriophages were also used by Rieux et al. (268) to trace sources of infection, especially from waterborne diseases. These workers also used detection of bacteriophages as an index of fecal pollution of water.

F. Sampling of Water and Waste Water for Viruses

Samples for virological examination can be obtained by one of two methods, the grab sample or the gauze pad techniques. A grab sample is simply obtained by dipping a container into water or waste water and removing a portion for subsequent laboratory examination for viruses. The recommendations in the 12th and the proposed 13th editions of *Standard*

Methods(*23,26*) for pretreatment of collection glassware and the taking and handling of water samples should be consulted. In addition, Berg(*269*) emphasized that some samples of waste water may contain substances toxic to virus assay methods (animals or cell cultures) and thus will require pretreatment. It was suggested(*269*) that sewage be centrifuged to remove heavier particles and larger microbes, or it may be pretreated by procedures suggested by Kelly(*270*), Melnick et al.(*271*), or Gravelle and Chin(*272*). The latter three procedures involve concentration of the viruses in the grab sample by adsorption onto ion exchange resin, ammonium sulfate, or gelatin, followed by the separation of the viruses by elution or dialysis, and centrifugation, coupled with antibiotic or ether treatment. However, the grab sample technique may not be completely quantitative because of adsorption of some viruses to the centrifuged discarded materials and the sensitivity of some viruses to ether and the preparatory procedures.

The gauze pad (or swab) method was developed because of the need for detection of low levels of viruses in water and waste water. Cotton-filled pads are suspended in water for varying time periods, often for several days. Sanitary or maternity napkins (containing additional additives besides cellulose) or cheesecloth strips tied loosely together [see Sec. I.C.7.f.(1)(b)] can also be used. The gauze pads are removed from the water and placed in a plastic bag or other suitable container. The pH is adjusted to 8.0 with dilute sodium hydroxide. The latter procedure supposedly elutes the concentrated viruses from the pads. The pad is then squeezed (through the plastic) and the collected expressed fluid is tested for viruses. The gauze pad technique is a qualitative procedure since:

(1) There is no way to determine the actual quantity of virus that flowed through the pad while it was immersed in water.

(2) Determination is made only of the virus that is adsorbed onto the pad that later can be eluted.

(3) The total volume of water flowing through the pad is not known.

(4) It is not possible to determine when the virus was actually adsorbed.

(5) There might have been varying concentrations and types of viruses present throughout the exposure period.

Kollins(*273*) pointed out that the probable nonuniform deposition of virus in the pad during one or several short periods may be considered advantageous since, if virus release occurred infrequently, a grab sample might miss its presence completely. Based upon the studies of Kelly(*270*) and Melnick et al.(*271*) the gauze pad technique appears superior to intermittent grab samples for detection of low levels of viruses in water.

G. Concentration and Detection of Low Levels of Enteric Viruses in Large Volumes of Water

1. INTRODUCTION

The present and proposed editions of *Standard Methods* (23,26) both state that routine examination of water and waste water for enteric viruses is not practical or even meaningful at the present time, but that special circumstances may require certain waters to be examined for the presence of viruses. However, as pointed out by the Committee on Viruses in Water (274) of the American Water Works Association:

> There is still considerable room for research, both laboratory and epidemiologic, to determine if there is a problem in virus disease transmission by water; to determine if the coliform index is always adequate...; to devise better techniques for measuring viruses in water; to develop a laboratory method of detecting viruses of infectious hepatitis; and to develop a sound method of detecting small numbers of viruses in large volumes of water.

Thus, a challenge has been made to the scientific community for effective and meaningful studies in water virology to resolve the above-stated problem areas. I will confine myself here, however, to methods for the detection of enteric viruses in water.

As pointed out by Berg (275), only small volumes of waste water (such as raw sewage, primary effluents, and often secondary effluents) are required for effective viral examination since they usually contain large numbers of enteric viruses. These waste waters can be assayed for enteric virus content using available sampling methods (grab sample or gauze pad) or modifications of them. For instance, Kelly (270) increased the sensitivity of virus detection in grab samples or gauze pad expressions by adsorbing the viruses present onto ion exchange resins. The problem in virus assay arises when large volumes of water need to be examined to detect the presence or absence of enteric viruses. Usually, the numbers of viruses of human origin in water are low compared to the numbers of bacteria, partly because viruses do not multiply outside living hosts. In addition, to begin with, we are dealing with lower levels of these microbial agents. For example, the enteric virus density in feces on a per capita basis has been computed to be about 200 virus units per gram of feces (216). Using the data of Geldreich et al. (276) on total coliform bacteria in feces, Clarke et al. (216) calculated the relative enteric virus density to total coliform density in human feces to be about 15 virus units for every million coliforms, or a 1:65,000 ratio. The enteric virus density of domestic sewage was then estimated at 700 virus units/100 ml of sewage and 0.5–1.5 virus units/100 ml of polluted surface water. As pointed out by Berg(275), their numbers also decrease "even in that most nutritional environment constituted by domestic waste."

In recent years, a variety of sensitive and quantitative physical and chemical techniques have been developed to concentrate low levels of viruses from large volumes of water and waste water, leading to their subsequent detection in virus host systems. These methods include the gauze pad, direct cell culture adsorption of virus from large volumes of water, virus flotation, hydroextraction, two-phase polymer separation, forced flow electrophoresis, high speed centrifugation, filters (soluble ultrafilters, membrane, or other filters), precipitation or coagulation by chemicals, and adsorption on and elution from chemicals. The Committee on Viruses in Water(274), after a review of the available literature, concluded that the following five of these methods merited further investigation: soluble ultrafilters, hydroextraction, chemical precipitation followed by low speed centrifugation, adsorption onto and elution from iron oxide, and the two-phase polymer separation procedure. Berg(275) noted that we may not be able to achieve a universal recovery system that can be used efficiently with all types of water. Instead, we may have to modify the recovery system for the water being examined. In any case, the proposed 13th edition of *Standard Methods*(26) recommends the gauze pad method for qualitative studies where high sensitivity to the presence of virus during a time period is required. This method (see Sec. II.F) permits the passage of large volumes of water through the pad body. The membrane filter procedure, however, is tentatively recommended for quantitative recovery of virus from large volumes of very clear water(26). It also has the potential of unlimited volume sampling and thus the greatest sensitivity to the presence of viruses.

In the following pages, methods for the isolation of enteric viruses from water are discussed, stressing the low level quantitative recovery techniques. Also, it should be kept in mind that a suitable method for detection of enteroviruses in water, according to Chang(222), should fulfill the following criteria:

(1) The method should be capable of concentrating small numbers of virus particles from large volumes of water.

(2) Concentrated viruses should be suitable for inoculation into tissue cultures for determination of viral density.

(3) The method should separate the virus from other microbes and from toxic substances, which can produce harmful effects on tissue culture cells.

2. METHODS OF CONCENTRATION AND DETECTION

a. Gauze Pad Method

The gauze pad (or swab) method was discussed previously as useful for qualitative studies where high sensitivity was desired. Gravelle and Chin(272) compared three different methods for effectiveness of entero-virus isolation from sewage (see Table 7) and found that concentration

TABLE 7

Comparison of Three Methods of Treatment
of Gauze Pad Expressions as Determined by
the Frequency of Enterovirus Isolations[a]

	Number of samples		%
Sample treatment	Tested	Positive	Positive
None	108	34	31.2
Ultracentrifugation	108	57	52.6
Resin adsorption	108	34	31.2

[a]Abstracted and summarized from Ref. 272, Table 1.

by ultracentrifugation of the viruses in gauze pad expressions yielded more virus than when no concentration or concentration by adsorption with an ion exchange resin was undertaken. Their results are at variance, however, with the previously cited research of Kelly(270), where ion exchange treatment of grab samples and expressions from gauze pads increased the isolation of viruses from sewage. Berg(269) suggested that the apparent lack of agreement may be due to differences in the viruses encountered or in the sensitivities of the host systems used. In any case, a 20-fold virus concentration was obtained using the resin method of Kelly(270), whereas the centrifuge technique of Gravelle and Chin(272) showed a 10-fold concentration of the starting material.

Coin et al.(6) introduced a floating gauze ribbon method [previously described in Sec. I.C.7.f.(2)(b)] similar to the one recommended in the pro-posed edition of Standard Methods(26). When city water supplies were examined, the floating gauze was placed inside a standing test tube with the inlet connected with the tap and the outlet connected with a meter that measured the quantity of circulating water passing through the test tube. This method allowed greater contact between the water and the gauze, a regulated standardized rate of water circulation, and an accurate measure-ment of the water volume passing through the test tube. Although Coin's technique of sampling using floating gauze ribbons in a closed chamber has definite advantages, it is still not possible to predict with absolute certainty that *all* the viruses in *all* the water passed through some portion of the gauze. Thus, the result is a more quantitative procedure, but certainly not completely quantitative.

Little effort has been directed toward investigating the viral adsorptive and desorptive phenomena of gauze pads to increase the quantitation of the method. As previously noted in Sec. II.F, after the gauze pad is placed in a plastic bag the pH is adjusted to 8.0 supposedly for elution of virus from the gauze fibers(271,277). Although they did not work with gauze pads, Phillips and Grim(278) demonstrated that adsorption of entero- and rhinoviruses from virus-buffer mixtures onto cotton and wool swabs used to obtain clinical specimens was similar at pH 4.0, 7.0, and 8.0 at 24 and 37°C. Elution of viruses from both of these swabs was not significantly different at pH 5.5, 7.1, or 8.4. Their results conflicted with those of Wenner(279), who showed that poliovirus was eluted best from cotton swabs when the diluent was alkaline at pH 8.0. Differences in technique might account for the observed results. For instance, Wenner (279) worked with poliovirus in the form of a mouse brain suspension, whereas Phillips and Grim(278) used a more precise tissue culture assay system along with prototype strains of poliovirus 1 (Mahoney), echovirus 1 (Farouk), Coxsackievirus A9, and rhinovirus.

Duff(280) filtered 25 liters of artificially contaminated tap water through sewer swabs (i.e., gauze pads) placed in a large glass filter funnel. The water flow was slow and was continued over a 5- to 6-hr period. Initial and final virus levels, and those of swab eluates, were assayed to evaluate the effectiveness of sewer swabs in concentrating virus particles in the water by an adsorptive mechanism. The results indicated that neither poliovirus 1 (Mahoney) nor Coxsackievirus A8 were adsorbed onto cotton fibers of gauze pads under laboratory conditions of study.

b. Adsorption of Virus on Susceptible Cells

Berg et al.(281) described a sensitive quantitative method for the recovery of small amounts of viruses from large volumes of water. The method, however, was limited by the small amount of water that still could be sampled (1–2 gal), which was directly related to the cost of the method, since large numbers of cell cultures were required for precise viral quantitation. In this procedure the water to be assayed for viruses was used to prepare the liquid medium in which cell cultures were grown. The viruses in the fluid were adsorbed on susceptible cells after periods of extended contact between the virus-laden fluid and the cells. Cellular destruction resulting from virus adsorption was detected microscopically, and determinations of virus concentrations were made by a most probable number (MPN) procedure, using the methods of Cochran(282), Crow (283), and Chang et al.(284).

Godbole et al.(285) suspended monkey kidney cells in the sample water containing enterovirus to which concentrated M + Hanks medium was added. This suspended cell culture was incubated at 36°C for 7 days. The need for concentration of the sample water was eliminated since they detected as few as 12.5 $TCID_{50}$ enterovirus units/100 ml of artificially polluted drinking water.

c. Virus Flotation

The concentration of viruses from water and waste water by foam separation techniques, and their subsequent quantitation, has been suggested by several researchers. Hopper and Khoobyarian(286) reported the use of a flotation system for recovery of influenza A virus (strain PR8) suspended in sterile distilled water. Ten ppm of a quarternary ammonium compound, cetyl pyridinium chloride, was added, followed by aeration of the system. The copious foam that resulted contained the concentrated virus. Increased air pressure was used to blow off the foam, and the harvested foam was dispersed by the addition of a small amount of silicone. The authors found that the silicone appeared to have no adverse effect on the virus. The quarternary ammonium compound was applied to the original mixture a second time and the process was repeated, resulting in additional virus recovery in the foam. The authors noted that the virus did not show any evidence of denaturation or loss of activity. It was suggested that flotation may be applied to viruses in general as a method of concentration. In another paper(287) these workers investigated the increase in hemagglutinating activity of the concentrated influenza A virus (PR8 strain) that accompanied a decrease in infectivity. When phosphate buffer was used as the diluent for the virus instead of distilled water there was a decrease in both hemagglutinin titer and infectivity. The antigenic characteristic of the virus was not altered and remained similar before and after aeration of the liquid.

Foam flotation was also used by Bagdasaryan and Zheverzheeva(288) to concentrate polio virus suspended in dechlorinated tap water. Bovine serum was used to adsorb the virus and to serve as a foaming agent. They concluded that the method could be used to detect enteroviruses in surface waters.

d. Hydroextraction

Shuval et al.(289) recommended hydroextraction as an effective and inexpensive technique for the concentration and quantitation of viruses in water and waste water. A water sample (usually 1 liter) was placed in a 3-in.-diameter dialyzing bag which was surrounded by about 1 kg of the hydrophilic agent, polyethylene glycol (Carbowax 4000 with a molecular weight of 3000–3700). The glycol extracted the water in the dialyzing bag by the mechanism of osmotic ultrafiltration, and this eventually resulted in a considerable reduction in the volume of the test sample. Large, nondialyzable molecules, including viruses, were retained inside the bag along with a few milliliters of water after about 18 hr of hydroextraction. Adhering viruses on the inside surfaces of the bag were hopefully removed by flushing with a few milliliters of phosphate buffer solution. The final volume of about 10 ml was then removed and assayed for virus. In their laboratory studies the viruses used to seed the test samples were echovirus 9 (PL88) and poliovirus 1, which were isolated locally.

Shuval et al. (289) reported that virus concentration factors of 100 and more were achieved with this method, along with recovery efficiencies of between 40 and 50%. They believed that concentration factors of 100 or more would be obtainable with further development of the method. Initial virus levels as low as 0.57 PFU/ml were detected, although these workers indicated that they expected that lower levels (10 PFU/liter or less would be detectable in the future.

Certain limitations of the technique were pointed out by Shuval et al. (289). For instance, a certain percentage of the virus was believed to have adhered to or been entrapped in the dialyzing bag. They noted that Cliver's research (290) revealed that virus can adsorb to the matrix of membrane filters (porosities ranged from 50 to 220 nm) and that extensive or total loss of virus may result. Toxic substances that may be present in the water may also be concentrated along with the viruses by the hydro-extraction process. These substances may cause a reduction in the virus titer. Kohn (291), however, used this method to concentrate protein from fluids, and he found that the electrolyte content of the concentrate was the same as that in the initial fluid because of free passage of electrolytes across the membrane. This indicated to Shuval et al. (289) that low molecular weight toxic substances were not concurrently increasing in concentration during hydroextraction. Finally, polyethylene glycol counterdialysis occurred and contaminated the water samples being concentrated. However, Shuval et al. (289) believed that it is probably not virucidal since polyethylene glycol has been used by others (292) in direct contact with virus during purification procedures. Further limitations of the hydroextraction procedure in addition to virus loss by adsorption to the dialysis tube were reviewed by Cliver (293). He observed that besides requiring great dexterity, practice, and "four hands," usual precautions in the handling of infectious materials are not possible, and the method has low reproducibility. However, the equipment required is inexpensive, and there is a saving in the number of tissue cultures required for final assay purposes.

Gibbs and Cliver(294) achieved about a 100-fold concentration of reoviruses with the hydroextraction procedure after 2–3 hr at room temperature. A virus recovery of 46–81% was noted. Cliver(293) also used the hydroextraction procedure to concentrate enteroviruses (poliovirus 1, Coxsackievirus B2, and echovirus 6) from large volumes of fluid. His method varied somewhat from that of Shuval et al.(289) previously described. A virus seed was suspended in different fluids, including tap or deionized waters, and 100 ml were usually placed in a dialyzing tube (23/1000, Union Carbide). The tube was surrounded by 100 g of polyethylene glycol (Carbowax 20,000, with a molecular weight of about 20,000) in 100 ml of water/100 ml of fluid sample in the tube. The insides of some dialysis tubing were pretreated with 2% gelatin or agamma newborn bovine serum, Bo, to prevent virus adsorption. Cliver had noted in other work(290) that gelatin prevented adsorption of enteroviruses to filter membranes composed of modified cellulose. However, the gelatin did not improve the efficiency of the hydroextraction method when results were compared with untreated tubes. The use of undiluted Bo was also found to be undesirable since it formed a firm gel that interfered with virus recovery. Concentration of the virus sample was done at 5, 23, and 37°C for various time periods in order to determine efficiencies of recovery, but no statistically significant differences were noted. It was concluded that the concentration process could be performed at any temperature between 5 and 37°C that would permit completion within a convenient length of time. The initial 100 ml of fluid in the dialysis tube that were previously seeded with virus were preferably concentrated to almost zero volume. The virus now concentrated in the tube was eluted with 2 ml of an eluant, preferably either a salt solution or tissue culture medium containing about 2% serum. Gibbs and Cliver(294) and Cliver(293) attributed the toxicity of the eluate (containing concentrated virus plus eluant) for tissue cultures used for virus assay to low molecular weight polyethylene glycol that had dialyzed into the fluid sample. However, minimal amounts of polyethylene glycol were found to remain in each dialysis tube when concentration proceeded until no fluid remained. Prolonged outside rinsing of the dialysis tubes to remove residual polyethylene glycol also drew a variable quantity of water back into the tubing. It was found that 2–5 min of rinsing in a large volume of sterile distilled water at room temperature was effective in removing polyethylene glycol from the tube surfaces and eliminated the need for such prolonged rinsing.

It was estimated by Cliver(293) that with the hydroextraction procedure there was a 50% probability of detecting virus if 6.64 PFU were present in a 100-ml sample. The efficiency of the method when used to concentrate enteroviruses was low, and this constituted its principal disadvantage. Cliver(293) reported only a 10–30% recovery of initial enterovirus levels when using this procedure, although higher recoveries were noted previously for reoviruses.

e. Two-Phase Polymer Separation

Several investigators have reported success at concentrating viruses from large volumes of water by use of two-phase polymer separation systems. This method is an application of the research of Albertsson (295) and Philipson et al. (292), who used this technique for partial concentration and purification of animal and bacterial viruses, such as vaccinia, adenovirus, influenza, mumps, Newcastle disease, poliovirus, echoviruses, T2 bacteriophage, and others. Albertsson (296) reviewed different polymer phase systems from the standpoint of their preparation, the distribution of viruses in them, and their application for viral purification and concentration; his review should be consulted for further references.

When this method is applied to the recovery of small quantities of viruses from large volumes of water the following procedure is used. First, several liters of the viral-contaminated water are mixed with a combination of organic polymers, dextran sulfate, and polyethylene glycol. After a detention period in a separatory funnel, two phases are produced (hence the term "two-phase" polymer separation). Viruses in the water will concentrate in the smaller, lower phase of dextran sulfate. After the bottom phase has been drained out through the funnel stopcock it is centrifuged, and the supernatant is assayed for virus content.

Several polymer systems have been used in purification and concentration procedures, such as dextran-polyethylene glycol, dextran sulfate-polyethylene glycol, dextran-methyl cellulose, and dextran sulfate-methyl cellulose systems. The viruses will be distributed between the two phases and in the interphase depending upon their surface properties. Philipson et al. (292) reported that all the viruses that they studied, except echoviruses in the dextran sulfate-methyl cellulose system, could be efficiently concentrated into the small lower phase of the systems dextran sulfate-methyl cellulose, -polyethylene glycol, or -polyvinyl alcohol. The dextran sulfate-polyethylene glycol phase system is the one preferred for detection of low viral levels in large volumes of water. In the latter system when the NaCl concentrations are low ($0.15-0.3\,M$) the viruses are found mainly in the lower or dextran sulfate phase. At high NaCl concentrations, $1\,M$, the viruses are concentrated in the upper phase. Thus, the NaCl concentration is critical and determines virus distribution in this water-polymer two-phase system.

Shuval et al. (289) and Lund and Hedström (297) reported their use of the two-phase separation technique for the concentration and detection of low levels of viruses in water at the Symposium on the Transmission of Viruses by the Water Route, held in Cincinnati, Ohio, in 1965. Shuval et al.(289) added a test sample (usually 640 ml, but varying between 630 and 1280 ml) to a mixture of 9 ml of 0.2% (w/w) sodium dextran sulfate (A. B. Pharmacia, Sweden) aqueous solution, 193 ml of 6.45% (w/w) polyethylene glycol (Carbowax 4000) aqueous solution, and 54 ml of 0.3 M NaCl. The shaken mixture was then poured into a 2-liter separatory funnel and left undisturbed for 12–18 hr at 4°C. Then the bottom phase and the interphase of 6–32 ml were withdrawn through the funnel stopcock. This gave a calculated virus concentration factor of 100–200. KCl was added to the drained fluid to give a final concentration of 1 M in order to precipitate the dextran sulfate. After centrifugation of this mixture at 2000 rpm for 5–10 min the supernatant was tested for virus. Shuval et al.(289) also used a two-step, two-phase polymer separation technique previously described by Philipson et al.(292). NaCl was added to give a final concentration of 1 M to the small drained lower phase that contained the concentrated viruses. Dextran sulfate was not precipitated in this latter procedure. A new two-phase system was now effected, but the viruses were now concentrated in the small top phase. Since a concentration factor of about 100 can usually be achieved in the one-step, two-phase system, and an additional factor of about 10 may be achieved in the second step of the two-step procedure, a total virus concentration factor of about 1000 was possible. The actual concentration factors achieved with poliovirus 1 in a number of experiments varied between 52.5 and 200 with the single-step procedure. The efficiency of virus recovery based upon initial virus concentration was between 30 and 67%. When recovery efficiencies were based upon controls, a range of 37–98% was obtained. It was noted that sometimes 89 and 98% recoveries based on control titers were achieved. In one study using the two-step procedure, a concentration factor of 274 was achieved, while the recovery efficiency was 51%. Shuval et al.(289) anticipated that future research with the polymer two-phase separation system would allow virus detection of 10 PFU/liter or less.

Lund and Hedström(297,298) also used a one-step, two-phase system of dextran sulfate and polyethylene glycol for isolation of viruses from sewage. An initial test sample was usually 200 ml. The dextran sulfate (lower) layer and the interphase each contained 2–2.5 ml of fluid. It was noted that the lower phase and the interphase could contain different types of viruses. Comparison was also made with the procedure of Melnick et al.(271) for concentration of virus. The latter procedure, which involved ammonium sulfate precipitation of virus followed by ultracentrifugation, is discussed in Sec. II.G.2.g. Lund and Hedström(297) reported a100-fold concentration with both of the above methods, but noted that the polymer one-step, two-phase separation system was the simpler of the two. When the interphase in the two-phase procedure was also examined, the number of virus-positive samples increased to 150% of the number found in untreated sewage.

Shuval et al. (299) reported on the further development and refinement of the two-step, two-phase separation system and evaluated its efficiency under both laboratory and field conditions. They reported achieving a concentration factor of about 500 in samples of water contaminated with poliovirus 1. In the first step, the average concentration factor was 164 with a median of 173, while the average concentration factor for both steps was 487 with a median of 520. Thus, the viruses contained in a 5-liter water sample can be concentrated in a volume that is $\frac{1}{500}$th of the original volume, or about 10 ml. The median efficiency of recovery of poliovirus 1 in water was 87%, although the average efficiency of recovery was 102%. Poliovirus was also added to sewage effluents, but was concentrated using a one-step procedure. These investigators found that the average concentration factor achieved in the sewage samples using this technique was 224, while the median concentration factor was 172. It was again found that virus recovery efficiencies were over 100% with the average being 172% and the median 134%. The high molarity of NaCl, 1.0 M, that the viruses were exposed to during the phase separation process apparently resulted in increased titers. The authors found that virus counts increased as the molarity of the diluent increased from 0.15 to 1.0 M. At the latter molarity the virus counts achieved were about three times greater than the controls run at 0.15 M. Although Lund and Hedström (298) had recommended etherization of the virus concentrate prepared from sewage samples prior to inoculation into cell cultures as a means of contamination control, Shuval et al. (299) disagreed. The latter noted that when etherization and centrifuge treatment were compared for effectiveness in contamination removal, centrifugation at 15,000 g for 30 min was superior. In fact, they reported that when samples of sewage effluent were seeded with poliovirus, 50% higher counts were obtained with the centrifuge method than after ether treatment. It was emphasized, however, that trace amounts of ether in the concentrate might have affected the tissue cultures, or other unknown factors might have been involved that were responsible for lower titers after etherization. Shuval et al. (299) concluded that it might be possible to detect, in about 85% of the time, virus concentrations in water as low as 1–2 PFU/liter. It was suggested that the two-step method when coupled with the one suggested by Berg et al. (281) would make possible routine detection of virus in 10 liters of drinking water containing virus levels less than 1 PFU/10 liters.

Recent studies by Grindrod and Cliver(*300*) examined the limitations of the polymer two-phase system of dextran sulfate and polyethylene glycol for detection of low levels of viruses in large volumes of fluid. They found that although seven enteroviruses studied were efficiently concentrated in the lower dextran sulfate phase, three of these were inhibited when the lower phase was directly tested in primary rhesus monkey kidney tissue cultures by the plaque technique involving an agar overlay. Coxsackievirus A9, however, was not inhibited significantly in cultures that were maintained with liquid L-15 medium as the overlay, but both Coxsackievirus B2 and echovirus 6 were inhibited in tissue cultures with both agar and liquid overlays. Echovirus 6 recovery under liquid L-15 could only be made if the lower phase was diluted prior to inoculation. The three types of poliovirus and Coxsackievirus B3 were detectable with the two-phase system followed by the plaque assay procedure and did not pose any problem. However, Coxsackievirus B2 and echovirus 6 could not be detected with this method. It appeared that the lower dextran sulfate phase containing the concentrated viruses was inhibitory to the above two viruses and, in addition, to influenza A (PR8 strain). Grindrod and Cliver(*300*) attempted to remove the dextran sulfate by precipitating it out with KCl or BaCl₂, but the resulting solution was not significantly less inhibitory to Coxsackievirus A9. They noticed that Lund et al. (*301*), in an 18-month field study using this two-phase method, found four types of Coxsackievirus B viruses (but not Coxsackievirus B2), several types of echoviruses (but not echovirus 6), and no type A Coxsackieviruses in sewage samples. Coxsackievirus B2 was isolated from two unconcentrated fecal specimens, and it was suggested that this virus at least was not detectable because of the inhibitory effect of the dextran sulfate lower phase. Grindrod and Cliver(*300*) stressed that investigators should be cognizant of limitations of this concentration technique for some of the enteroviruses studied. They were aware that others diluted the lower phase before virus assay, and suggested that this might have modified the inhibitory effect of the dextran sulfate layer. Philipson et al. (*297*) had earlier reported, however, that both phases appeared to be innocuous for the viruses that they tested. Obviously, further extensive research is necessary to clarify the following extremely important questions: Can this method be used to concentrate and therefore detect *all* the enteric viruses that may be present in a water sample? If not, which viruses will or will not be detectable by this concentration procedure? What are the other limitations of this method? These questions should provide a profitable area of future research for investigators, although Berg(*275*) pointed out that the phase separation technique does present the disadvantage of overnight incubation while the viruses are being concentrated.

f. Forced-Flow Electrophoresis

Electrophoresis has been used as a technique for the characterization and purification of viruses based upon their ability to migrate in an electrical field. Viruses, like other microbes, have characteristic mobilities and are usually negatively charged at neutral pH values. Bier et al. (302) used the technique of forced-flow electrophoresis to concentrate the model virus, $T1$ bacteriophages, from water. They suggested that the electrophoretic device and procedure that they developed may be useful for the routine monitoring of water for viruses. The monitoring cell that was constructed consisted of two semipermeable dialyzing membranes (Visking regenerated cellulose casing, Union Carbide Corporation) placed on both sides of a filter (battery separators of microporous polyvinyl chloride from the ESB-Reeves Corporation, or membrane filters from Gelman Instrument Company and Millipore Filter Corporation) that were all separated by plastic spacers. Any number of such cells can be assembled in parallel, and the pack can be secured by end plates containing the platinum electrodes. Electrophoretic transport in the monitoring cell can cause selective adsorption of bacteriophages on the semipermeable dialyzing membranes, resulting in a concentration effect. Direct culturing of bacteriophages adsorbed on dialyzing membranes was accomplished by overlaying the membranes on solidified dilute nutrient agar containing the host bacterium. Since the dialyzing membranes are transparent, plaque formation was easily visible. It was found that there was little adsorption of bacteriophage on the dialyzing membranes in the absence of an electric field. Significant adsorption occurred when the current was applied for only 10 min, resulting in an increased concentration of bacteriophage on the anodic dialyzing membrane. No filter had been placed in the latter experiments between the two dialyzing membranes. When a millipore membrane filter (0.45- or 3-μm porosities) was placed between the two membranes for 30 min of water flow without application of current, bacteriophages presumably adsorbed on the membrane filter. Passage of the bacteriophage through the membrane filter into the anodic compartment of the monitoring cell, after the membrane filter was saturated with bacteriophage, occurred after application of an electric current. This provided a means of separation of bacteria from bacteriophages, since the electric current will reduce the adsorption of the bacteriophages on the membrane filter and facilitate their passage to the anodic dialyzing membrane. The bacteria in the sample, however, are mechanically retained by the fine porosity membrane filter (0.45 μm) on the cathodic side of the monitoring cell. The overall data of Bier et al. (302) also showed that the best retention of bacteriophages in the monitoring cell occurred with the application of 20 V or more of current.

Bier et al.(*302*) also did studies with a larger preparative electrophoretic apparatus that was used in other biological work and in water purification and was previously described by Bier(*303,304*). This apparatus was able to concentrate bacteriophages, but the initial levels had to be high to minimize loss of bacteriophage due to adsorption on the membranes. This adsorption prevented its use when initial bacteriophage levels were low. The concentration of bacteriophages in the effluent from this apparatus was, however, reduced by a factor of 10^7 to 10^8. The use of forced-flow electrophoresis in water purification may then be of some importance. For other possible applications of this method, consult Bier et al.(*302*).

To summarize, the advantage of a monitoring cell based on the principles of forced-flow electrophoresis are(*302*): Large volumes of water can be processed in a relatively short time, both the equipment and procedure are simple, and separation of bacterial contaminants from the virus is possible.

g. High Speed Centrifugation

Ultracentrifugation has been used alone or in combination with other procedures for the concentration and detection of viruses in water and waste water, and at one time was recommended as the method of choice (*23,269,305*). A number of investigators have studied the use of this technique either by itself or in association with other virus concentration methods. For instance, Melnick et al.(*271*) described a procedure for the isolation of Coxsackieviruses from sewage that involved concentration by ammonium sulfate precipitation followed by ultracentrifugation for 1 hr at an average force of about 105,000 g. Gravelle and Chin(*272*) found that concentration of enteroviruses in gauze pad expressions by ultracentrifugation at 39,000 rpm for 1 hr was superior to the other methods that they investigated. A 10-fold concentration of original material was reported achieved with this method. Cliver and Yeatman(*306*) evaluated ultracentrifugation as a method for concentrating high, medium, and low titers of enteroviruses (poliovirus 1 and Coxsackievirus B2) in suspensions. Initial titers used ranged from 1.7×10^8 to 1.6×10^{-2} PFU/ml. The No. 50 rotor of a Spinco Model L ultracentrifuge was run at 50,000 rpm (maximum, 198, 425 g), while the No. 30 rotor was run at 30,000 rpm (maximum, 105, 651 g). The tube capacity of the No. 50 rotor was about 9.7 ml each, whereas that of the No. 30 rotor was about 34 ml each. It was found that there was at least a 50% probability of detecting viruses present initially at levels as low as 0.12 PFU/ml while using a No. 50 rotor. When a No. 30 rotor was used, initial levels as low as 0.025 PFU/ml could be detected. Although Lund and Hedström(*297,298*) used the ammonium sulfate precipitation and ultracentrifugation method of Melnick et al.(*271*) and achieved a 100-fold increase in virus titer, they found it laborious. It might be added that ultracentrifuges are expensive and, as noted by Shuval et al.(*289*), are not generally available in water laboratories.

Anderson et al.(*307*) used new rotor systems developed for subcellular fractionation and virus isolation to investigate natural waters for particles that possess sedimentation and banding properties of known viruses. Fractionation of the classes of particles found in water was achieved by either rate-zonal or isopycnic-zonal centrifugation. In rate-zonal centrifugation (called simply zonal centrifugation) the particles are separated on the basis of differences in sedimentation rates in a density gradient. Thus, particles with different sedimentation rates can be separated from each other. Separation of particles with the same sedimentation rates into fractions of different densities is accomplished by the use of the second technique, isopycnic-zonal centrifugation. It was noted that the second procedure could be combined with continuous flow centrifugation. The latter involves the flow of a continuous stream of untreated water over a density gradient in a continuous flow centrifuge rotor. It was noted that any combination of rotor systems using different density gradients and different flow rates can be placed in series or cascaded for a complete analysis of raw water constituents in one system. Rotor units were originally designed for virus and virus subunit isolation from large volumes of cultures, such as in vaccine production. However, the same systems can can also be used for low levels of viruses in large volumes of natural waters. For example, it was found that a high performance continuous flow centrifuge (rotor B-V, where B is the rotor series for the 5000- to 60,000-rpm range, and V designates the rotor modification or type of the series) removed over 95% of suspended poliovirus at a flow rate of 2–3 liters/hr. In this technique the sedimented material was pelleted directly onto the rotor wall and was either removed by resuspension in the fluid remaining in the rotor (about 135 ml) or scraped off the wall after rotor disassembly. Recovered material can then be separated into subfractional species on the basis of sedimentation by using rate-zonal centrifugation in the A-XII or B-IV rotor systems. Since certain virus types were inactivated after pelleting, continuous flow rotors were developed where the flowing stream moved over a stationary density gradient. In the latter system, virus particles were never pelleted but were banded isopycnically in the gradient. The gradient now contained the separate particle zones and these were recovered undisturbed for further analysis at the end of the run. Anderson et al.(*307*) subsequently constructed two such one-step experimental systems (B-VIII and B-IX rotors). These were successfully tested with adenovirus 2 and respiratory syncytial virus. Electron microscopy can be used to examine the variously separated fractions. Grabow(*308*) pointed out that Anderson's procedure coupled with the study of viruses in these fractions by electron microscopy may allow us to examine viruses for which no conventional biological assays exist, such as infectious hepatitis. In any case, Anderson et al. (*307*) already reported the recovery of large numbers of particles with virus dimension and morphology from seawater by first concentrating a water sample with a B-V rotor at a flow rate of 1.7 liters/hr at 40,000 rpm, and then examining the sediment under the electron microscope. Although the above systems are far too complicated for routine use by water laboratories, it is obvious that this is an excellent approach to investigating the morphology, biophysics, and ecology of particles of viral dimension that exist in natural waters (see Chap. 12).

h. Filters

Soluble ultrafilters and membrane filters have been used for the detection and the quantitative recovery of enteric viruses in water and waste water. In the following pages these filters are discussed along with certain other new commercially available forms. Soluble ultrafilters were among those recommended for continued investigation by the Committee on Viruses in Water of the American Water Works Association(*274*). The proposed 13th edition of *Standard Methods* (*26*), however, has tentatively recommended the membrane filter for quantitative recovery of viruses from large volumes of water.

(1) Soluble Ultrafilter. The soluble ultrafilter does not allow the passage of viruses, and is soluble in appropriate solvents after the filtration process. The origin and development of the filter was due to the efforts of Thiele(*309*), Thiele and Schyma(*310*), and Schyma and co-workers (*311–314*). The recovery of small viruses with this technique was reported in 1964(*315*), while in the same year Witt(*316*) examined bathing waters with the soluble ultrafilter for vaccine polioviruses. In the 42nd Report by the Metropolitan Water Board(*317*) on the results of the bacteriological, chemical, and biological examination of London waters for the years 1965–1966, viruses were reported isolated from river water by using the method of ultrafiltration. A grab sample was first filtered through a preliminary cellulose acetate membrane filter to remove debris, fungi, and bacteria from the water. The filtrate containing the viruses was now passed through a soluble alginate membrane ultrafilter. After filtration each filter was dissolved in sodium citrate solution. The resultant mixture was inoculated in tubes or bottles containing monolayers of monkey kidney

cells. The tissue cultures were then incubated with a nutrient agar overlay at 36°C. A further overlay containing neutral red was later added to distinguish the plaques. The results were recorded in PFU. This method detected only the following viruses that could form plaques in rhesus or cynomulgus monkey kidney cells: the three polioviruses, the six group B Coxsackieviruses, some of the echoviruses, and a few of the group A Coxsackieviruses. This method of ultrafiltration was compared with the 2-day swab ion exchange method for isolation of viruses, using water from the Thames and Lee Rivers. It was found that ultrafiltration of grab samples gave higher recoveries.

Gärtner(*318*) reviewed the origin and application of the soluble ultrafilter in the quantitative recovery of viruses from water and waste water. The retention and recovery of the three types of polioviruses on soluble ultrafilters were also reported by him in this paper. Soluble ultrafilters were prepared from a 1% solution of sodium alginate and a 2:1 mixture of an electrolyte solution (0.5 M solution of lanthanum nitrate and 0.5 M solution of aluminum chloride). The alginate filter formed was capable of withstanding negative pressures up to 700 mm Hg (or 60 mm Hg, absolute), although Gärtner filtered his virus-containing solutions at a negative pressure of about 20 mm Hg (or 740 mm Hg, absolute). The filter itself consisted of three layers, from the bottom up: a primary gel membrane, an intermediate layer, and a capillary zone. The primary gel membrane consisted of a dense layer of horizontally oriented alginate threads, and filter permeability was actually determined by this membrane. The thickness of the primary gel membrane depended on the ions present in the electrolyte solution. The direction of filtration was from the top of the filter through the capillary zone, then through the intermediate network, and finally through the primary gel membrane. Gärtner found that bacteria, bacteriophages, and larger viruses were retained by the intermediate layer and accumulated in the lower parts of the capillary zone. Small viruses, however, were able to penetrate the intermediate layer and reach the primary gel membrane. Three types of water and waste water were examined: drinking water, surface and bathing water, and sewage samples. Poliovirus suspensions were made in all of the water types and filtered through alginate filters. A 3.8% solution of sodium citrate was used to dissolve each filter. It took 1.5 ml of the solution to dissolve a membrane that was 7.5 cm in diameter. Gärtner found that the alginate-citrate solution had no virus-inactivating or cytotoxic activities in primary cultures of human amnion or monkey kidney cells although premature degeneration was observed at times in HeLa cells. Baby mice were not harmed by the solution. Virus recoveries in quantitative studies ranged from 25 to 100%, with an average recovery of 66% in six studies, when 10 liters of tap water seeded with virus were filtered. Gärtner noted that small losses may have been due to the formation of virus aggregates. With this technique the recovery of 10 $TCID_{50}$ from 10 liters of water was possible.

Field studies were conducted by Gärtner(318) from July to September using 31 untreated sewage and effluent samples from purification plants. It was found that 87% of the samples contained viruses when the soluble ultrafilter technique was used. Only 55% were positive for viruses when the samples were inoculated directly into monkey kidney cell cultures. Poliovirus yield, however, was only 22% additional with the use of the ultrafilters. On the other hand, with the ultrafilter technique there was an 80% increase in positive results over the direct inoculation method with Coxsackieviruses, and an increase of 133% with other viruses. It was felt that many of the latter were echo-viruses.

(2) Membrane Filters. Membrane filters with pores smaller in diameter than the viruses being filtered were used by Metcalf(319) to recover influenza viruses from aqueous suspensions. S & S (The Carl Schleicher and Schuell (S & S) Company) filters used were of ultrafine, coarse, and medium grade porosity. The filters obtained from the Millipore Filter Corporation were of the VC (virus coarse), VM (virus medium), and VF (virus fine) types. After filtration the filters were pulped to liberate the contained viruses. Metcalf(319) found, however, that the virus could be washed off the membrane to give comparable recoveries, and he concluded that retention was simply due to deposition of virus on the filter surface. He speculated that electrostatic forces could be involved in virus filtration, since virus was retained to some extent by membranes with greater porosity diameters than the virus. His results showed that when he prefiltered a bacteria- and virus-containing mixture through a bacteria-retaining Millipore HA membrane filter, some loss of the virus also occurred. Retention loss of the virus during filtration varied from an average value of 10% determined by chick embryo infectivity titrations, ID_{50}, to an average value of 7% as measured by hemagglutination tests. Toxicity of the metal surfaces of the filter apparatus to the virus was investigated and found to be negative. Gärtner(318) noted that the main disadvantages of these methods were that the viruses could not be separated from the filter material or that the dissolved filter material was not favorable for culturing.

While investigating the factors involved in the membrane filtration of enteroviruses, Cliver(290) noted adsorption of virus to the membrane matrix regardless of the porosity used. Membrane porosities studied ranged from 50 to 220 nm. This adsorption could be minimized by the incorporation of 2% bovine or chicken serum into the virus suspension before filtration, or by overnight pretreatment of the membranes with serum or 2% gelatin solution. Differences were observed in the behavior of the Gelman and Millipore membranes that were used in Cliver's studies, and were believed to be due to their chemical composition. Gelman membranes are composed of cellulose acetate, whereas Millipore membranes are primarily cellulose nitrate. Cliver(320) later noted: "Because enteroviruses adsorbed to the matrices even of membranes whose pore diameters exceeded the virus diameter, it seemed likely that this adsorption could be put to use." Using the procedure of "membrane chromatography," Cliver(320) did put his previous observation to use and reported the following method for the detection of low levels of enteroviruses in large volumes of water. Although he used additional enteroviruses, results for only Coxsackievirus A9 were presented by him in this study. It was found that 99% or more of Coxsackie A9 suspended in deionized water, tap water, or phosphate-buffered saline was adsorbed onto Millipore HA (not Gelman GA) membranes. The pore diameters could be as great as 0.45 μm, even when the virus suspension was previously passed through a 50-nm filter. Viruses in urine or throat washings were also reported to be adsorbed as efficiently as those in phosphate-buffered saline. Viruses adsorbed to the 25-mm-diameter membranes could be eluted with some 80–90% efficiency when the membranes were soaked with agitation for 30 min in 1 ml of phosphate-buffered saline containing 30–50% agamma chicken serum. On the basis of studies with artificially contaminated tap water, it was concluded that there was at least a 50% probability of detecting virus under the experimental conditions used if 2 PFU are present in a 1-liter sample.

Berman(320a) reported that in tests done at the Robert A. Taft Sanitary Engineering Center, Cincinnati, Ohio, Cliver's results were confirmed. One- and 4-liter volumes of boiled distilled and tap waters that were seeded with less than 100 PFU of virus were filtered through 47-mm-diameter, 0.45-μm Millipore filter membranes. Adsorbed viruses were eluted from the membranes with 5-ml portions of fetal bovine serum. After a 5-min soaking, 5 ml of Earle's balanced salt solution were added, and the mixture was assayed for virus. The results showed a 100% recovery of poliovirus 1 from both the 1- and 4-liter volumes, but some loss occurred in tap water, especially when the 4-liter volume was used. Echovirus 7 was similarly completely recovered from 1- and 4-liter volumes of both tap and distilled water. It was found that the serum used enhanced the titer of this virus, so that it was necessary to titrate the virus initially inoculated into the test waters in the presence of 50% serum.

Otherwise, the amount of virus recovered on the filter would exceed the amount of virus added to the water.

Studies reported by Wallis and Melnick(321,322) in 1967 dealt with concentration of viruses using membrane adsorption techniques. In one report(321) the concentration and detection of viruses in large volumes (usually 3.78 liters) of sewage were investigated using modifications of Cliver's(320) procedure. Basically the method used involved, first, removal of bacteria from sewage samples by preliminary clarification by filtration through a 293-mm-diameter Millipore AP 20 glass-fiber prefilter, followed by passage of the sample through a 293-mm-diameter GS Millipore membrane (0.22-μm porosity). Bacteria were thus removed, whereas enteroviruses passed through and were present in the filtrate. Enteroviruses were not adsorbed due to the presence of membrane-coating components (MCC) in sewage and the hypotonicity of sewage. The problem now was to concentrate the virus onto membranes. This was accomplished by removing the MCC by passage of the sewage through a resin column. Dowex anion resin (50–100 mesh), 1-X8(Cl$^-$), was used in the ratio of 240 g to each 3.78 liters of sewage. The resin was shown not to adsorb virus. The salt concentration of the resin filtrate was also increased with $MgCl_2$ to give a final concentration of 0.05 M. The addition of the latter chemical was found in another study(322) to enhance enterovirus adsorption. The sewage sample was now filtered through a 47-mm or 90-mm-diameter HA Millipore membrane of 0.45-μm porosity. After filtration the membrane was placed in a mortar along with 2 g of Alundum and ground up. Then 4 ml of medium B containing 10% bovine fetal serum were added, and the mixture was triturated again. The resultant homogenate was settled to remove the Alundum, and the supernatant was assayed for virus. According to Wallis and Melnick(321) the procedure provided 1000-fold concentrates of sewage. Comparisons between the direct inoculation of unconcentrated sewage into tissue cultures and the membrane filter procedure used by them were also made. The superiority of their procedure was clearly established when in a 7-month period only four virus strains were isolated from cultures inoculated with unconcentrated sewage, whereas 2795 virus isolates were detected by the membrane adsorption and elution procedure. Ten sewage samples were examined during this period. It was suggested by Wallis and Melnick (321) that virus levels in water and waste water in remote areas could be monitored by the use of their procedure. Viruses could be adsorbed to membranes in the field and be shipped to the laboratory for assay. The membranes could be stabilized in transit by immersing them in 2 M $MgCl_2$. Quantitative recovery from the membranes and 80- to 100-fold concentrations of virus were usually achieved.

Studies done at the Robert A. Taft Sanitary Engineering Center by Berg et al.(275,323), and reported also by Chang(222), confirmed Cliver's (293) work. Their initial procedure with clean water systems was previously discussed(320). In a later investigation(323) of poliovirus 1 removal from secondary effluents by lime flocculation and rapid sand filtration, a modified method was used to detect quantitatively the presence of virus. One-liter water samples were filtered through HA Millipore filters (0.45-μm porosity), although sometimes the water was prefiltered through Millipore fiber glass prefilters. Elution of adsorbed viruses was accomplished by soaking each filter in 5.1 ml of an aqueous solution of 3% beef extract for 30 min. This method was reported to give results similar to those obtained with fetal calf serum, but is less expensive and is a more consistent eluant. A final rinse for 15 min of 5.1 ml of Earle's balanced salt solution was then given to the filter, and the washings were combined with the beef extract. One ml of the resulting 10-ml suspension was inoculated onto each of 10 cell cultures. Only 41–59% of the virus was recovered from a liter of effluent. Chang(222) noted that effluent organic matter might have reduced membrane adsorption sites, as previously reported by Wallis and Melnick(321). It was also suggested(222) that if the water sample was too soft 100 ppm of calcium (as $CaCl_2$) can be added to enhance virus adsorption onto the membrane.

Rao and Labzoffsky(324), based on a suggestion of Chang(222), described a combined fiberglass prefilter pad and membrane filter unit to facilitate the detection and quantitation of low levels of poliovirus 1 in artificially contaminated natural waters. Test samples were passed through both the prefilter and membrane filter in one operation, and then the adsorbed viruses were eluted from each with 3% beef extract in situ, using procedures similar to those previously discussed. Poliovirus was found to be adsorbed to a considerable degree by the prefilters used to clarify turbid waters under the conditions of these experiments. Other investigators(321,323) used prefilters but did not attempt to elute virus from them. The use of this procedure also provided bacteria-free solutions of virus that could be inoculated into tissue cultures without the addition of antibiotics. This was possible because the addition of the beef extract to the surfaces of the in situ filters eluted the adsorbed viruses from both the prefilter and the membrane filter, but left the bacteria behind.

i. Precipitation or Coagulation by Chemicals

(1) Aluminum Phosphate, Aluminum Hydroxide, and Calcium Phosphate Precipitates. Wallis and Melnick(325,326) described a relatively simple method for the concentration of viruses on aluminum phosphate ($AlPO_4$) or aluminum hydroxide [$Al(OH)_3$] precipitates. The usual pro-

cedure was to hold the well-mixed virus-precipitate mixture for 30 min at 25°C, inverting the mixture every 5 min. The precipitate sediment was then removed by centrifugation for 5 min at 2000 rpm, resuspended, and then assayed for virus content. They reported that more than 99% of the test virus, herpes virus, was adsorbed to $AlPO_4$ precipitates at the pH levels tested (6–9 pH), although more virus was removed from the system at 6 pH. The adsorption of herpesvirus to $AlPO_4$ at 25°C was found to be almost immediate, while at other temperatures (4 and 37°C) no effect on the adsorption rate of the virus was observed. It was noted that 0.4 g of $AlPO_4$ adsorbed almost all the herpesvirus present in an undiluted virus solution with a maximum volume of 100 ml and adjusted to 6 pH with HCl. Adsorption studies were also done with representative members of the eight major virus groups. Wallis and Melnick reported that only the acid-sensitive viruses (pox, herpes, myxo, arbo groups, and rhinovirus) were absorbed to $AlPO_4$, whereas almost all the viruses tested were adsorbed on $Al(OH)_3$. Reovirus could not be adsorbed on any of the salts used. Adeno, papova SV_{40}, polio, echo, and Coxsackie viruses were found to be readily adsorbed onto $Al(OH)_3$ but not on $AlPO_4$.

In a study(325) directed toward the detection of small quantities of virus in large volumes of fluid, 5 ml of $Al(OH)_3$ (or 0.25 ml of packed precipitate) suspended in a pH 6 buffer were first added to a 1-liter mixture of saline and virus. The virus in 1 ml of the virus-saline solution could not be detected, but it was calculated that 100 PFU were present in each liter batch. After gentle agitation on a magnetic stirrer for 1 hr at 25°C, the mixture was filtered by vacuum through a 47-mm-diameter HA Millipore filter with a 0.45-μm porosity. The precipitate retained on the membrane surface was suspended in 1 ml of saline and inoculated in 0.1-ml quantities into 10 tissue cultures for assay purposes. The precipitate was found not to be toxic for the tissue culture cells. The following recovery rates were obtained: 80 and 84% for poliovirus, 84% for herpesvirus, 50% for measles virus, and 82% for echovirus 7. In all cases the viruses were concentrated from solutions where they could not be detected by direct inoculation into tissue cultures.

In similar studies by Wallis and Melnick(326), $CaHPO_4$ precipitates were also used to adsorb and thereby concentrate viruses suspended in large volumes of fluid. All the viruses studied, except reovirus, were capable of being concentrated and subsequently detected when adsorbed on $CaHPO_4$.

The above precipitate concentration method is adequate only when small volumes are being examined for virus content. Berg(275) pointed out that the large quantities of chemicals required for each unit volume of water tested limited the volumes of water that could be accommodated.

(2) Protamine Sulfate Precipitation. Protamine sulfate precipitation of extraneous material in a virus-containing suspension, leaving viruses in the supernatant, was initially suggested by Warren et al.(*327*) to be a rapid and effective means for partial purification of those viruses that did not precipitate. Thirteen viruses were examined, eight which were not precipitated by the protamine sulfate and were thus found in the supernatant, and five that were precipitated.

England(*328*) found that she could precipitate reoviruses and adenoviruses, but not most enteroviruses, from waste waters with protamine sulfate, and obtain virus concentrations of up to 250-fold. Protamine sulfate was added as a 1% solution to give a final concentration of 0.05% in samples of sewage or treated effluents. The latter waste waters were previously supplemented with 0.25% bovine albumen. The precipitate containing the viruses was collected by centrifugation or by filtration through a Millipore prefilter pad that was previously treated with 0.1% Tween 80 to prevent virus adsorption to the pad. The harvested precipitate was dissolved in a small volume of $1.0M$ NaCl with the addition of water to achieve isotonicity, and then assayed for virus content.

Berg(*275*) commented that protamine precipitation of larger viruses from $Al(OH)_3$-adsorbed effluents was an important approach to the effective recovery of viruses from heavily contaminated waters.

(3) Alum Flocculation. Aluminum sulfate [alum, $Al_2(SO_4)_3 \cdot 18H_2O$] flocculation was used for the concentration of Coxsackievirus from dilute suspensions(*329*) and was found to be superior to the ion exchange resin adsorption technique of Kelly(*270*). It was found by Stevenson et al.(*329*) that it was possible to detect as little as $0.00625LD_{50}/0.02$ ml in the starting water, where the LD_{50} is a measure of the amount of virus that will kill within a stated period of time 50% of the animals inoculated. In their procedure floc formation occurred in 600-ml beakers that contained, in order of addition, 370.8 ml of sterile distilled water, 0.4 ml of SiO_2 suspension, 10 ml of tryptose broth, 10 ml of $NaHCO_3$, and 1 ml of the diluted virus. After the mixture had been stirred for 2 min, 7.8 ml of a 1% solution of $Al_2(SO_4)_3 \cdot 18H_2O$ were added and floc formation was observed within 1 or 2 min. After 30 min of stirring, the floc was settled for 60–90 min, and the supernatant fluid was separated from the floc by suction. The floc was then concentrated by low speed centrifugation, resuspended in a buffer of appropriate pH, and held at room temperature for 1–3 hr with intermittent agitation. There were no significant differences when floc redispersing fluid at different pH values (7.9, 8.5, and 8.9) was used for recovery of viruses from the flocs formed with 100 ppm of aluminum sulfate, and a 1- or 3-hr redispersing time. However, the $NaHCO_3$-HCl buffer at pH 7.5 was not effective in virus separation from the floc.

j. Adsorption and Subsequent Elution

(1) Insoluble Polyelectrolytes. Berg(275) in a state of the art report noted that "there is another filtration approach currently in a state of reincarnation that offers promise for quantitative recovery of viruses from water—the ion exchange resin, more voguishly, the insoluble polyelectrolyte."

Johnson et al.(330) investigated some insoluble polyelectrolytes and found that they adsorbed 100% of tobacco mosaic virus and more than 99.99% of poliovirus from aqueous suspensions. Polyelectrolytes used were polymers based on divinylbenzene cross-linked styrene or maleic anhydride copolymers. Their procedure consisted of placing 100 mg of cationic polyelectrolyte derivatives in contact with 0.5 ml of virus suspension in 4.5 ml of distilled water. The resultant mixture was agitated on a shaker at room temperature for 1 hr and filtered through filter paper, and the filtrate was assayed for virus content. They found in preliminary studies that the 100% imide methyl iodide quaternary salt was most effective in removal of essentially all the tobacco mosaic virus. The critical variables involved in virus removal using polyelectrolytes were stated as (i) the ratio of virus to polymer, (ii) time of contact, (iii) particle size (i.e., surface area) of the adsorbent, and (iv) degree and type of derivatization. One great advantage of polyelectrolytes is their avid adsorptive capacity.

Jonnson et al.(330) eluted a polymer-virus complex by shaking for 1 hr with 5 ml of 1 *M* NaCl, and found that 52% of adsorbed virus was liberated from the polymer. This was important in demonstrating the regenerative capacity of the polyelectrolytes if they were to be practical in water treatment, and the possible use of these polymers for the concentration and subsequent detection of the eluted virus. Further adsorptive studies showed that an animal virus (poliovirus) behaved in a fashion similar to that of the tobacco mosaic virus already described. The authors pointed out that they could not ascertain whether the loss of virus infectivity was due to polymer adsorption or inactivation of the virus by the presence of the polymer. However, they pointed out that other studies have shown that viable virus can be eluted from ion exchange resin-virus complexes.

Studies by Wallis et al.(331) compared three methods for concentration and subsequent detection of viruses from sewage and excreta. The insoluble polyelectrolyte method was found to be superior to the aluminum hydroxide and the cellulose membrane procedures both in the efficiency of recovery and in the time required for sample processing, as shown in Table 8. The procedure used by them consisted of adding 400 mg of PE 60 (an insoluble, cross-linked copolymer of isobutylene and maleic anhydride, 100-mesh powder) to each gallon sample of clarified (solid-free)

TABLE 8
Comparison of Three Methods for Concentration
and Recovery of Poliovirus Added to Sewage[a]

Method	Processing time, hr	Recovery, %
None	None	0
Al(OH)$_3$	3.5	56
Cellulose membrane	3.0	64
PE 60[b]	1.25	93

[a]From Ref. 331.
[b]An involuble, cross-linked copolymer of isobutylene and maleic anhydride, used as a 100-mesh powder (Monsanto Co., St. Louis, Mo.).

sewage, and then adjusting the acidity to pH 5.5–6.0 with HCl to enhance virus adsorption on the polyelectrolyte. The AP20 fiber glass pads used for clarification were pretreated with 200 ml of 10% fetal calf serum to prevent virus adsorption. Unpublished data of Wallis, Melnick, and Fields, cited in Ref.(331), showed that PE 60 preferentially adsorbed viruses in the presence of organic compounds, and thus the removal of the organic compounds on ion exchange resins wasn't necessary. The PE 60-virus mixture was stirred at 25°C for 1 hr and then filtered through a 47-mm-diameter fiber glass pad to harvest the polyelectrolytes on the pad. Virus was eluted off the harvested polyelectrolytes in a tube by addition of 3–5 ml of 10% fetal calf serum in either pH 8 phosphate buffer or pH 9 borate buffer. After centrifugation at 500 g for 5 min, the supernatant fluid was passed through a serum-pretreated 0.22-μm Millipore membrane to remove bacteria but allow the passage of viruses. The resultant sterile filtrate was then assayed for virus content.

An apparatus for field studies was assembled by Wallis et al.(331) that consisted of 1 g of polyelectrolytes packed to give a 1- to 1.5-mm-thick layer of polyelectrolytes sandwiched between two 90-mm-diameter fiber glass pads that were held together in a Millipore filter holder. When a gallon of sewage was passed through, the top fiber glass pad removed solids, while the polyelectrolyte layer removed viruses from the sample. The polyelectrolytes were treated as previously discussed, and then assayed. The latter field procedure was shown to give virus recoveries that were similar to their previously described "standard" method. Although their apparatus was adequate for 1-gal samples, when larger volumes (50–100 gal) of sewage or other natural fluids were to be used Wallis et al.(331) anticipated difficulties. A larger filtration setup (293-mm-diameter) containing about 8 g of PE 60 would provide rapid and efficient adsorption of viruses but would present a problem when the virus was eluted from the polyelectrolytes, since larger volumes of eluant would be needed.

They met this problem by reconcentration of the virus from a larger eluant volume with a second polyelectrolyte, PE 52. The latter was an insoluble cross-linked polyelectrolyte, based on ethylene-maleic anhydride. This polymer can adsorb viruses in the presence of proteins (such as the serum eluant) in hypotonic fluids, but viruses will not adsorb to PE 52 in the presence of isotonic salt solutions. Thus, PE 52 was used to reconcentrate virus eluted from PE 60, and then this adsorbed virus was eluted with isotonic salt solutions. Their procedure included, first, elution of adsorbed virus from PE 60 with 200 ml of 5% fetal calf serum in distilled water adjusted to pH 9 with NaOH. The eluted virus in the filtrate was then concentrated on PE 52 for 1 hr at 25°C with stirring, and then the suspension was centrifuged. The PE 52 pellet was treated with 3 ml of saline with vigorous mixing for 15 sec to elute the adsorbed virus. After centrifugation, the 3-ml supernatant fluid, now the PE 52 eluate, was treated with 0.3 ml of undiluted fetal calf serum to prevent virus adsorption to Millipore membranes (0.22 μm) during filtration to remove bacteria. An efficient recovery of virus added to sewage was obtained by Wallis et al.(*331*) using this method.

Berg(*275*) reported that when small amounts of viruses in 1-liter volumes of distilled water were concentrated using the aforementioned method of Wallis et al.(*331*), relatively poor recoveries resulted. Poliovirus 1 recovery sometimes was over 80%, whereas that of echovirus 7 was sometimes lower than 30% and reovirus 1 was sometimes lower than 20%. However, Berg(*275*) concluded that despite the low and erratic efficiency of the polyelectrolyte method, it appeared to be the most sensitive technique available in 1970 for large volumes of water.

(2) Magnetic Iron Oxide. Based on the studies of Warren et al.(*350*), Rao et al.(*332*) described a method for the concentration and detection of small numbers of viruses in large volumes of water using a magnetic iron oxide (MO 2530) adsorption system. Their procedure involved passing virus suspensions through 25 g of magnetic iron oxide in a glass column at a flow rate of 25 ml/min, and then eluting the adsorbed virus with a 3% beef extract solution or fetal calf serum that was adjusted to pH 8. In studies with Coxsackievirus A9, a 500-ml water sample containing 100 PFU of the virus was passed through the column, the virus was eluted with beef extract, and the eluate was assayed. Three other iron oxides, including a nonmagnetic one, were studied, but MO 2530 was the easiest to work with and gave the best results. In experiments with high virus loads, 45,000 PFU of Coxsackievirus A9 in 500 ml of water were passed through a column of MO 2530 iron oxide, and the column was

flushed with 20 liters of tap water at a flow rate of 25 ml/min. No virus was detected in the tap water effluent, indicating that the adsorbed virus could not be washed away by large volumes of sample water. After the virus adsorbed to the iron oxide in the column was eluted as previously described, about 87% of Coxsackievirus A9 was recovered from the eluate. However, in other experiments virus recovery was not as great at virus input levels of less than 12 PFU/ml when 25 g of iron oxide and flow rates of 25 ml/min were used. When the flow rates were lowered to 10 ml/min and only 5 g of iron oxide were used, a greater virus recovery was observed at low virus input levels. Tests were done with a variety of different-sized viruses containing either DNA or RNA, and the results indicated complete virus removal from water. In studies with sewage effluent, river water, and tap water, seeded Coxsackievirus A9 removals were found to be 93.5, 70.6, and 86%, respectively. The Committee on Viruses in Water(274) recommended this procedure for detection of viruses in water as one deserving of further investigation.

(3) Adsorption on Activated Carbon. Cookson and North(333) and Cookson(334) have studied the mechanism of virus adsorption on activated carbon, using the T4 coliphage as the test virus. The latter were not inactivated by adsorption or desorption. The kinetics of bacteriophage T4 adsorption on activated carbon was described as a reversible second-order equation. Adsorption was first-order with both virus concentration and carbon sites. They noted that adsorption obeyed the Langmuir isotherm and was reversible. However, there was inefficient use of the available carbon surface area for coliphage adsorption. Desorption was accomplished by the addition of tryptone broth to the activated carbon-virus complex. They found that adsorption was best at pH 7 and an ionic strength of 0.08.

H. Detection of Bacterial Viruses

The methods discussed in Sec. II.G of this chapter may also be applicable for bacteriophages. In fact, several of the methods described in the above section were evaluated by the use of bacterial viruses. In this section, therefore, I limit my discussion to two techniques that have been reported to improve the recovery of low levels of bacteriophages from solutions without the necessity of concentration to improve detection.

1. FILTRATION METHOD

Loehr and Schwegler(335) described a filtration method for bacteriophage detection involving membrane filtration of the sample. The T2 coliphage was used in these investigations. Their procedure was to filter a diluted T2 bacteriophage-*E. coli* mixture through Millipore membrane filters, presumably of 0.45-μm porosity. The filter was removed and incubated at 37°C on an absorbent pad previously saturated with M-Endo broth. After 24 hr the plaques that developed on the membrane surface were enumerated. One of the shortcomings of the method, as pointed out by the authors, was that only phage that had adsorbed to host cells before filtration were measurable. Unadsorbed coliphage would pass through the filter and not be counted. The filtration method produced titers that were lower by a factor of about 20 than those obtained by the soft agar technique of Adams (*335a*). However, the authors felt that their filtration method was useful when low levels of bacteriophages were present in a solution, since any quantity of liquid could be passed through the membrane.

2. MOST PROBABLE NUMBER

A most probable number procedure was reported by Kott (*336*) for estimation of low numbers of coliphages in large volumes of fluid. The method used made it possible to detect as low as two bacteriophages/100 ml of sample. Kott's procedure involved planting 10 ml of a seawater sample into each of five tubes of double-strength phage assay base (PAB) broth. A second set of five tubes containing 10 ml of single-strength PAB broth were inoculated with 1 ml of the seawater sample, and a third set of five tubes containing 10 ml of single-strength PAB broth were inoculated with 1 ml of a 1:10 dilution of the seawater sample. Each of the tubes was inoculated with the host, *E. coli* B culture, and the tubes were incubated at 37°C for about 16 hr. After incubation a loopful of the broth from each tube was streaked on the surface of freshly seeded *E. coli* B PAB agar plates, and these were incubated for 6 hr at 35°C. The plaques that developed were enumerated, and the most probable number tables for total coliforms in *Standard Methods* (*23*) were consulted to estimate the most probable number of bacteriophages present in the seawater sample. Comparisons with the direct plaque counts were good.

III. Future Methodology

There are many additional promising methods described in the literature that may prove useful in detection and quantitation of both indicator and pathogenic species or strains of bacteria and viruses in water and waste water. For instance, Levin et al. (337) proposed a rapid method for total counts of microbes in aerospace potable water systems that utilized the bioluminescent reaction of the firefly to assess the presence of microbial-containing adenosine triphosphate (ATP). Oleniacz et al. (338) described a chemiluminescent method for the detection of microbes in water that was based on the measurement of light emission resulting from the interaction of microbial cells with alkaline luminol in the presence of sodium perborate or sodium pyrophosphate peroxide. Rogers and Purcell (339) studied spectrophotofluorometric methods for rapid, sensitive identification of bacteria, and suggested their usefulness in the examination of bacteria in polluted waters or waste-processing operations. Gas chromatography is another exciting technique that has shown promise in detecting the presence of specific bacteria by their metabolic products. Since distinctive chromatographic patterns are found for each of the bacteria examined, it may be possible to determine not only total numbers but also what specific bacteria or other microbes are present in a water sample after isolation of pure cultures (340,341). Cecchini and O'Brien (342) described a procedure for differentiating E. coli from other bacteria by direct gas chromatographic analysis of the culture media. Fluorescent antibody (FA) detecting of microbes when they are exposed to homologous-labeled antibody labeled with fluorescein dyes is becoming increasingly popular for both bacteria and viruses (121) and may have future utility in water pollution control (343). For example, a membrane filter-fluorescent antibody method for the detection and enumeration of bacteria (E. coli) in water has been described by Guthrie and Reeder (344). The research of Stevens and Watkins (345) points the way to rapid identification of viruses using the technique of immunofluorescence. Levin et al. (346) first reported in 1956 a rapid radioactive test for coliform organisms using ^{14}C that appears to hold much promise for the future. Their test depended upon the report by Roberts et al. (347) that 86% of the carbon utilized by E. coli as formate was converted to CO_2, and on the use of formate ricinoleate broth for the detection of coliform organisms in milk, water, and other substances of sanitary significance.

The carbon-14 radioisotopic technique for the detection of fecal pollution of water supplies can be completed in 4 hr and is of definite value in times of emergency. [See Ref. 348 for a complete discussion on the advantages of this technique.] However, this procedure at this time does not allow us to compare pollution sources or to quantitatively determine levels of pollution. The use of the electron microscope to examine bacteria of pollutional significance after lactose broth cultivation has also been suggested by Baylis and Scarce (349).

The development of new methodology in the field of water microbiology is progressing rapidly. However, not all new methods need be an improvement and a final solution of old problems. The age of a technique should not be the sole criterion for its demise. In this chapter I have attempted to review the old, the present, and the possible future techniques in this area that have been, are, and may be relevant, with a strong emphasis on the present. A quick, easy, one-step technique has obviously never been found to assay at one time for the presence of all polution-significant bacteria and viruses in a water sample. Perhaps the latter goal will never be realized, and may not be really necessary. However, the problems inherent in simply the collection of a representative water sample and its subsequent transport in an unaltered state to the laboratory for analysis do merit a considerably more detailed study. After all, the investigator's final interpretation of the bacterial and viral quality of a water is only as valid as the initial proper selection and subsequent handling (including storage) of the water sample. If the sample is not representative of the body of water from which it was originally obtained, or if its transport to the laboratory was beset with questionable practices and delays, the significance of careful laboratory analysis is very difficult to determine. Although the methods presently employed do provide a reasonable, practical measure of safety to the user, the search for more rapid and exact methods for the assay of pollution-significant bacteria and viruses in water and waste water needs to be continued. The formulation of a standard method and a minimum standard for enterovirus levels in water is also badly needed. Methods should be constantly reevaluated to determine their relevancy in light of newer knowledge, and they should be discarded, improved upon, or replaced, as appears most reasonable. Methods established for analysis of bacteria and viruses in water should never be looked upon as sacred cows, but should be continuously reviewed. Methods for the analysis of bacteria and viruses in water and waste water, it should be constantly recalled, are only a means to an end (the safety of the user) and not an end in themselves.

REFERENCES

1. W. Bullock, *The History of Bacteriology,* Oxford University Press, London, 1960.
2. J. Snow, *Snow on Cholera,* Hafner, New York, 1965.
3. A. E. Greenberg and H. J. Ongerth, *J. Am. Water Works Assoc.,* **58**, 1145 (1966).
4. G. Berg (ed.) *Transmission of Viruses by the Water Route,* Wiley, New York, 1967.
5. J. D. Mosley, Ref. *4,* pp. 5–23.
6. L. Coin, M. L. Menetrier, J. Labonde, and M. C. Hannoun, in *Advances in Water Pollution Research* (O. Jaag, ed.), Vol. 1, Pergamon, Oxford, 1967, pp. 1–10.
7. L. Coin, in *Transmission of Viruses by the Water Route* (G. Berg, ed.), Wiley, New York, 1967, pp. 367–368.

8. G. Berg, Ref. *4*, p. 462.
9. S. L. Chang, *J. Am. Water Works Assoc.*, **53**, 288 (1961).
10. G. T. Moore, W. M. Cross, D. McGuire, C. S. Mollohan, N. N. Gleason, G. R. Healy, and L. H. Newton, *New Engl. J. Med.*, **281**, 402 (1969).
11. W. Burrows, J. W. Moulder, and R. M. Lewert, *Textbook of Microbiology* 18th ed., W. B. Saunders, Philadelphia, 1963.
12. S. L. Chang, *J. Am. Water Works Assoc.*, **53**, 288 (1961).
13. U.S. Bureau of the Census, *Statistical Abstracts of the United States: 1969*, 90th ed., Washington, D.C., 1969.
14. Committee on Pollution, *Waste Management and Control, Publ. 1400*, National Academy of Sciences and National Research Council, Washington, D.C., 1966.
15. World Health Organization, *Chron. World Health Organ.* **22**, 362 (1968).
16. World Health Organization Expert Committee on Water Pollution Control in Developing Countries, *World Health Organ. Tech. Rept. Ser.*, No. 404 (1968). Report discussed in *Chron. World Health Organ.* **23**, 173 (1969).
17. J. M. Dennis, *J. Am. Water Works Assoc.*, **51**, 1288 (1959).
18. S. R. Weibel, F. R. Dixon, R. B. Weidner, and L. J. McCabe, *J. Am. Water Works Assoc.*, **56**, 947 (1964).
19. L. Červa and K. Novák, *Science*, **160**, 92 (1968).
20. L. Červa, V. Zimák, and K. Novák, *Science*, **163**, 575 (1969).
21. D. F. Spino, *Appl. Microbiol.*, **14**, 591 (1966).
22. F. T. Brezenski, R. Russomanno, and P. DeFalco, *Health Lab. Sci.*, **2**, 40 (1965).
23. *Standard Methods for the Examination of Water and Wastewater*, 12th ed., American Public Health Association, New York, 1965.
24. *Public Health Service Drinking Water Standards, Publ. No. 956*, Public Health Service, Washington, D.C., 1962.
25. National Technical Advisory Committee, *Water Quality Criteria*, Federal Water Pollution Control Administration, Washington, D.C., 1968.
26. *Standard Methods for the Examination of Water and Wastewater*, 13th ed., American Public Health Association, New York, in press.
27. G. J. Bonde, *Bacterial Indicators of Water Pollution*, 2nd ed., Teknisk Forlag, Copenhagen, 1963, p. 422.
28. G. J. Bonde, *Health Lab. Sci.*, **3**, 124 (1966).
29. *International Standards for Drinking Water*, 2nd ed., World Health Organization, Geneva, Switzerland, 1963.
30. D. A. A. Mossel, in *Intern. Congr. Microbiol., 7th Congr., Rept. Proc.*, Stockholm, Sweden, 1958, p. 440.
31. H. Gyllenberg and S. Niemelä, *J. Sci. Agr. Soc. Finland (Maataloustieteellinen Aikakauskirja)*, **31**, 94 (1959).
32. H. Gyllenberg, S. Niemelä, and T. Sormunen, *Appl. Microbiol.*, **8**, 20 (1960).
33. *Difco Manual*, 9th ed., Difco Laboratories, Inc., Detroit, Mich., 1953.
34. *Difco Supplementary Literature*, Difco Laboratories, Inc., Detroit, Mich., 1966.
35. *B.B.L. Products*, 4th ed., Baltimore Biological Laboratory, Inc., Baltimore, Md., 1956.
36. P. A. Rohde, ed., *B.B.L. Manual of Products and Laboratory Procedures*, 5th ed., Bio Quest, Division of Becton, Dickinson, and Co., Cockeysville, Maryland, 1968.
37. A. Goetz, *Fiat Rev. Ger. Sci.*, Rept. 1312 (1947).
38. A. Goetz and N. Tsuneishi, *J. Am. Water Works Assoc.*, **43**, 943 (1951).
39. R. Zsigmondy and W. Bachman, *Z. Anorg. Allgem. Chem.*, **103**, 119 (1918).
40. H. F. Clark, E. E. Geldreich, H. L. Jeter, and P. W. Kabler, *Public Health Rept.*, **66**, 951 (1951).

41. Standard Methods for the Examination of Water, Sewage, and Industrial Wastes, 10th ed., American Public Health Association, New York, 1955.

42. E. E. Geldreich, H. L. Jeter, and J. A. Winter, *Health Lab. Sci.*, **4**, 113 (1967).

43. R. Koch, *Deut. Ärtzblatt*, **137**, 244 (1883) (in German); in *Microbiology* (R. N. Doetsch, ed.), Rutgers Univ. Press, New Brunswick, N.J., 1960, pp. 122–131 (English transl.).

44. Committee on Standard Methods of Water Analysis, *Standard Methods of Water Analysis*, 1st ed., American Public Health Association, New York, 1905.

45. *Ibid.*, 2nd ed., 1912.

46. *Ibid.*, 5th ed., 1923.

47. Standard Methods for the Examination of Water and Sewage, 6th ed., American Public Health Association, New York, 1925.

48. Ministry of Health, *The Bacteriological Examination of Water Supplies*, revised ed., Rept. Public Health and Medical Subjects, No. 71, London, 1939.

49. Standard Methods for the Examination of Water and Sewage, 9th ed., American Public Health Association, New York, 1946.

50. H. F. Clark, H. L. Jeter, E. E. Geldreich, and P. W. Kabler, *J. Am. Water Works Assoc.*, **44**, 1052 (1952).

51. *Microbiological Analysis of Water*, Application Rept. AR-81, Millipore Corp. Bedford, Mass., 1969.

52. G. M. Cooke, E. Duffy, and H. Wolochow, *Stain Technol.*, **32**, 63 (1957).

53. R. E. Ecker and W. R. Lockhart, *J. Bacteriol.*, **77**, 173 (1959).

54. P. W. Kabler, *J. Am. Water Works Assoc.*, **43**, 969 (1951).

55. *Evaluation of Water Laboratories*, Publ. No. 999-EE-1, Public Health Service, Washington, D.C., 1966.

56. Recommended Practice for Design, Equipment and Operation of Swimming Pools and Other Public Bathing Places, 10th ed., American Public Health Association, New York, 1957.

57. Suggested Ordinance and Regulations Covering Public Swimming Pools, American Public Health Association, New York, 1964.

57a. E. Hormaeche and P. R. Edwards, *Intern. Bull. Bacteriol. Nomenclature and Taxonomy*, **10**, 71 (1960).

58. F. Kauffmann, *Zentr. Bakteriol. Parasitenk., I. Orig.*, **165**, 344 (1956).

59. F. Kauffmann, P. R. Edwards, and W. H. Ewing, *Intern. Bull. Bacteriol. Nomenclature and Taxonomy*, **6**, 29 (1956).

60. P. R. Edwards and W. H. Ewing, *Identification of Enterobacteriaceae*, Burgess, Minneapolis, 1962, p. 258.

61. M. Grimes and A. J. Hennerty, *Sci. Proc. Roy. Dublin Soc.*, **20** (N.S.), 89 (1931).

62. E. K. Borman, C. A. Stuart, and K. M. Wheeler, *J. Bactoriol.*, **48**, 351 (1944).

63. V. Moeller, *Acta Pathol. Microbiol. Scand.*, **35**, 259 (1954).

64. P. H. A. Sneath and V. B. D. Skerman, *Intern. J. Systematic Bacteriol.*, **16**, 1 (1966).

65. T. Rosebury, *Microorganisms Indigenous to Man*, McGraw-Hill, New York, 1962.

66. W. Litsky, W. L. Mallmann, and 'C. W. Fifield, *Am. J. Public Health*, **43**, 873 (1953).

67. H. F. Clark and P. W. Kabler, *J. Am. Water Works Assoc.*, **56**, 931 (1964).

68. P. W. Kabler and H. F. Clark, *J. Am. Water Works Assoc.*, **52**, 1577 (1960).

69. P. W. Kabler, H. F. Clark, and E. E. Geldreich, *Public Health Rept.*, **79**, 58 (1964).

70. C. B. Taylor, *J. Hyg.*, **41**, 17 (1941).

71. S. C. Prescott, C. E. A. Winslow, and M. H. McCrady, *Water Bacteriology*, 6th ed., Wiley, New York, 1946, pp. 80–84.

72. A. J. Salle, *Fundamental Principles of Bacteriology*, 6th ed., McGraw-Hill, New York, 1967, pp. 533–534.

73. J. E. Holt-Harris and O. Teague, *J. Infectious Diseases*, **18**, 596 (1916).

74. M. Levine, *J. Infectious Diseases*, **23**, 43 (1918).

75. M. Levine, *J. Am. Water Works Assoc.*, **8**, 151 (1921).

76. E. S. Wynne, L. J. Rode, and A. E. Hayward, *Stain Technol.*, **17**, 11 (1942).

77. S. Endo, *Zentr. Bakteriol. Parasitenk., I. Orig.*, **35**, 109 (1904).

78. C. Neuberg and F. F. Nord, *Biochem. Z.*, **96**, 133 (1919).

79. L. A. Margolena and P. A. Hansen, *Stain Technol.*, **8**, 131 (1933).

80. *Standard Methods for the Examination of Water and Wastewater*, 11th ed., American Public Health Association, New York, 1960.

81. H. F. Clark, P. W. Kabler, and E. E. Geldreich, *Water Sewage Works*, **104**, 385 (1957).

82. E. L. Shipe and A. Fields, *Appl. Microbiol.*, **2**, 382 (1954).

83. E. E. Geldreich, H. F. Clark, and P. W. Kabler, 55th Annual Meeting, American Water Works Association, Indianapolis, Ind., February, 1963.

84. C. C. Croft and G. H. Eagle, *Acceptance of the Membrane Filter Procedure for the Bacteriological Examination of Water*, Announcement, State of Ohio, Department of Health, Columbus, October 16, 1961.

85. E. L. Shipe and G. M. Cameron, *Appl. Microbiol.*, **2**, 85, (1954).

86. A. J. Gaspar and J. M. Leise, *J. Bacteriol.*, **71**, 728 (1956).

87. A. J. Gaspar and J. M. Leise, *Bacteriol. Proc. (Soc. Am. Bacteriologists)*, 1956, p. 31.

88. R. D. Cahn, *Science*, **155**, 195 (1967).

89. G. B. Morgan, P. Gubbins, and V. Morgan, *Health Lab. Sci.*, **2**, 227 (1965).

90. P. Kabler, *Am. J. Public Health*, **44**, 379 (1954).

91. H. A. Thomas, R. L. Woodward, and P. W. Kabler, *J. Am. Water Works Assoc.*, **48**, 1391 (1956).

92. L. W. Slanetz and C. H. Bartley, *Appl. Microbiol.*, **3**, 46 (1955).

93. E. E. Geldreich, *Water Sewage Works*, **114**, R98 (1967).

94. E. E. Geldreich, *Sanitary Significance of Fecal Coliforms in the Environment*, *Publ. WP-20-3*, Federal Water Pollution Control Administration, 1966.

95. A. A. Hajna and C. A. Perry, *Am. J. Public Health*, **33**, 552 (1943).

96. C. A. Perry and A. A. Hajna, *Am. J. Public Health*, **34**, 735 (1944).

96a. E. E. Geldreich, H. F. Clark, C. B. Huff, and L. C. Best, *J. Am. Water Works Assoc.*, **57**, 208 (1965).

97. S. C. Prescott, C. E. A. Winslow, and M. H. McCrady, *Water Bacteriology*, 6th ed., Wiley, New York, 1946, pp. 212–215.

98. W. Morris and R. H. Weaver, *Appl. Microbiol.*, **2**, 282 (1954).

99. T. F. Medrek and W. Litsky, *Appl. Microbiol.*, **8**, 60 (1960).

100. J. O. Mundt, J. H. Coggin, and L. F. Johnson, *Appl. Microbiol.*, **10**, 552 (1962).

101. E. E. Geldreich, B. A. Kenner, and P. W. Kabler, *Appl. Microbiol.*, **12**, 63 (1964).

102. E. E. Geldreich, L. C. Best, B. A. Kenner, and D. J. Van Donsel, *J. Water Pollution Control Federation*, **40**, 1861 (1968).

103. E. E. Geldreich and B. A. Kenner, *J. Water Pollution Control Federation*, **41**, R336 (1969).

104. E. E. Geldreich, *J. Am. Water Works Assoc.*, **62**, 113 (1970).

105. L. W. Slantez, D. F. Bent, and C. H. Bartley, *Public Health Rept.*, **70**, 67 (1955).

106. L. W. Slantez and C. H. Bartley, *J. Bacteriol.*, **74**, 591 (1957).

107. B. A. Kenner, H. F. Clark, and P. W. Kabler, *Appl. Microbiol.*, **9**, 15 (1961).

108. W. H. Welch and G. H. F. Nuttal, *Bull. Johns Hopkins Hosp.*, **3**, 81 (1892).

109. R. S. Breed, E. G. D. Murray, N. R. Smith, and ninety-four contributors, *Bergey's*

Manual of Determinative Bacteriology, 7th ed., Williams and Wilkins, Baltimore, 1957, p. 1094.

110. A. T. Willis, *J. Appl. Bacteriol.*, **20**, 61 (1957).

111. S. C. Prescott, C. E. A. Winslow, and M. H. McCrady, *Water Bacteriology*, 6th ed., Wiley, New York, 1946, pp. 224–237.

112. A. A. Hajna, *Public Health Lab.*, **9**, 23 (1951).

113. B. Moore, E. L. Perry, and T. S. Chard, *J. Hyg.*, **50**, 137 (1952).

114. R. Ferramola, R. H. Leiguardia, E. M. Ansiaume, O. A. Peso, and A. Z. Palazzola, *Rev. Obras. Sanit. Nación* (Buenos Aires), **33**, 94 (1954).

115. S. M. Kelly, M. E. Clark, and M. B. Coleman, *Am. J. Public Health*, **45**, 1438 (1955).

116. J. E. Jameson, *J. Hyg.*, **60**, 193 (1962).

117. H. Raj, *Appl. Microbiol.*, **14**, 12 (1966).

118. E. E. Geldreich, in Literature Review, Microbiology, *J. Water Pollution Control Federation*, **41**, 1053–1069 (1969).

119. W. I. Taylor, *Bacteriol. Proc. (Soc. Am. Bacteriologists)*, 1964, p. 55.

120. A. A. Hajna, *Public Health Lab.*, **13**, 59 (1955).

121. J. E. Blair, E. H. Lennette, and J. P. Truant, eds., *Manual of Clinical Microbiology*, American Society for Microbiology, Bethesda, Md., 1970, p. 727.

122. B. M. Gibbs and F. A. Skinner, *Identification Methods for Microbiologists*, Academic, New York, 1968, Part A, p. 211; Part B, p. 145.

123. V. B. D. Skerman, *A Guide to the Identification of the Genera of Bacteria*, Williams and Wilkins, Baltimore, 1967, p. 303.

124. W. P. Dunbar, *Z. Hyg. Infektionskrankh.*, **21**, 295 (1896).

125. W. P. Dunbar, *Gesundh. Arb.*, **10**, 142 (1896).

126. E. K. Dunham, *Z. Hyg. Infektionskrankh.*, **2**, 337 (1887).

127. O. Felsenfeld, *Bull. World Health Organ.*, **34**, 161 (1966).

128. K. H. Lewis and L. F. Rettger, *J. Bacteriol.*, **40**, 287 (1940).

129. B. D. Davis, R. Dulbecco, H. N. Eisen, H. S. Ginsberg, and W. B. Wood, *Microbiology*, Harper and Row, New York, 1968, p. 1464.

130. A. H. Eggerth and B. H. Gagnon, *J. Bacteriol.*, **25**, 389 (1933).

131. L. Zubrzycki and E. H. Spaulding, *J. Bacteriol.*, **83**, 968 (1962).

132. F. J. Post, A. D. Allen, and T. C. Reid, *Appl. Microbiol.*, **15**, 213 (1967).

133. F. Kauffmann, *J. Immunol.*, **57**, 71 (1947).

134. F. Kauffmann and A. Dupont, *Acta Pathol. Microbiol. Scand.*, **27**, 552 (1950).

135. F. Kauffmann, *The Bacteriology of the Enterobacteriaceae*, E. Munksgaard, Copenhagen, 1966.

136. R. Seigneurin, R. Magnin, and M. L. Achard, *Ann. Inst. Pasteur*, **89**, 473 (1951).

137. N. Peterson and J. R. Boring, *Am. J. Hyg.*, **71**, 134 (1960).

138. W. H. Ewing, *J. Infectious Diseases*, **110**, 114 (1962).

139. B. D. Davis, R. Dulbecco, H. N. Eisen, H. S. Ginsberg, and W. B. Wood, *Microbiology*, Hoeber Medical Division of Harper and Row, New York, 1968, pp. 893–896.

140. G. S. Wilson and A. A. Miles, *Topley and Wilson's Principles of Bacteriology and Immunity*, Vol. 2, Williams and Wilkins, Baltimore, 1964, pp. 2190–2206.

141. A. D. Alexander, in *Manual of Clinical Microbiology* (J. E. Blair, E. H. Lennette, and J. P. Truant, eds.), American Society for Microbiology, Bethesda, Md., 1970, Chap. 30.

142. R. W. H. Gillespie and J. Ryno, *Am. J. Public Health*, **53**, 950 (1963).

143. R. C. Johnson and P. Rogers, *J. Bacteriol.*, **88**, 1618 (1964).

144. J. L. Braun and W. F. McCulloch, *Appl. Microbiol.*, **16**, 174 (1968).

145. S. L. Chang, M. Buckingham, and M. P. Taylor, *J. Infectious Diseases*, **82**, 256 (1948).

146. N. M. Blagoveshchenskaya and K. F. Goncharova, *Gigiena Sanit.*, **24**, 12 (1959).
147. D. Smith and H. Self, *J. Hyg.*, **53**, 436 (1955).
148. C. E. G. Smith and L. H. Turner, *Bull. World Health Organ.*, **24**, 35 (1961).
149. J. M. Appelman and P. H. van Thiel, *Zentr. Bakteriol. Parasitenk.*, **133**, 244 (1935).
150. J. Pokorny and O. Havlik, *Geskoslov epidemiol. Mikrobiol. Immunol.*, **6**, 204 (1951); abstr. in *Bull. Hyg.*, **32**, 1197 (1957).
151. M. B. Rittenberg, W. D. Linscott, and M. G. Ball, *J. Bacteriol.*, **76**, 669, (1958).
152. J. L. Braun, *Dissertation Abstr.*, **27**, 2973 (1967).
153. C. D. Cox and A. D. Larson, *J. Bacteriol.*, **73**, 587 (1957).
154. R. Yanagawa, personal communication, 1960, Bacteriology Section, The National Institute of Animal Health, Tokyo; cited by M. M. Galton, *Ann. N.Y. Acad. Sci.*, **98**, 675–685 (1962).
155. J. B. Baseman, R. C. Henneberry, and C. D. Cox, *J. Bacteriol.*, **91**, 1374 (1966).
156. B. D. Davis, R. Dulbecco, H. N. Eisen, H. S. Ginsberg, and W. B. Wood, *Microbiology*, Herber Medical Division of Harper and Row, New York, 1968, pp. 865–867.
157. K. W. Newell, *Bull. World Health Organ.*, **34**, 827 (1966).
158. R. C. Cochrane, (ed.), *Leprosy in Theory and Practice*, John Wright and Sons, Bristol, England, 1959, p. 114.
159. L. F. Badger, in Ref. *158*, p. 51.
160. G. S. Wilson and A. A. Miles, *Topley and Wilson's Principles of Bacteriology and Immunity*, Vol. 2, Williams and Wilkins, Baltimore 1964, pp. 1654–1667.
161. A. T. Laird, C. L. Kite, and D. A. Stewart, *J. Med. Res.* **29**, 31 (1913).
162. K. E. Jensen, *Bull. World Health Organ.* **10**, 171 (1954).
163. A. E. Greenberg and E. Kupka, *Sewage Ind. Wastes*, **29**, 524 (1957).
164. K. Heicken, *Zentr. Bakteriol. Parasitenk., Abt. I. Orig.*, **165**, 156 (1956).
165. D. Pramer, H. Heukelekian, and R. A. Ragotzkie, *Public Health Rept.*, **65**, 851 (1950).
166. D. Pramer and H. Heukelekian, *Sewage Ind. Wastes*, **22**, 1123 (1950).
167. H. Heukelekian and M. Albanese, *Sewage Ind. Wastes*, **28**, 955 (1956).
168. H. Heukelekian and M. Albanese, *Sewage Ind. Wastes*, **28**, 1094 (1956).
169. B. Moore, *Monthly Bull. Min. Health Public Health Lab. Serv. (Brit.)*, **7**, 241 (1948).
170. L. C. Wayne, *J. Bacteriol.*, **69**, 92 (1955).
171. L. C. Wayne, *Am. J. Clin. Pathol.*, **28**, 565 (1957).
172. *Techniques for Microbiological Analysis, Adm. 40*, Millipore Corp., Bedford Mass., 1967.
173. A. R. Prévot, *Manual for the Classification and Determination of the Anaerobic Bacteria*, translated by V. Fredette from the French), 1st American ed., Lea and Febiger, Philadelphia, 1966, p. 402.
174. H. Haenel, *Z. Kinderheilk*, **78**, 592 (1956); cited in Ref. *32*.
175. H. Haenel and W. Müller-Beuthow, *Zentr. Bakteriol. Parasitenk. I. Orig.*, **167**, 123 (1956).
176. J. Dehnert, *Zentr. Bakteriol. Parasitenk. I. Orig.*, **169**, 66 (1957).
177. C. A. Hunter and P. R. Ensign, *Am. J. Public Health*, **37**, 1166 (1947).
178. L. M. Ringen and C. H. Drake, *J. Bacteriol.*, **64**, 841 (1952).
179. V. L. Sutter, V. Hurst, and C. W. Lane, *Health Lab. Sci.*, **4**, 245 (1967).
180. A. E. Hussar and H. L. Holley, *Antibiotics and Antibiotic Therapy*, Macmillan, New York, 1954, p. 259.
181. F. Selenka, *Arch. Hyg. Bakteriol.* **142**, 569 (1958).
182. J. Potel, *Zentr. Bakteriol. Parasitenk.*, **162**, 44 (1955).
183. H. Kleinmaier and C. Quincke, *Arch. Hyg. Bakteriol.*, **143**, 125 (1959).
184. A. C. Houston, *2nd Rept. Roy. Comm. Treating and Disposal of Sewage*, London, 1902, pp. 55, 135; cited in Ref. *27*.

185. R. Buttiaux, *L'Analyse Bacteriologique des Eaux de Consommation*, 1st. ed., Paris, 1951; cited in Ref. *27*.
186. R. Reitler and R. Seligman, *J. Appl. Bacteriol.*, **20**, 145 (1957).
187. A. W. Hoadley and E. McCoy, *Health Lab. Sci.*, **3**, 20 (1966).
188. C. H. Drake, *Health Lab. Sci.*, **3**, 10 (1966).
189. F. Selenka and R. Ruschke, *Arch. Hyg. Bakteriol.*, **149**, 273 (1965).
190. A. W. Hoadley, *Dissertation Abstr.*, **27**, 4231 (1967).
191. A. W. Hoadley, *J. New Engl. Water Works Assoc.*, **82**, 99 (1968).
192. B. Lanyi, M. Gregacs, and M. M. Adam, *Acta Microbiol. Acad. Sci. Hung.*, **13**, 319 (1966–1967); *Bull. Hyg.*, **42**, 1067 (1967).
193. H. M. Taylor, *J. Am. Med. Assoc.*, **113**, 891 (1939).
194. W. W. Cothran and J. B. Hatlen, *Stud. Med.*, **10**, 493 (1962).
195. M. S. Favero, C. H. Drake, and G. B. Randall, *Public Health Rept.*, **79**, 61 (1964).
196. M. S. Favero and C. H. Drake, *Public Health Rept.*, **79**, 251 (1964).
197. F. R. Georgia and C. F. Poe, *J. Bacteriol.*, **22**, 349 (1931).
198. E. O. King, M. K. Ward, and D. E. Raney, *J. Lab. Clin. Med.*, **44**, 301 (1954).
199. N. W. Chmura and M. J. Pelczar, *J. Bacteriol.*, **77**, 518 (1959).
200. J. A. Clark, *Can. J. Microbiol.*, **15**, 771 (1969).
201. I. L. Shklair, F. L. Losse, and A. N. Bahn, *Bacteriol. Proc.*, 1963, p. 71.
202. F. Selenka, *Arch. Hyg. Bakteriol.*, **144**, 627 (1960).
203. J. Lederberg and E. M. Lederberg, *J. Bacteriol.*, **63**, 399 (1952).
204. E. B. Masurovsky, S. A. Goldblith, and J. Voss, *J. Bacteriol.*, **85**, 722 (1963).
205. M. J. Thornley, *J. Appl. Bacteriol.*, **22**, i (1959).
206. M. J. Thornley, *J. Appl. Bacteriol.*, **23**, 37 (1960).
207. M. P. Horwood, B. S. Goud, and H. Shwachman, *J. Am. Water Works Assoc.*, **25**, 124 (1933).
208. C. Ritter and E. L. Treece, *Am. J. Public Health*, **38**, 1532 (1948).
209. E. D. Robinton, E. W. Mood, and L. R. Elliot, *Am. J. Public Health*, **47**, 1101 (1957).
210. E. B. Seligmann, Ph.D. Thesis, Michigan State Univ., East Lansing, 1951.
211. A. H. Stevenson, *Am. J. Public Health*, **43**, 529 (1953).
212. A. M. Woodruff and E. W. Goodpasture, *Am. J. Pathol.*, **7**, 209 (1931).
213. G. Berg, *J. New Engl. Water Works Assoc.*, **78**, 79 (1964).
214. A. J. Rhodes and C. E. Van Rooyen, *Textbook of Virology*, Williams and Wilkins, Baltimore, Md., 1968, p. 966.
215. J. F. Enders, T. H. Weller, and F. C. Robbins, *Science*, **109**, 85 (1949).
216. N. A. Clarke, G. Berg, P. W. Kabler, and S. L. Chang, in *Advances in Water Pollution Research* (B. A. Southgate, ed.), Vol. 2, Macmillan, New York, 1964, p. 523.
217. C. W. Northington, S. L. Chang, and L. J. McCabe, in *Water Quality Improvements by Physical-Chemical Processes* (N. F. Gloyna and W. W. Eikenfelder, Jr., eds.), Univ. Texas Press, Austin, 1970, pp. 49–56.
218. B. England, R. E. Leach, B. Adame, and R. Shiosaki, in *Transmission of Viruses by the Water Route* (G. Berg, ed.), Wiley, New York, 1967, pp. 401–417.
219. S. M. Kelly and W. W. Sanderson, *Sewage Ind. Wastes*, **31**, 683 (1959).
220. W. N. Mack, J. R. Frey, B. J. Riegle, and W. L. Mallman, *J. Water Pollution Control Federation*, **34**, 1133 (1962).
221. G. Berg, R. B. Dean, and D. R. Dahling, *J. Am. Water Works Assoc.*, **60**, 193 (1968).
222. S. L. Chang, *Bull. World Health Organ.*, **38**, 401 (1968).
223. F. L. Horsfall and I. Tamm, (eds.), *Viral and Rickettsial Infections of Man*, 4th ed., Lippincott, Philadelphia, 1965.
224. S. A. Plotkin and M. Katz, in *Transmission of Viruses by the Water Route* (G. Berg, ed.), Wiley, New York, 1967, pp. 151–166.

225. M. Katz and S. A. Plotkin, *Am. J. Public Health*, **57**, 1837 (1967).
226. F. D'Herelle, *The Bacteriophage and Its Behavior* (English transl. by G. H. Smith), Williams and Wilkins, Baltimore, Md., 1926.
227. E. H. Hankin, *Ann. Inst. Pasteur*, **10**, 511 (1896).
228. G. S. Wilson and A. A. Miles, *Topley and Wilson's Principles of Bacteriology and Immunity*, Williams and Wilkins, Baltimore, Md., 1964, pp. 421–422.
229. R. S. Safferman and M. E. Morris, *Science*, **140**, 679 (1963).
230. E. Gildemeister and H. Watanabe, *Zentr. Bakteriol. Parasitenk., Abt. I, Orig.*, **122**, 566 (1931).
231. E. Gildemeister and H. Watanabe, *Gesundh. Ing.*, **55**, 241 (1932).
232. K. Schlossmann, *Z. Hyg. Infektionskrankh.*, **114**, 65 (1932).
233. F. Diénert, *Bull. Acad. Méd.* (Paris), **112**, 611 (1934).
234. F. Diénert, P. Etrillard, and M. Lambert, *Compt. Rend.*, **199**, 102 (1934).
235. P. Etrillard and M. Lambert, through *Water Pollution Abstr.*, **9**, No. 977, p. 292 (1936).
236. R. Abdoelrachman, *Antonie van Leeuwenhoek J. Microbiol. Serol.*, **9**, 143 (1943).
237. A. Guélin, *Ann. Inst. Pasteur*, **69**, 219 (1943).
238. A. Guélin and J. Le Bris, *Ann. Inst. Pasteur*, **73**, 508 (1947).
239. A. Guélin, *Ann. Inst. Pasteur*, **75**, 485 (1948).
240. A. Guélin, *Ann. Inst. Pasteur*, **79**, 186 (1950).
241. A. Guélin, *Ann. Inst. Pasteur*, **74**, 104 (1948).
242. A. Guélin, *Ann. Inst. Pasteur*, **79**, 447 (1950).
243. F. Diénert, *Compt. Rend.*, **221**, 574 (1945).
244. F. Diénert, *Bull. Acad. Méd.* (Paris), **128**, 660 (1944).
245. M. Morzycka and J. Georgiades, *Bull. State Inst. Marine and Trop. Med. (Gdánsk, Poland)*, **4**, 399 (1952).
246. D. A. Cornelson, I. Sechter, G. Zamfir, V. Avram, H. Tudoranu, and H. Feller, *Igiena (Bucharest)*, **6**, 317 (1957).
247. V. Lenk and H. W. Ackermann, *Zentr. Bakteriol. Parasitenk., Abt. I, Ref.*, **178**, 77 (1961).
248. A. F. Carlucci and D. Pramer, *Appl. Microbiol.*, **8**, 254 (1960).
249. Y. Kott and E. F. Gloyna, *Water Sewage Works*, **112**, 424 (1965).
250. N. Buras and Y. Kott, *Israel J. Med. Sci.*, **2**, 660 (1966).
251. Y. Kott, in *Advances in Water Pollution Research* (J. Paz Maroto and F. Josa, eds.), Vol. 3, Water Pollution Control Federation, Washington, D.C., 1967, p. 112.
252. J. Suñer and J. Piñol, in *Advances in Water Pollution Research* (J. Paz Maroto and J. Josa, eds., Vol. 3, Water Pollution Control Federation, Washington, D.C., 1967, p. 105.
253. L. W. Slanetz, in *Advances in Water Pollution Research* (J. Paz Maroto and F. Josa, eds.), Vol. 3, Water Pollution Control Federation, Washington, D.C., 1967, p. 115.
254. F. Couture, *Rev. Hyg. Méd. Prévent.*, **58**, 371 (1936).
255. W. Emilianowicz, *Bull. State Inst. Marine and Trop. Med. (Gdánsk, Poland)*, **4**, 342 (1952).
256. O. A. Peso and R. M. Mignone, *Rev. Obras Sanit. Nación (Buenos Aires)*, **19**, 433 (1955).
257. S. Zieminska, *Roczniki Pánstwowego Zakladu Hig.*, **9**, 225 (1958).
258. South African Council for Scientific and Industrial Research, National Institute for Water Research, *Report of the Director for 1961, C.S.I.R. Spec. Rept. No. W20*, 1963; through *Water Pollution Abstr.*, **37**, No. 546, p. 111 (1963).
259. E. M. J. Carstens, O. J. Coetzee, H. H. Malherbe, and R. M. Harwin, *C.S.I.R. Res. Rept. No. 241*, 1965; through *Water Pollution Abstr.*, **41**, No. 478, p. 129 (1968).

260. O. J. Coetzee, *Public Health* (Johannesburg), **66**, 45 (1966).
261. T. G. Metcalf, in *Advances in Water Pollution Research* (S. H. Jenkins, ed.), Pergamon, London, 1969, pp. 831–833.
262. C. Joyce and H. H. Weiser, *J. Am. Water Works Assoc.*, **59**, 491 (1967).
263. Y. Kott, H. B. Ari, and N. Buras, in *Advances in Water Pollution Research* (S. H. Jenkins, ed.), Pergamon, London, 1969, pp. 823–829.
264. C. Berg, *ibid.*, pp. 833–834.
265. P. G. H. Gell, B. C. Hobbs, and V. D. Allison, *J. Hyg.*, **44**, 120 (1945).
266. O. A. Peso, *Rev. Obras Sanit. Nación* (*Buenos Aires*), **12**, 337 (1948).
267. J. Hruby, *Higijena* (*Belgrade*), **5**, 1 (1953); through *Water Pollution Abstr.*, **27**, No. 1929, p. 322 (1954).
268. C. G. Rieux, R. Buttiaux, and G. Muchemble. *Hydrobiologica*, **1**, 105 (1949).
269. G. Berg, *Health Lab. Sci.*, **3**, 90 (1966).
270. S. M. Kelly, *Am. J. Public Health*, **43**, 1532 (1953).
271. J. L. Melnick, J. Emmons, E. M. Opton, and J. H. Coffey, *Am. J. Hyg.*, **59**, 185 (1954).
272. C. R. Gravelle and T. D. Y. Chin, *J. Infect. Diseases*, **109**, 205 (1961).
273. S. A. Kollins, in *Advances in Applied Microbiology* (W. W. Umbreit, ed.), Vol. 8, Academic, New York, 1966, pp. 145–193.
274. Committee on Viruses in Water, *J. Am. Water Works Assoc.*, **61**, 491 (1969).
275. G. Berg, presented at the National Specialty Conference on Disinfection, University of Massachusetts, Amherst, July 8–10, 1970.
276. E. E. Geldreich, R. H. Bordner, C. B. Huff, H. F. Clark, and P. W. Kabler, *J. Water Pollution Control Federation*, **34**, 295 (1962).
277. G. A. Lamb, T. D. Y. Chin, and L. E. Scarce, *Am. J. Hyg.*, **80**, 320 (1964).
278. C. A. Phillips and C. A. Grim, *Appl. Microbiol.*, **13**, 457 (1965).
279. H. A. Wenner, *Proc. Soc. Exp. Biol. Med.*, **60**, 104 (1945).
280. M. F. Duff, *Appl. Microbiol.*, **19**, 120 (1970).
281. G. Berg, D. Berman, S. L. Chang, and N. A. Clarke, *Am. J. Epidemiology*, **83**, 196 (1966).
282. W. G. Cochran, *Biometrics*, **6**, 105 (1950).
283. E. L. Crow, *Biometrika*, **43**, 423 (1956).
284. S. L. Chang, G. Berg, K. A. Busch, R. E. Stevenson, N. A. Clarke, and P. W. Kabler, *Virology*, **6**, 27 (1958).
285. S. H. Godbole, S. J. Illavia, and B. D. Rawal, *Environ. Health* (*India*), **8**, 70 (1966); through *Water Pollution Abstr.*, **40**, No. 378, p. 108 (1967).
286. S. H. Hopper and N. Khoobyarian, *Am. J. Trop. Med. Hyg.*, **5**, 388 (1956).
287. S. H. Hopper and N. Khoobyarian, *Am. J. Trop. Med. Hyg.*, **6**, 379 (1957).
288. G. A. Bagdasaryan and V. F. Zheverzheeva, *Gigiena i Sanit.*, **32**, 68 (1967); through *Biol. Abstr.*, **49**, 9141 (1968) and *Water Pollution Abstr.*, **42**, No. 683, p. 150 (1969).
289. H. I. Shuval, S. Cymbalista, B. Fatal, and N. Goldblum, in *Transmission of Viruses by the Water Route* (G. Berg, ed.), Wiley, New York, 1967, pp. 45–55.
290. D. O. Cliver, *Appl. Microbiol.*, **13**, 417 (1965).
291. J. Kohn, *Nature*, **183**, 1055 (1959).
292. L. Philipson, P.-Å. Albertsson, and G. Frick, *Virology*, **11**, 553 (1960).
293. D. O. Cliver, in *Transmission of Viruses by the Water Route* (G. Berg, ed.), Wiley, New York, 1967, pp. 109–120.
294. T. Gibbs and D. O. Cliver, *Health Lab. Sci.*, **2**, 81 (1965).
295. P.-Å. Albertsson, *Biochim. Biophys. Acta*, **27**, 378 (1958).
296. P.-Å. Albertsson, in *Methods in Virology* (K. Maramorosch and H. Koprowski, eds.), Academic, New York, 1967, pp. 303–321.

297. E. Lund and C.-E. Hedström, in *Transmission of Viruses by the Water Route* (G. Berg, ed.), Wiley, New York, 1967, pp. 371–377.

298. E. Lund and C.-E. Hedström, *Am. J. Epidemiol.*, **84**, 287 (1966).

299. H. I. Shuval, B. Fatal, S. Cymbalista, and N. Goldblum, *Water Res.*, **3**, 225 (1969).

300. J. Grindrod and D. O. Cliver, *Arch. Ges. Virusforsch.*, **28**, 337 (1969).

301. E. Lund, C.-E. Hedström, and O. Strannegard, *Am. J. Epidemiol.*, **84**, 282 (1966).

302. M. Bier, G. C. Bruckner, F. C. Cooper, and H. E. Roy, in *Transmission of Viruses by the Water Route* (G. Berg, ed.), Wiley, New York, 1967, pp. 57–73.

303. M. Bier, in *Methods in Enzymology* (S. P. Colowick and N. O. Kaplan, eds.), Vol. 5, Academic, New York, 1962, pp. 33–50.

304. M. Bier, U.S. Pat. 3,079,318 (1963).

305. N. A. Clarke and P. W. Kabler, *Health Lab. Sci.*, **1**, 44 (1964).

306. D. O. Cliver and J. Yeatman, *Appl. Microbiol.*, **13**, 387 (1965).

307. N. G. Anderson, G. B. Cline, W. W. Harris, and J. G. Green, in *Transmission of Viruses by the Water Route* (G. Berg, ed.), Wiley, New York, 1967, pp. 75–88.

308. W. O. K. Grabow, *Water Res.*, **2**, 675 (1968).

309. H. Thiele, *Naturwissenschaften*, **36**, 123 (1941).

310. H. Thiele and D. Schyma, *Naturwissenschaften*, **40**, 583 (1953).

311. D. Schyma, *Zentr. Bakteriol. Parasitenk., Abt. I. Orig.*, **178**, 229 (1960).

312. D. Schyma, H. Gärtner, and G. Moll, *Zentr. Bakteriol. Parasitenk., Abt. I. Orig.*, **178**, 562 (1960).

313. D. Schyma, H. Gärtner, and G. Moll, *Zentr. Bakteriol. Parasitenk., Abt. I. Orig.*, **181**, 22 (1961).

314. H. Gärtner and D. Schyma, *Arch. Hyg. Bakteriol.*, **145**, 81 (1961).

315. H. Gärtner and R. F. V. Schnurbein, *Arch. Hyg. Bakteriol.*, **148**, 183 (1964).

316. G. Witt, *Arch. Hyg. Bakteriol.*, **148**, 188 (1964).

317. Metropolitan Water Board, London, *42nd Report on the Results of the Bacteriological, Chemical, and Biological Examination of the London Waters for the Years 1965–1966*, 1968, p. 140, through *Water Pollution Abstr.*, **44**, No. 1776, p. 438 (1968).

318. H. Gärtner, in *Transmission of Viruses by the Water Route* (G. Berg, ed.), Wiley, New York, 1967, pp. 121–127.

319. T. G. Metcalf, *Appl. Microbiol.*, **9**, 376 (1961).

320. D. O. Cliver, in *Transmission of Viruses by the Water Route*, (G. Berg, ed.), Wiley, New York, 1967, pp. 139–141.

320a. D. Berman, in *Transmission of Viruses by the Water Route* (G. Berg, ed.), Wiley, New York, 1967, pp. 146–147.

321. C. Wallis and J. L. Melnick, *Bull. World Health Organ.*, **36**, 219 (1967).

322. C. Wallis and J. L. Melnick, *J. Virology*, **1**, 472 (1967).

323. G. Berg, R. B. Dean, and D. R. Dahling, *J. Am. Water Works Assoc.*, **60**, 193 (1968).

324. N. U. Rao and N. A. Labzoffsky, *Can. J. Microbiol.*, **15**, 399 (1969).

325. C. Wallis and J. L. Melnick, in *Transmission of Viruses by the Water Route* (G. Berg, ed.), Wiley, New York, 1967, pp. 129–138.

326. C. Wallis and J. L. Melnick, *Am. J. Epidemiol.*, **85**, 459 (1967).

327. J. Warren, M. L. Weil, S. B. Russ, and H. Jeffries, *Proc. Soc. Exp. Biol. Med.*, **72**, 662 (1949).

328. B. L. England, *Bacteriol. Proc., Am. Soc. Microbiol.*, *70th Annual Meeting, 1970*, pp. 194–195.

329. R. E. Stevenson, S. L. Chang, N. A. Clarke, and P. W. Kabler, *Proc. Soc. Exp. Biol. Med.*, **92**, 764 (1956).

330. J. H. Johnson, J. E. Fields, and W. A. Darlington, *Nature*, **213**, 665 (1967).
331. C. Wallis, S. Grinstein, J. L. Melnick, and J. E. Fields, *Appl. Microbiol.*, **18**, 1007 (1969).
332. V. C. Rao, R. Sullivan, R. B. Read, and N. A. Clarke, *J. Am. Water Works Assoc.*, **60**, 1288 (1968).
333. J. T. Cookson, Jr., and W. J. North, *Environ. Sci. Technol.*, **1**, 46 (1967).
334. J. T. Cookson, Jr., *J. Am. Water Works Assoc.*, **61**, 52 (1969).
335. R. C. Loehr and D. T. Schwegler, *Appl. Microbiol.*, **13**, 1005 (1965).
335a. M. H. Adams, *Bacteriophages*, Wiley (Interscience), New York, 1959.
336. Y. Kott, *Appl. Microbiol.*, **14**, 141 (1966).
337. G. V. Levin, E. Usdin, and A. R. Slonim, *Aerospace Med.*, **39**, 14 (1968).
338. W. S. Oleniacz, M. A. Pisano, M. H. Rosenfeld, and R. L. Elgart, *Environ. Sci. Technol.*, **2**, 1030 (1968).
339. C. J. Rogers and T. C. Purcell, *Environ. Sci. Technol.*, **3**, 764 (1969).
340. Y. Henis, J. R. Gould, and M. Alexander, *Appl. Microbiol.*, **14**, 513 (1966).
341. R. T. O'Brien, *Food Technol.*, **21**, 78 (1967).
342. G. L. Cecchini and R. T. O'Brien, *J. Bacteriol.*, **95**, 1205 (1968).
343. A. V. Titova, I. K. Laikunas, and G. N. Nedoshopa, *Gigiena i Sanit.*, **30**, 66 (1965).
344. R. K. Guthrie and D. J. Reeder, *Appl. Microbiol.*, **17**, 399 (1969).
345. T. D. Stevens and H. M. S. Watkins, *Appl. Microbiol.*, **17**, 384 (1969).
346. G. V. Levin, V. R. Harrison, and W. C. Hess, *J. Am. Water Works Assoc.*, **48**, 75 (1956).
347. R. B. Roberts, P. H. Abelson, D. B. Cowie, E. T. Bolton, and R. J. Britten, *Studies of Biosynthesis in Escherichia coli*, Publ. 607, Carnegie Institute, Washington, D.C., 1957.
348. G. V. Levin, in *Advances in Applied Microbiology* (W. W. Umbreit, ed.), Academic, New York, 1963, pp. 95–133.
349. J. R. Baylis and L. Scarce, in *Public Health Hazards of Microbial Pollution of Water*, Proc. Rudolfs Res. Conf., Dept. Sanitation, College of Agriculture, Rutgers Univ., New Brunswick, N.J., 1961, pp. 285–351.
350. J. Warren, A. Neal, and D. Rennels, *Proc. Soc. Exp. Biol. Med.*, **121**, 1250 (1966).

Chapter **14** **Toxicity Bioassay Techniques Using Aquatic Organisms**

Max Katz
COLLEGE OF FISHERIES
UNIVERSITY OF WASHINGTON
SEATTLE, WASHINGTON

I. Introduction

The regulatory agencies which are concerned with our aquatic resources, and the management of industrial establishments whose wastes might be lethal or harmful to fish and other aquatic life, must know the degree of dilution or treatment that must be provided to a toxic waste to prevent damage to the organisms in the receiving waters. Much of the desired toxicological data has been determined using fish, invertebrates, and various algae of importance in the aquatic ecosystem as biological reagents. Results obtained by the use of toxicity bioassays have dictated the expenditures of large sums for waste discharge facilities and waste treatment procedures and, in many cases, have affected the selection of plant sites. In addition, regulatory agencies such as Departments of Fisheries of the federal and state governments, and the various pollution control agencies, have sometimes used toxicity bioassays to advise their enforcement divisions of potential toxic pollution problems.

It was hoped at one time that the toxicity of wastes to aquatic organisms could be determined by an analysis of the chemical constituents of the waste and then by reference to a master table or series of tables listing the toxicities of the various substances in the waste to fish or other aquatic organisms. This goal, although reasonable and most desirable, has not proved to be feasible for many reasons. In many cases, for example, the only toxicity data for a certain compound or effluent were derived from tests with a fish foreign to the waters concerned; regulatory agencies concerned with valuable salmon and striped bass populations, for example, would be hesitant to apply toxicity data derived from experiments with goldfish or eels. In other cases, the tests reported in the literature may have been carried on in a water supply which contained large concentrations of dissolved salts, while the water in the river concerned might be relatively lacking in dissolved minerals. Other variables that might make the use of tabulated material invalid are differences in water temperature, size of fish, seasonal tolerance of various species, testing procedures, physiology, previous history, nutritional state, and certain laboratory conditions such as lighting and disturbance which may have affected the results of the test.

Most of the experienced workers in the field of water quality who are faced with a problem regarding the possible effects of a toxic waste on a valuable aquatic population have learned that they cannot affort to accept the data in the literature unless they are quite familiar with the professional competence of the investigator or have some other excellent reasons to accept published data. Hence, the toxicity bioassay has developed by necessity into one of the more important tools available to the worker concerned with water quality in its relation to fish and invertebrate populations.

II. Historical Background

The use of fish to establish the toxic effects of water pollution is not new. Over 100 years ago, Penny and Adams(1) examined the River

Leven, a tributary of the Clyde, which was polluted by effluents from a dye works. They carried out laboratory experiments with water from the polluted river and with solutions of the various acids, salts, and other substances present in the effluents. The assay fish used were minnows, which they regarded as being typical of the more sensitive species resident in the stream, and goldfish, whose tolerance permitted a variety of observations which were useful for determining the mode of action of the various toxicants.

The next important effort in evaluating the toxicity of substances to fish was that of Weigelt et al. (2). These workers had a good insight into the practical needs to be filled by toxicity bioassays. They conducted some bioassays with fish in flowing water systems and determined the toxicity to fertilized trout eggs of 11 different acids, alkalies, and salts. The experiments with trout eggs were conducted for 12 days, and the percentage surviving after this exposure period was determined.

Most of the tests conducted by Weigelt et al. (2), however, were short-term toxicity bioassays in which fish were placed into various solutions and were observed until they died. These experiments were carefully controlled according to the standards prevailing at that time. The sizes of fish used in the experiments were recorded. The trout were segregated into large, medium, and small fish. The concentration of toxicant and the water temperature were recorded. Most of the experiments lasted only a few hours. These workers conducted 230 experiments with 43 different compounds that were known to be present in industrial wastes. Most experiments were conducted with a single fish—either a trout or the tench (*Tinca tinca*). In some cases, however, as many as 16 fish were used to determine the toxicity of a single substance.

Kupzis(3) was perhaps the first worker to conduct experiments to determine the concentration at which various toxicants were not lethal. He determined the length of time required before the fish became agitated, came to the surface, turned over on their sides, failed to respire, and died. He dissolved 3, 5, 10, and 20 mg/liter of naphthenic acid in water and observed the reactions of fish to these concentrations. Observations were sometimes continued for as long as 120 hr, although in most experiments observations were concluded before 48 hr. Kupzis also studied the toxicity of the same substance to crayfish and frogs and continued observations with these organisms for up to six days.

Since the time of Kupzis, many concerned individuals and agencies have conducted bioassay studies to determine the toxicity of substances and their components to fish. Some of these studies were done by biologists concerned with the fish as a resource(4–8); other studies were made by physiologists and pharmacologists whose concern was either entirely academic or who were interested in finding organisms that would be useful in evaluating the action of drugs for use in medicine(9–15). Several of these workers, especially Shelford and Powers(14), diverted their pharmacological interest into the study of the effects upon fish of toxic substances present in wastes and made contributions which led directly to the standardization of fish bioassays. Among the most influential of these studies was that of Powers(15) entitled "The Goldfish as a Test Animal in the Study of Toxicity." Although this paper was intended as a pharmacological study, it proved to be an influential guide for aquatic biologists who were looking for more precise techniques that could be useful in correlating toxicity with time and concentration.

It became apparent at this time to some critical workers that although some creditable work had been done in evaluating the toxicity of substances to fish, much of this work could not be applied by other workers because of the lack of uniformity of procedures. Belding(16), concerned with the lack of uniformity in the procedures used by aquatic biologists who were trying to collect data that could be applied to water pollution problems, gave a paper on toxicity bioassay procedures at the meeting of the American Fisheries Society in 1927. Belding, a competent physiologist and pharmacologist, realizing that his audience consisted mainly of fish culturists and aquatic biologists who were largely untrained in the laboratory disciplines, devoted a large segment of his paper to the factors that could affect the results of toxicity tests performed in the laboratory. He discussed the effects upon experimental data of the individual variation of fish and stressed the use of appropriate controls. In his discussion of family and species, he pointed out that different species of fish might have different tolerances to a specific toxicant and emphasized that data obtained with one species could not be applied routinely to another species. In the paragraph on age, he observed that the tolerance of a fish to a substance could vary with its age and state of development. He further observed that the size and weight of fish vary at different times and pointed out that fish may be more sensitive immediately after spawning, in extremely warm water, and during periods of food scarcity. He also pointed out that fish acclimated to laboratory conditions were more useful for experimental studies than wild fish.

Belding also enumerated experimental variables that would affect the data. The water used in an experiment might produce different results if the chemical composition differed markedly from that of water used in a previous experiment. Although Belding obviously was not well versed in water chemistry and did not seem to be aware of the many differences in water composition and their effect on toxicity experiments, his discussion should have alerted those who were aware of differences that exist in natural water supplies. He pointed out that the ratio of the size and number of fish in each test container should be considered. He recommended that tests be made with no flow of water, probably because he realized the technical problems involved in regard to the creation of the constant flow apparatus and the undue stress that a current might place upon a fish already affected by the toxicant. The necessity of maintaining adequate dissolved oxygen, either by allowing sufficient surface area for atmospheric diffusion or by artificial reaeration, was pointed out. Finally, the necessity of maintaining constant temperature in the test aquaria was emphasized. Belding's recommendations, although sound and useful, did not receive wide recognition, although his paper was far more useful to the average aquatic biologist than that of Powers(15).

Steinmann(17), in Germany, also discussed the variables that would affect the results of toxicity bioassays.

A. The Compilation of Ellis

Perhaps the most influential of the earlier studies was the paper by Ellis(18) which was published by the U.S. Bureau of Fisheries. This widely accepted report was the culmination of extensive field and laboratory studies which had been carried on by the author throughout the United States from 1930 to 1935. A good deal of the impact of this report was due to the increasing concern with water pollution throughout the United States at this time rather than to the intrinsic merit of the publication as a guide to toxicity bioassay procedures.

Although water pollution and its effects upon fisheries resources in the United States were of great concern to fisheries agencies and conservationists, at the time of the publication of Ellis's study(18) nothing effective was being done to collect the biological information required to combat the problem. Conservationists, however, were becoming more vocal and effective, and in several of the states in which the fisheries interests could exert the political pressures necessary, they were insisting that state pollution control agencies become concerned with other than public health problems of water pollution and consider the problems of industrial wastes in regard to the fishery resource.

In addition, certain industrial groups, in particular the pulp and paper and petroleum industries, were reacting to public pressure. They were also concerned with losses of raw material and finished products which were being discharged into waterways. These industries, although far from being entirely altruistic, were concerned with their water pollution problems and did fish toxicity work in their own laboratories.

The Ellis compilation, therefore, appeared at an opportune time and was eagerly seized upon by biologists who were concerned with water pollution and fisheries. The ready acceptance of Ellis's study was further enhanced by the fact that the study was sponsored, financed, and published by the U.S. Bureau of Fisheries. The federal sponsorship gave it an authoritative status despite some serious deficiencies. Although Ellis emphasized repeatedly that caution should be exercised in the use of his compilations of literature regarding the lethality of substances to fish, these warnings were almost uniformly disregarded by workers in the field. A typical caution was inserted in his section on trade waste. On page 430, Ellis stated: "Already much confusion, often to the detriment of fisheries interests, has resulted from the misuse in this connection of various statements in the literature concerning the tolerance of fishes for a given number of parts per million of a particular waste, when these observations were intended to apply to a specific case."

Most of the workers in the field of water pollution, unfortunately, did not recognize the complexities inherent in experimentation with fish and uncritically seized upon the last major section of Ellis's study, which was entitled "Lethal Limits of 114 Substances Which May be Found in Stream Pollutants," as the authoritative answer to their toxicological problems. These workers accepted this compilation as a bible of fish toxicology and failed to heed Ellis's repeated cautions.

Ellis presented a rather brief and unorganized discussion of the toxicity bioassay methods which he used. He also presented some experimental results in a series of tables which failed to indicate the reproducible precision which was being obtained regularly by other workers with adequate experience in fish experimentation.

Ellis et al. (18a) later published a brief section on bioassay techniques as part of a larger report on the chemical and physical methods for the determination of water quality parameters for fish and aquatic life. The brief instructions in this report, although perhaps of interest to experienced biologists, did not give sufficient detail for the neophyte or for the technician in an industrial laboratory who was usually assigned the biological studies.

The recklessness with which many workers applied Ellis's toxicity data to their own problems, without, of course, regarding his warnings, made it apparent to thoughtful scientists working with industry, and some biologists working with conservation agencies, that a formal standardization of toxicity bioassay methods was urgently required. For example, the reports cited by Ellis frequently did not specify temperatures at which tests were carried on, the chemistry of the solute waters were frequently not given, and many other parameters which could be readily controlled or measured were not included. Standardization of technique in determining the toxicity of substances to fish was obviously needed.

B. The Hart, Doudoroff, and Greenbank Procedure

The first purposeful and still highly regarded effort to establish a standard method for determining the toxicity of substances to fish was by Hart, Doudoroff, and Greenbank(19). Hart, whose original training was in pharmacology, was in charge of waste control operations for the Atlantic Refining Company of Philadelphia. His professional duties brought him into contact with Doudoroff, an experimental physiologist, and Greenbank, an ichthyologist, both of whom were working on water pollution problems for the Louisiana Conservation Department. They were aware that industries concerned with waste disposal problems and the conservation agencies concerned with the effects of waste disposal were unhappy that much of the data in the literature could not be applied because of lack of detail and precision, and that most of the data being collected were not comparable. These authors' training and research experience indicated that precise and reproducible physiological and toxicological data could be obtained. They were also convinced that other workers with a basic background in biology and chemistry could produce valid and useful data if sufficiently detailed standard procedures were available for guidance. A joint effort to formulate standard bioassay procedures was started in about 1942 by Hart and his associates at the Atlantic Refining Company and by Doudoroff and Greenbank in Louisiana. This effort culminated in a publication by the Atlantic Refining Company(19) which gave the detailed procedures necessary to conduct toxicity bioassays with fish. Although this initial small printing was designed for limited distribution as a preliminary to a revised edition with a wider distribution, financial considerations precluded the publication of the revised issue.

Judicious distribution of the procedures to competent workers and the application of these procedures by these workers soon indicated the value of these bioassay methods. With the exception of some details not required by the better-trained workers now working in fish toxicology, these procedures are the basis for the standard bioassay methods now widely and routinely used.

A glance at the Table of Contents and the Appendices of this work indicates the effort made by Hart, Doudoroff, and Greenbank to ensure that a worker with a minimum of biological experience could perform tests that would have validity and which could be replicated and used by other workers.

The procedures outlined by Hart, Doudoroff, and Greenbank won immediate acceptance and have formed the basis for the excellent toxicological work with fish that is now being reported routinely by American and foreign workers. As always, there was some criticism of these procedures, but the criticisms were actually compliments, for many stated that the bulk and detail of the procedures frightened many timid workers, especially untrained people in industrial laboratories and pollution control agencies. Hart, Doudoroff, and Greenbank tried unsuccessfully to assuage this anxiety with the statement: "Such a voluminous and apparently intricate presentation as that which follows may create the impression to the novice that the procedure is so involved, and the tests so difficult to perform, that they will not be usable for his purposes — particularly if he is unaccustomed to procedures of this nature. Careful study of the various sections will reveal, however, that the procedures are essentially simple, and require no unusual technique or equipment."

Unfortunately, what were essentially "simple techniques" to talented physiologists like Doudoroff (who wrote the above statement) were formidable psychological barriers to the unfortunate technician in an industrial laboratory who was delegated as plant biologist. The bioassay procedures of Hart, Doudoroff, and Greenbank were therefore regarded with some disfavor in many industrial laboratories. This was not an unmixed curse because some industries took the logical step of obtaining biological consultants to help with their toxicity work, or hired trained biologists to handle these assignments in their laboratories and to assist with other water resource problems.

C. The Doudoroff Committee Procedure

The limited printing of the Hart, Doudoroff, and Greenbank procedure and the need for some revision necessitated the publication of a revised procedure. The history of this revision is of some interest. Congress assigned to the Public Health Service the various phases of water pollution control activity which had been scattered throughout various federal agencies, and a recruitment began in 1948 of the nucleus of what subsequently became known as the Robert A. Taft Sanitary Engineering Center, in Cincinnati, Ohio. Among the first of an outstanding group of water quality biologists recruited to Cincinnati was Peter Doudoroff.

Doudoroff was invited to participate in the activities of the Research Committee of the Water Pollution Control Federation. His two committee assignments were to the literature review committee and to the chairmanship of a special committee on bioassay methods. The duties of these two assignments fortified Doudoroff's belief in the necessity of standardized bioassay procedures. The extremely varied and often erroneous toxicity values reported for the same substance by various workers were the result of the use of unstandardized procedures(20,21). The anguish involved in the compilation of the reviews by Doudoroff and Katz(20,21) emphasized the necessity of providing a widely distributed and authoritative bioassay procedure to ensure that future research would be standardized. In addition, the flagrant abuse of tabulated toxicological data by uncritical water resource workers led Doudoroff and Katz to the decision not to prepare in their reviews the "useful," but always abused, tabular compilations of data. They presented the toxicity data obtained from the literature in text form. A worker who wanted to use the data was forced to read the paper thoroughly and was compelled to note the variables that gave rise to the results found by different workers. If he misused the data in the reviews, and this happened frequently, the error was his and not that of the reviewers.

For the committee to develop the bioassay procedures, Doudoroff selected a group of competent biologists and engineers from federal agencies, universities, industry, and state conservation agencies, with experience in conducting bioassays with fish and invertebrates. Several of these, especially George Burdick, made important contributions, although others of the committee never attended any of the meetings or just made ceremonial appearances. Certain consultants attended several of the meetings and made valuable contributions. Among those who participated as consultants were M. Katz and C. M. Tarzwell of the Public Health Service, C. Henderson of the U.S. Fish and Wildlife Service, and C. B. Kelley of New York.

The procedures developed by the committee were essentially a modification and condensation of the earlier Hart, Doudoroff, and Greenbank report, and were developed in a series of three meetings held at Cincinnati, Ohio, the Woods Hole Marine Laboratories, Massachusetts, and the U.S. Fish and Wildlife Service Fish Disease Laboratory at Kearneysville, West Virginia. The recommended bioassay methods were published in 1951(22). It had been the plan of the committee to develop bioassay procedures for zooplankton, particularly *Daphnia*, of importance as fish food, and for oysters, but in time, new professional assignments, etc., broke up the committee and no new formal procedures were developed. The stimulus provided by the bioassay procedures that were published is indicated by the high quality of toxicological data now routinely published by other investigators working with fish and other species.

D. The ASTM and Standard Methods Procedures

The bioassay procedures received wide and immediate acceptance in the United States and abroad. They proved to be so useful that there was soon a demand to give them a more formal status. A committee of the American Society for Testing and Materials headed by Roy Weston (an associate of Hart at the time of the development of the Hart, Doudoroff, and Greenbank procedures, and an engineer with considerable experience in toxicity bioassays with fish) prepared a revision of the bioassay procedures and adapted the Doudoroff committee report to fit the format of the ASTM (23).

At about the same time, the committee of the American Public Health Association appointed C. M. Tarzwell of the Public Health Service to head a special committee to revise the bioassay methods for inclusion in the 11th edition of the authoritative handbook, *Standard Methods for the Examination of Water and Wastewater* (24). Tarzwell invited Doudoroff to revise his procedure for the standard methods handbook. Although Doudoroff's name does not appear among those credited for the APHA procedure, his contribution is as important and direct as was his contribution to the Atlantic Refining Company report and the *Sewage and Industrial Wastes* report of 1951.

III. Toxicity Bioassay Methods with Fish

It is not deemed necessary in this chapter to go into the details of the procedures for the bioassay methods for fish because these are readily available in the Doudoroff report (22), the ASTM procedures (23), and *Standard Methods* (24). The author's experience with the procedures suggests some comments that are useful.

A. Choice and Selection of the Test Fish

Whenever possible, test fish should be a species native to or resident in the body of water under study. If possible, one should select a species of some economic importance, such as a game fish or a fish of commercial value. However, the investigator is frequently compelled to use whatever fish species is readily available from commercial aquaria, minnow dealers, or from nearby bodies of water. Hence, much of the toxicological literature reports tests with bluegills, guppies, and goldfish, although the latter species is not highly regarded because of its tolerance. The fathead minnow, *Pimphales promelas*, which is of little importance apart from its role as a forage species for bass, has been usefully employed by the talented workers at the Robert A. Taft Sanitary Engineering Center. English workers, who usually prefer to use rainbow trout, have found that a tropical fish, the cyprinid *Rasbora*, has about the same tolerance as the rainbow, and have advocated its use as a standard laboratory fish(25). Their supplies of trout are obviously still adequate, however, as they continue to use rainbow trout for most of their studies.

An extremely useful species for long-term bioassay studies is the Japanese rice fish, *Oryzias latipes*, which is available from aquarium dealers. Its habit of producing eggs daily for up to 2 months, the easy control of its spawning by the regulation of water temperature and laboratory lighting, and its rapid growth to maturity make it valuable for studies in which the effects of a substance on the total life cycle of a fish must be evaluated.

1. IDENTIFICATION OF TEST ANIMALS

If the investigator collects his own fish, it is imperative that only fish of a single species be used in a test. Although closely related species may vary only slightly in their tolerance to a toxicant, there are several instances of certain species that are specifically sensitive to certain substances. This specific sensitivity is the basis for the use of TFM (3-trifluoromethyl-4-nitrophenol) to control the sea lamprey(26) and Squaxin (1,1'-methylene-bis-2-naphthol)(26a) to control the predatory squawfish. Although experienced workers will sometimes apply good toxicity data obtained with one species of fish to the solution of a toxicological problem involving other closely related fish, it is good practice to conduct tests with the species involved. There is no way of predicting with assurance that the species concerned will not be very sensitive to the substance of concern. It must be observed, however, that the three compounds known to be specifically toxic to a certain species of fish—pyridyl mercuric acetate to rainbow trout(27), TFM to sea lamprey larvae, and Squaxin to the squawfish *Pytocheilus*—are rather complex organic compounds which may have specific interaction with an enzyme system of importance in the physiology of a particular species.

2. SIZE OF THE TEST ANIMALS

Although Doudoroff et al.(23) specified that the length of the largest fish in an industrial bioassay should not be more than 1.5 times the length of the smallest individual used, subsequent experience has indicated that if great precision is desired, extreme care should be used to select fish varying in length by only a few millimeters. It must be remembered that the weight of a fish increases as the cube of its length, and a fish half again as long as another fish may weigh several times as much as the smaller fish. An objection can be raised, however, to the use of a group of fish that vary in size by only a few millimeters: A natural population of fish is varied in size and the application of toxicity data derived from a very uniform group of fish to problems involving natural populations may be questionable.

Workers who use salmonids over a protracted period of time face the problem of working with a rapidly growing species which will double in length and quadruple in weight over the period of a summer. Thus, data obtained for fish in May and the following October may not be comparable.

3. Holding of Test Animals

Holding of test animals requires a high degree of biological know-how. Even the maintenance of enough guppies to meet the demands of a continuing bioassay program in which a constant supply of fish is required demands a considerable amount of time and effort. Salmonids and bluegills are relatively easy to maintain if the laboratory water supply is of good quality and if diseases can be avoided.

B. Acclimatization and Fitness of Test Animals

Whether fish are collected by the investigator in the field or purchased from a minnow dealer, a substantial loss due to the stress of capture and the rigors of transportation frequently occurs. After the third or fourth day in the laboratory, mortalities will decline if the fish are healthy, and the subsequent loss rate should be very low or nonexistent. Many species of fish adapt quite readily to laboratory conditions and will often begin to feed within a week or 10 days. Other species, such as the lake emerald shiner used by Van Horn et al. (28,29), are difficult to maintain in the laboratory; heavy losses due to disease usually occur within a month, necessitating the frequent procurement of fresh stocks of fish. If disease breaks out, it is best to remove the lot of fish and get a fresh stock unless one has good reason to believe that the disease is due to a nutritional deficiency. Sometimes supplemental feedings of brine shrimp (*Artemia*) will return a laboratory stock to excellent condition.

1. Selection and Preparation of the Experimental Water

The standard bioassay procedures were designed to provide the solution to toxicity problems relating to a specific industrial effluent that would be discharged into a particular body of water; hence, it was specified that the diluent water, as well as the acclimatization water, be from the body of water concerned. The diluent water should be collected from a point above the entrance of the effluent into the waterway.

There are some who have advocated the use of a standard dilution water that approximates the average dissolved salt content of the waters of the United States. This suggestion has not met with favor because results obtained with this standard water might not be applicable to the waterway under consideration. In addition, the practical aspects of preparing large amounts of water necessary for experimentation would outweigh the few advantages to be derived from the use of a standard water. These practical considerations have won the field, and there have been very few cases in which fish toxicity studies have utilized a standard water.

In some laboratories fortunate enough to have both soft and hard water supplies, parallel experiments with each type of water can be carried out with certain toxicants. With certain heavy metals, Pickering and Henderson(30) observed significant differences in toxicity in hard and soft waters, while with other compounds, particularly chlorinated hydro-carbon insecticides(31), the differences are only negligible.

This writer made a series of studies with the euryhaline fish, the stickle-back, in water of various salinities. Marine water was diluted with river water at concentrations of 5–25 parts per thousand to determine the toxicity of some chlorinated hydrocarbon insecticides at different salin-ites(32). There was no consistent or significant difference in the toxicity at various salinities. On the other hand, there was a marked difference in the toxicity of soap to fathead minnows in hard and soft water(33) (see Table 1).

TABLE 1

TLm of Soaps to Fathead Minnows in Soft and Hard Waters[a]

| Household soaps | TLm[b] mg/liter of packaged product | | | | | |
| | Soft water | | | Hard water | | |
	24 hr	48 hr	96 hr	24 hr	48 hr	96 hr
S-1	32	29	29	1100	920	920
S-2	43	41	32	1800	1700	1700
S-3	42	42	42	1800	1800	1800

[a]Reprinted from Ref. 33 by courtesy of the Water Pollution Control Federation.
[b]Median tolerance limit (see Sec. III, C. 6).

Table 1 illustrates not only the difference in toxicity of some substances in waters of different hardness but emphasizes vividly the dangers inherent in casually using tables that list the toxicity of substances to aquatic species. One who must use these tables, when there is no other alternative, should have a good idea of the chemistry of the substances involved before he makes important decisions on the possible toxicity of any waste.

Thus, to avoid error, an investigator should use unpolluted water from the body of water in question. If this is not readily available, he should use water of a similar chemical composition. If an artificial water must be prepared, the Doudoroff committee report(22) suggests diluting a harder water with demineralized or distilled water until the desired mineral content is obtained.

The writer has successfully used water from a river which received domestic and nontoxic organic wastes. Large amounts of water were brought into the laboratory and filtered through glass wool to remove particulate matter. The water was allowed to stabilize in the laboratory for at least a week and was filtered again, this time to remove the zooplankton which had developed; it was then used very successfully.

C. Other Prescribed Experimental Conditions

1. WATER TEMPERATURES

It was recommended that tests be performed at uniform temperatures (22). For warm water fish, temperatures between 20 and 25°C were recommended; in the Taft Center, studies with warm water fish were usually conducted at 25°C. For cold water species, temperatures between 12 and 18°C were recommended. On the other hand, when I shared a laboratory maintained at 20°C I carried on several series of experiments with salmonids, which are cold water species, at that temperature. The introduced error was small but significant and favored conservative answers which emphasized the great toxicity of the chlorinated hydrocarbon insecticides tested(34).

Maintaining the temperature of the test solution is a minor problem in most well-equipped laboratories; adequately engineered water baths can be regulated very precisely with the instrumentation and refrigeration systems now available.

2. CHOICE OF CONTAINER

It was recommended that test containers be made of glass(22). Some workers have recommended the use of aquaria, but these are expensive, heavy, and difficult to clean. For most purposes, the writer uses 5-gal glass pickle jars, which are readily available in most cities. Polyethylene containers of many sizes are now available for use as inexpensive aquaria. Cumming(35) describes a portable bioassay laboratory for field studies which consists of wooden frames and disposable polyethylene bags. One is cautioned, however, to consider the fact that polyethylene and other plastic containers can sorb some organic substances and may selectively remove some or all of the toxicants in solution.

3. Depth and Volume of Solution

The depth of liquid in test containers should never be less than 6 in., to limit the escape of volatile components in the tested solution. If one is forced to use jars of several dimensions, the volumes should be varied to ensure that a uniform depth is maintained in all jars if the waste is suspected of having volatile components.

The dissolved oxygen content of the solution tested should not fall below 5 ppm when using cold water fish, or below 4 ppm when using warm water fish. To avoid having to discard otherwise useful tests, experienced investigators vigorously aerate the diluent water before the beginning of the test, especially if it is taken from a natural body of water, to satisfy the BOD (biological or biochemical oxygen demand) that may be present and to ensure an adequate supply of dissolved oxygen. If the number of fish is not too large for the volume of water, if the waste does not have an appreciable BOD, or if the fish are not disturbed by the toxicant sufficiently to increase their metabolic rate, atmospheric diffusion may often suffice to keep the oxygen content at a satisfactory level.

If the dissolved oxygen falls to the level at which the fish compensate by increasing their respiratory rates, then erroneous results may be obtained. It is well documented that the lethality of many compounds is increased at low dissolved oxygen contents. This is explained by the fact that fish will compensate for a low dissolved oxygen content by increasing their respiratory rates. Hence, more toxicant is passed over their gills and can be absorbed.

Sometimes it is necessary to work with a test solution which is known to have a high BOD. The investigator should first try to compensate by reducing the number of test animals in the test container. If the amount of waste available for testing is limited, then controlled aeration is recommended. A method of controlled aeration (a controlled artificial oxygenation of liquids during tests) is given in the Auxiliary Methods of Ref. (22).

Sometimes it is necessary to obtain a solution of a toxicant which is not readily soluble in water. Acetone, which is not highly toxic to fish, has been used often to make stock solutions of toxicants. Organic solvents often exert a considerable BOD which may remove the dissolved oxygen. The writer has used a simple aeration method which compensated for the BOD of the solvent, with no obvious effect on the test results. A simple glass tube was connected to a laboratory air supply and the air was allowed to bubble out at a rate slow enough to produce single, large air bubbles. An adequate dissolved oxygen content was thus maintained. In the above case, however, the toxicant was a nonvolatile chlorinated hydrocarbon insecticide. This procedure is not advisable, of course, if the toxicant is volatile. For volatile wastes, the apparatus mentioned above (22) should be used.

Chadwick and Kiigemagi(36) developed a procedure for introducing constant amounts of chlorinated hydrocarbon insecticides into testing chambers. This procedure can also be used to introduce other compounds which are only slightly soluble in water, yet which are soluble in volatile solvents. A large glass column is filled with quartz aquarium sand or small glass beads. The column, which is stoppered at the bottom, is filled with a solution of solvent (acetone) saturated with the toxicant. The solution is immediately drained off and the remaining acetone is volatilized by a current of air. The sand grains or glass beads are thus covered with a thin film of the toxicant. Water is allowed to flow through the column until a constant toxicity is attained. This may take a few days to several weeks; then the toxicity will remain constant for several months. With this technique, experiments can be conducted for long periods of time without the necessity of preparing stock solutions and replenishing the toxicant supplies at frequent intervals.

4. THE RENEWAL OF TEST SOLUTIONS

The ideal toxicity bioassay should attempt to duplicate natural conditions, but this goal is not possible in the laboratory. Data obtained by the use of the standard bioassay procedure, in which the fish is immersed in a jar, are questionable when applied to natural systems. In a stream into which an effluent is being discharged continuously, for example, the organisms are being subjected to a constantly renewed toxicant. To duplicate this situation, it is desirable to conduct a bioassay in a constant flow system in which a continuous stream of water containing the desired concentration of waste is introduced into the aquarium system. A constant flow system is not practical in most laboratories because of the relatively large amount of space needed, the complicated experimental apparatus, the large amounts of wastes and diluent waters required, and the infrequency with which a particular toxicity problem may arise. Yet one is sometimes called upon to work with a volatile waste or one in which the toxic substance is destroyed or removed from the solution either by volatilization, precipitation, or detoxification by the test fish. This problem is sometimes solved by the periodic transfer of the test fish to freshly prepared solutions of the toxicant at regular intervals dictated by experience; many workers make this change at 12- or 24-hr intervals.

In recent years there has been a well-justified trend toward the use of constant flow toxicity bioassays for several reasons. It has been demonstrated repeatedly that fish in standing water bioassays can frequently detoxify solutions that would be quite lethal if constantly renewed. Tolerance values derived from these standing water experiments are several times greater than those observed in the flowing water bioassays which, of course, are more typical of field conditions. In addition, workers now have developed the techniques required to carry out running water bioassays, and many of the more highly regarded fish toxicologists are doing these experiments routinely. Leaders in developing these techniques are Donald Mount and his associates at the Federal Water Pollution Control Laboratories in Duluth, Minnesota.

Furthermore, it is evident that our water quality problems are increasing in complexity and severity. There can be no justification for not employing useful methods that will get the experimental data needed for the preservation of our biological resources, even if these procedures call for extra skill and ingenuity.

5. The Duration of Toxicity Bioassay Tests

One of the factors that necessitated the formulation of standard bioassay methods was the inconsistency in the times of exposure of fish to toxic solutions. Some of the earlier workers felt that fish in a stream would be exposed for only a few moments to high concentrations of wastes that were discharged to the receiving waters at widely separated and irregular intervals. They further assumed, with no substantiating evidence, that fish in the affected areas detect and avoid highly toxic solutions. Thus these workers felt that a dilution in which the fish could survive for an hour was adequate for the protection of fishery resources. Some of the older literature, therefore, reports data from experiments in which the fish were tested for an hour. Other workers took concentrations of substances that were present in typical wastes and determined how long fish could survive in these wastes. How these data could be applied is not clear, unless these workers took the position, which cannot be substantiated, that fish would leave the toxic areas.

In some European laboratories, principally French and Belgian, the standard time for a bioassay procedure seems to be 6 hr. There is no rationale given for this time period. One has to assume that the 6-hr time period fits neatly into a working day; hence, data can be obtained in 1 day. Even the 96-hr test proposed by Doudoroff and his committee(22) is an arbitrary selection designed to fit within the 5-day working week of most American governmental and industrial laboratories. This allocation of 96 hr allows the first half of Monday for preparation of the test, four days for observations, and the afternoon of Friday for the necessary analyses and calculations and for planning the next week's tests. Doudoroff and his committee, however, were careful to label tests of up to 96-hr duration as acute toxicity determinations. They termed any tests over 96 hr as prolonged tests and suggested that these prolonged tests be used when it was obvious that some of the fish were seriously affected at the end of 96 hr and might die. However, it was cautioned that toxicity bioassay tests should never be prolonged past the point at which the control fish begin to die. Doudoroff suggests termination when the controls show a 10% mortality.

The biologist seeking to use the data derived from a short-term toxicity bioassay test lasting for 96 hr is in a quandary. In most industrial situations, there is a fairly continuous discharge of effluent into the receiving waters. It is therefore imperative that the biologist recommend a concentration that will allow healthy animal populations to exist and flourish throughout their life history in the waters receiving this effluent. To obtain these data, a toxicity bioassay must be conducted during the life cycle of fish from the time they emerge from the egg until they grow, become sexually mature, spawn their own eggs, and the eggs hatch. In many circumstances, to conduct these procedures calls not only for some excellent fish husbandry techniques but also it may involve time periods up to a year. The technical aspects, as well as the expenses involved in laboratory space, manpower, etc., are prohibitive for most laboratories. Tests of this sort, however, lasting for up to a year, are now made routinely in the Federal Water Pollution Control Laboratory at Newtown, Ohio(37) and at some other research laboratories.

A solution that may be satisfactory for some laboratories is suggested by Johnson(38), who used the medaka, *Oryzias latipes*. This is an excellent laboratory fish which requires only 2–3 months to develop from egg to sexual maturity. One could determine the medaka's (or any other suitable fish) tolerance to the waste throughout its entire life history, then conduct a standard 96-hr toxicity bioassay with both the medaka and the native fish that is being studied. Using these data, one could derive a value that might represent the waste dilution that the native fish species could tolerate indefinitely. But even a 3-month bioassay test represents a technical challenge as well as a formidable expense.

At times, the alert technician may find that the 96-hr bioassay is unnecessarily long and does not yield any more worthwhile information than does a 24- or 48-hr test. In one experiment (Table 2), in all of the mortalities occurred in the first 24 or 48 hr of the test. These data indicated that the 96-hr test was inefficient and unnecessarily long in this particular case, and that a 48-hr test produced all the information that a 96-hr test would provide.

TABLE 2
Time Factor in Toxicity Bioassay Tests[a]

Waste, ppm	pH	Fish survival							
		24 hr		48 hr		72 hr		96 hr	
		Living	Dead	Living	Dead	Living	Dead	Living	Dead
Replicate 1. July 21–July 24[b]									
55.0	7.68	0	10	0	10	0	10	0	10
44.0	7.69	10	0	10	0	10	0	10	0
16.5	7.83	10	0	10	0	10	0	10	0
0.39 (control)	7.89	10	0	10	0	10	0	10	0
Replicate 2. July 25–July 29[c]									
49.0	7.69	2	8	2	8	2	8	2	8
45.0	7.69	6	4	4	6	4	6	4	6
43.0	7.69	9	1	9	1	9	1	9	1
0.13 (control)	7.89	10	0	10	0	10	0	10	0

[a]Test conditions: flowing water, 1.5 liters/hr.
[b]TLm: 49 ppm waste.
[c]TLm: 46 ppm waste.

In cases similar to the above, the routine bioassays can then be limited to these shorter periods with, of course, a periodic confirmation of the shorter bioassay with the standard 96-hr procedure. On the other hand, one should always be alert to the possibility that the toxicant may be slow-acting. Thus, for some of the chlorinated hydrocarbon insecticides in dilute solutions, mortalities start on the third or fourth day. In this case, the alert technician should conduct a longer bioassay of 10 days or 2 weeks.

An excellent use of the toxicity bioassay in a control laboratory should be the correlation of the toxicity of the waste with the chemical composition of the waste. The laboratory should make precise analyses of the waste and set up a research program that would indicate the component or components of the waste that are responsible for the toxicity of the effluent. With a well-designed research program, a laboratory should then be able to predict the toxicity of a waste from its chemical composition. The laboratory would thus be able to dispense with the toxicity bioassay as a routine procedure and use it only as a periodic confirmatory test or as a test to evaluate changes in the toxicity resulting from changes in plant procedures. This approach has been used with good results by English biologists(39), who have been able to predict the toxicity to fish of effluents emanating from sewage treatment plants by their ammonia, phenol, cyanide, and heavy metals contents.

6. The Median Tolerance Limit

The term median tolerance limit (TLm) has been accepted by most biologists to designate the concentration of toxicant or substance at which 50% of the test organisms survive. In some cases, and for certain special reasons, the TL_{10} or the TL_{90} might be used. The TL_{90} might be requested by a conservation agency negotiating with an industry in an area where an important fishery exists, where the agency wants to establish waste concentrations that will definitely not harm the fish. The TL_{10} might be requested by a conservation agency which is buying toxicants designed to remove undesirable species of fish from fishing lakes. These two terms, TL_{10} and TL_{90}, are seldom used in the technical literature. They can be easily derived from the same data used to determine the TLm. The use of the TLm instead of the TL_{10} and TL_{90} is not only based upon good statistical mathematics; the TLm is actually the simplest and most reproducible measurement to obtain. Determination of the TL_{90} is often frustrated in the laboratory by the insistence of one apparently normal fish in the experimental group on dying almost immediately at an unrealistically low level of toxicant; and when trying to determine the TL_{10}, the investigator often finds one or two fish of a batch to be almost indestructible.

Those who have been trained in pharmacology or mammalian toxicology have long accepted the term LD_{50}. The LD_{50} is the toxicant dose which is lethal to 50% of the test organisms. The term TLm, which was proposed by the Doudoroff Committee(22), is a far more precise and descriptive term in its application to fish work. In pharmacology, the test animal is fed or otherwise administered a measured amount of the text substance. But in an experiment with fish, the fish are exposed to an environment containing a certain concentration of a toxicant. This concentration is often sufficient to kill most of the fish in an experiment and still retain a large degree of toxicity. In the case of certain chlorinated hydrocarbons, it is observed that fish will concentrate in their tissues many thousand times the concentration of the insecticide that is present in the solution, before dying(38).

Some workers(40) have adopted the term LC_{50} for 50% lethal concentration. Although this designation includes the concepts of the TLm and is not incorrect or confusing, it does not present any new concept or add to the precision inherent in the term TLm.

7. SUGGESTED EXPERIMENTAL CONCENTRATIONS

Most workers after gaining experience with a particular class of wastes will be able to select concentrations for testing that will be fairly close to the TLm. For example, an experienced worker trying to determine the toxicity of a waste containing a chlorinated hydrocarbon waste will select his preliminary dilutions to yield concentrations in the parts per billion range of active ingredient. If the waste sample contain heavy metals, his preliminary dilutions should result in heavy metal concentrations in the parts per million range.

The investigator working with an unfamiliar waste should select a series of concentrations containing 0.1, 1.0, 10, and 100% of the waste. If, for example, no animals are killed at 1.0% waste and all are killed at 10% waste, he may set up his second experiment with concentrations based on a progressive series of intervals on a logarithmic scale. A very suitable guide for the selection of experimental concentrations is given in Table 3(22). The same table is given in the ASTM procedure(23) and in several other publications giving toxicity bioassay procedures.

Although Table 3 gives a selection of progressive dilutions arrayed in five columns, it is seldom necessary to use more than the first three columns. This recommendation always distresses inexperienced workers, who feel that they will overlook pertinent data and who will insert a value from column 4, usually 7.5, into their dilution series. If the worker is in a small laboratory where he has to wash the experimental aquaria and care for the experimental animals, he learns very quickly that this added datum contributes little speeding up or adding precision to his work.

8. CALCULATION OF THE TLm VALUE

The number of fish living or dead in the various concentrations is recorded at the end of 24, 48, 72, and 96 hr or at whatever time deemed necessary. The data are then tabulated, and if the concentrations of toxicant are selected wisely, at some concentration all the fish will be alive and at some still higher concentration all the fish will be dead. If

TABLE 3

A Guide to the Selection of Experimental Concentrations, Based on Progressive Bisection of Intervals on a Logarithmic Scale[a]

Col. 1	Col. 2	Col. 3	Col. 4	Col. 5
10.0	—	—	—	—
—	—	—	—	8.7
—	—	—	7.5	—
—	—	—	—	6.5
—	—	5.6	—	4.9
—	—	—	4.2	—
—	—	—	—	3.7
—	3.2	—	—	—
—	—	—	—	2.8
—	—	—	2.4	—
—	—	—	—	2.1
—	—	1.8	—	—
—	—	—	—	1.55
—	—	—	1.35	—
—	—	—	—	1.15
1.0	—	—	—	—

[a]Reprinted from Ref. 22 by courtesy of the Water Pollution Control Federation.

these data are plotted on semilog paper, with the per cent animals surviving as the abscissa and the concentration as the ordinate, then the TLm can be obtained graphically by interpolation.

9. APPLICATION OF THE TLM

The toxicity bioassay has been of great value to industry for the solution of many toxicity problems. It gives the waste producer some idea of the toxicity of his waste. If it is determined that the waste is not very toxic and it is known that the waste is being discharged into an extremely large body of water with almost immediate and thorough mixing, then the industry would have good reason to believe that its chances of seriously affecting biological organisms are small.

But if, as is regrettably so often the case, the waste is of great toxicity and it must be discharged into a relatively small stream on which other water users make legitimate demands, or even into a large stream that is accepting other waste discharges, then the waste disposal problem is serious. In many cases, the derived toxicity information indicates that the plant management must construct some effective treatment facilities involving large and continuing expenses. The plant manager is informed by the conservation agencies that important biological resources in the areas receiving the plant effluents must be protected. He in turn asks his biologist what dilution or degree of treatment is necessary to meet the demands of the regulatory agency. At this point the weakness of the 96-hr TLm determination becomes painfully apparent. Although from the statistical standpoint the TLm is the most suitable value, the conservation agency and the fisheries interests could not be satisfied with a level of toxicity that would only allow 50% of a fish population to live, and the surviv-50% would not be strong, vigorous organisms but would be "half dead" in the sense that they would be affected to some undesirable degree by the waste. What is necessary is dilution or treatment that will ensure a healthy, vigorous, normally growing population of organisms that can carry on all of their life activities. The biologist cannot on the basis of the TLm provide data indicating the necessary degree of dilution.

A dilution factor of 10 (1/10 the TLm concentration) was suggested at one time as a dilution for a kraft pulping waste (40a). In this case, this dilution was adequate and a precedent was set. The dilution factor of 10 has been unofficially and unfortunately adopted as adequate by many agencies and has become rather firmly entrenched in practice, for no good reason. British workers who were cognizant of this inherent danger of the TLm avoided, to a large extent, the use of this measure and insisted on making toxicity tests to determine what could be called, in effect, the 0.0% toxicity level. In their experiments, which often lasted from 500 to 1000 hr, they determined the toxicity level at which the mortality of the fish in the toxicant did not differ from the mortality of the control. These procedures (although they gave data which were useful and which were adopted readily by American biologists) did not have the appeal and efficiency of the 96-hr TLm. In more recent years, some English workers (41) have adopted the 3-day TLm in studies on the toxicity of sewage effluents.

There were attempts by some biologists who were dealing with a few specific toxicants to develop formulas which would utilize the data obtained by short-term toxicity bioassays to determine the dilution required to protect aquatic populations. Matida (42) attempted to determine the threshold concentration (i.e., the concentration at which the fish are minimally affected) from data obtained in toxicity bioassays. He also explored the relationship between body size and TLm and concluded that the difference in TLm observed in fish of different sizes was due to the larger surface area of gill per unit body weight in the smaller fish. Abram(*43*) and Alabaster and Abram(*25*) made a detailed study of several methods to find the best method of determining the threshold value of toxicity of several compounds. All three methods were based to some extent on the equation:

$$t = \frac{K}{\log c - \log i}$$

where t is the harmonic mean survival time, K is a constant, c is the concentration of toxin, and i is the mean threshold concentration.

In his book, *Fish and River Pollution*, Jones(*44*) discusses other methods for determining the toxicity of substances to fish by continuous flow bioassay procedures.

The technical breakthrough which made the long-term constant flow bioassay a practical laboratory procedure was achieved by Mount and Warner(*45*). These workers developed a successful serial dilution apparatus designed to deliver continuously a series of concentrations of a toxicant. No electrical power is needed for operation — the entire apparatus depends upon gravity and siphons to circulate the water and to deliver the toxicant. The apparatus delivers accurate toxicant concentrations even if the influent water flow varies over a wide range, and once adjusted, it remains quite accurate with little need for servicing or further adjustment. Other useful constant flow systems have been developed recently (*45a*, *45b*).

In Mount's laboratory, continuous experiments have been carried on for a year with this apparatus, and some excellent data on the threshold concentrations of malathion and butoxyethanol ester of 2,4-D have become available(*37*). In this experiment, young fathead minnows were raised to sexual maturity and maintained through their spawning period. The 96-hr TLm values of malathion, an organic phosphorous compound, and the butoxyethanol ester of 2,4-D were compared to the highest concentration in which the fish were able to grow and produce viable young. For malathion, the 96-hr TLm was 45 times greater than the concentration that had no measurable effect during the lengthy exposure. For the 2,4-D, the 96-hr TLm was 19 times higher. Mount(*46*) exposed fathead minnows to copper sulfate for 11 months and found that they will grow and reproduce successfully at a concentration between 3 and 7% of the 96-hr TLm. Obviously, dilution factors must be obtained by experimentation rather than referral to precedent, showing the fallacy of using the value of 10.

Few industrial laboratory directors feel that they can afford the time and space required such long-term experiments. It is suggested that one use a fish with a short life history to determine the toxicity of a compound from hatching until the fish achieves sexual maturity and then produces its own eggs. After the long-term toxicity tolerance for the experimental fish has been ascertained, the 96-hr TLm of the experimental fish and the fish of concern can be determined. If one is willing to assume that both species of fish will have the same relative tolerance to the toxicant or waste throughout the various stages of their life history, one could calculate the concentration that would be sufficient to protect the species of concern. For example, say the 96-hr TLm of the laboratory fish is 10 ppm and the concentration that the fish can tolerate throughout all of its life history is 1/20 of the 96-hr TLm, or 0.5 ppm. If the fish in the area concerned is more sensitive and has a 96-hr TLm to the same toxicant of 5 ppm, the safe concentration might be calculated to be 0.25 ppm of the waste ($1/20 \times 5$ ppm).

IV. Other Specialized Bioassays

A. Avoidance Studies

Many wastes are discharged into waterways which do not have important resident populations of fish but which are migratory routes for important fish species. For example, on the West Coast of the United States, many of the larger cities or metropolitan complexes are located on the mouths or estuaries of large rivers, through which small salmonids, striped bass, or other species must pass on their way to the ocean and through which the adult fish later migrate on their return to the natal streams. Fisheries managers are concerned with the possibility that fish will not be able to detect and avoid the high and possibly lethal concentrations of wastes immediately downstream from industrial effluents. They are also concerned that fish may migrate into strong concentrations of waste and be so weakened, if indeed they are not killed, that they will lose their ability to swim upstream to their spawning areas. Many of the older short-term toxicity bioassays in which fish were subjected to toxicants for very short periods of time were justified on the premise (which was seldom tested in the field) that fish would rapidly detect lethal concentrations of waste and would promptly leave these areas for unpolluted sections of the stream. Although the short-term toxicity bioassay (less than 24 hr) has fallen out of favor, there has been a consistent interest in learning if fish can in fact detect and avoid toxic wastes. This interest has been particularly manifested by agencies managing salmon populations who are concerned that the salmon would be repelled by obnoxious or toxic wastes and would fail to enter their natal streams.

There have been several rewarding studies regarding the "avoidance reactions" of fish to wastes and to deleterious changes in water quality. Shelford(47) observed that fish often would not detect and avoid lethal concentrations of waste. He found, for example, that fish in a gradient apparatus would swim into and would select concentrations of ammonia that were rapidly lethal. This behavior has been reported in the field by other observers. Shelford found that the experimental fish, a sunfish (*Lepomis humilis*), also reacted positively to several other components of the gas waste which he was investigating.

Although to my knowledge no one has repeated Shelford's experiments, his study does cast serious doubts upon the rationale behind the short-term bioassay.

Jones conducted a long series of avoidance studies which are summarized in his book(44). These studies were concerned with the avoidance reactions of fish to low dissolved oxygen, heavy metals, and other substances present in industrial wastes. He used stickleback, small minnows, and trout fry in an apparatus which exposed the experimental animals to sharp differences in concentration (in contrast to the gradual gradient of the Shelford apparatus). Jones showed that sticklebacks were able to detect and learned to avoid low concentrations of dissolved oxygen at 13°C. At lower temperatures, 3°C, the avoidance response was also observed but the reaction was more gradual. In the same apparatus, Jones demonstrated that sticklebacks could learn to detect and avoid low concentrations of the soluble salts of heavy metals. Sticklebacks were able to detect Zn 0.0003 N. They were not capable of detecting and avoiding copper at concentrations of 0.01 and 0.001 N. In the case of lead, the fish seem to select high concentrations, 0.04 N. At lower concentrations, 0.004, 0.0004, and 0.00002 N, they showed definite avoidance.

Others have used various avoidance apparatus to determine the ability of fish to detect alterations in water quality. Jones et al.(48) used a relatively sophisticated avoidance channel which allowed the fish to select either a channel containing clean water or a channel receiving pulping waste. These investigations found that various species of salmon could detect and avoid solutions containing pulping wastes. Whitmore et al.(49), using the same type of apparatus(48), showed that Pacific salmon fingerlings would avoid water in which the dissolved oxygen content was 4.5 mg/liter or less. Bass and bluegills readily avoided dissolved oxygen concentrations of 1.5 mg/liter or less.

Ishio(50) developed a gradient tank which he believed gave a simpler gradient of toxicants than some of the previously employed systems. His studies indicated that the avoidance of toxic substances depends greatly upon the rate of change in the concentration of the toxic substance. He also felt that the attraction of fish to ammonia and copper salts was attributable to the relatively high pH in waters in which these substances were present in high concentrations.

Sprague et al.(51), who were concerned with the effect of copper and zinc pollution in the Miramichi River on the migratory pattern of Atlantic salmon, tested the avoidance reactions of juvenile salmon to copper and zinc solutions. Their avoidance apparatus, in contrast to Ishio's, was designed to give a sharp boundary between the clear water and the water containing metal salts. They found that the salmon fingerlings avoided 0.05 ILL (incipient lethal level)(51) of copper sulfate and 0.09 ILL of zinc sulfate. In the water that Sprague et al. used (20 mg/liter hardness), the incipient lethal level of copper was 48 μg/liter and for zinc, 600 μg/liter. Sprague observed, however, that in nature, mature salmon would migrate upstream until the concentration of copper and zinc reached 0.35–0.43 ILL.

The use of avoidance chambers to evaluate the avoidance reaction of fish to toxic solutions has not been completely satisfactory. Most workers who have used an avoidance apparatus have been aware that their procedures have some important shortcomings, but each feels that his procedure does give some useful information. Tamura(52), in a discussion of the paper by Sprague et al.(51), briefly summarized some studies he made using an avoidance apparatus developed by Sato et al.(53) which was based on a merotactic response of fish. Tamura indicated that a standard procedure should be developed for the determination of avoidance by fish of toxic wastes. Warner et al.(54) developed a system of evaluating the sublethal effects of pesticides by observing and measuring the behavior of goldfish. The responses of goldfish to light and shock before and after exposure to very small concentrations of pesticide were observed, and the authors concluded that their technique can measure patterns of behavior that will affect the survival mechanisms of fish subjected to sublethal concentrations of toxicants.

B. Activity Studies

Another important series of specialized bioassays was developed by physiologists who were interested in the swimming ability of fish(55) and by respiratory physiologists who were interested in the ability of active fish to utilize the oxygen in the water(56).

Among those concerned with the ability of fish to swim in water of reduced dissolved oxygen content were Katz et al.(57). Their studies were carried on in special apparatus in which water was forced through a tube by a pump. The fish in the tube were forced to swim to avoid being swept onto a grid. The water in the tube was replenished at a regular rate by water whose oxygen content was reduced by scrubbing with nitrogen. In this study it was demonstrated that small salmon could swim for as long as 48 hr in a moderate current [1 fps (foot per second)] in oxygen concentrations as low as 3 mg/liter. Below that level not all fish were able to swim for 24 hr, and at 2.5 mg/liter no fish were able to swim for 24 hr. In a later series of experiments, Davis et al. (58) used an improved swimming apparatus to test fish at higher velocities and also found that the ability for sustained swimming was dependent on the dissolved oxygen content of the water. The experiments of Katz and Davis and their associates were carried on in uncontaminated water in which only some of the dissolved oxygen was removed. Because of the experimenters' need to limit the variables under investigation, no other parameters were regulated except water temperature. Yet in most streams receiving industrial or domestic wastes that reduce the dissolved oxygen content, there are, more often than not, other toxicants in significant concentrations that will have some deleterious effect on fish. Because of the complex problems involved in handling many experimental variables, and the mathematical techniques required for analyzing the data, most biologists have been unable to set up toxicity experiments which duplicate field conditions. Alderdice (59,60), in an outstanding study, outlined mathematical techniques by which he determined the median resistance times of young salmon exposed to sodium pentachlorophenate at various levels of salinity, temperature, and dissolved oxygen. Although this study was a convincing demonstration of a very useful technique, there have been few additional studies using the statistical procedures that Alderdice has demonstrated.

C. Toxicity Bioassays with Organisms Other than Fish

Although fish have usually been recommended for use in toxicity bioassays, other aquatic organisms have also been used. Workers who are unfamiliar with fish will choose to use aquatic organisms with which they are more familiar. The use of invertebrates and some algae can be justified because they are known to be eaten by fish or are part of the food chain of desirable fish species. Sometimes fish are not readily available and it is felt that other aquatic organisms which can be maintained readily in the laboratory can give useful information which can be utilized profitably in the preliminary planning of a waste disposal system. In certain cases, oysters, mussels, and some crustaceans are the organisms of economic concern that are affected by the waste discharges, and the use of fish would be illogical.

1. THE LOWER INVERTEBRATES AND CRUSTACEANS

Perhaps the first worker to use organisms other than fish to evaluate the effects of water pollution was Kupzis(3), who determined the toxicity of naphthenic acids to frogs and crayfish as well as fish. Subsequent literature indicates that a wide range of freshwater and marine animals and plants have been used for toxicity bioassays. Veger(61) used several aquatic vertebrates and invertebrates to evaluate the toxicity of a detergent. Among other organisms he used two protozoans, *Tetrahymena* and *Paramecium*, both favorite laboratory organisms. In addition, he used the turbellarian flatworm, *Planaria gonocephala*.

a. Bioassays with Crustaceans

Daphnia, a small freshwater crustacean, has been a favorite organism for determining the toxicity of substances and, next to fish, is perhaps the favorite toxicity bioassay organism. It is not used as extensively as fish in the United States because most water pollution problems, from the administrative standpoint, are fish problems and both industrial groups and regulatory agencies prefer, whenever possible, to consider data obtained with fish. Yet *Daphnia* spp. have many advantages over fish as laboratory organisms. In addition, they are known to be eaten by many species of fish and often are used when an agency seeks data on the effect of a waste upon typical fish food organisms. They have been used for a long time as biological test organisms in pharmacology and in water toxicity studies(18,62). Anderson(63–65), in several extensive studies, standardized procedures for the use of *Daphnia*. These procedures were developed in studies designed to determine the toxicity of substances that are sometimes present in industrial wastes. Van Horn et al.(28) used *Daphnia* spp. to determine the toxicity of certain components of kraft pulping effluents. Their tolerance to these waste components was about the same as that of minnows that were found in the same waters.

Among many recent studies in which *Daphnia* spp. were used effectively as bioassay organisms are those of Cabejsek and Stasiak(66), Gillespie(67), Godzik(68), and Stroganov and Kolosova(69). Cabejsek and Stansiak(66) determined the toxicity to *Daphnia magna* of the heavy metals commonly found in industrial wastes. Copper was the most toxic, and the toxicity decreased in the following order: chromium, cobalt, nickel, and manganese.

Gillespie(67) determined the toxicity of the insecticide, malathion, to *Daphnia*. Godzik(68) used *Daphnia* to determine the toxicity of the anionic detergent, nekal BXG, and Stroganov and Kolosova(69) used *Daphnia* in a prolonged experiment to determine the effects of nylon wastes on the feeding, growth, molting, maturation, and reproduction of *Daphnia*, fish, and freshwater mollusks.

A wide variety of other freshwater crustaceans have been used in toxicity bioassays. Wurtz and Bridges(70) determined the lethal effects in hard and soft water of sodium chloride, zinc sulfate, copper sulfate, a detergent, and elevated temperature on nine different freshwater invertebrates including the crustacean *Asellus*. Nebeker and Gaufin(71) determined the toxicity of 14 substances, principally organic insecticides, to *Gammarus*, an amphipod crustacean of importance as a fish food organism. Lüdemann and Neumann(72, 72a) determined the toxicity of chlorinated hydrocarbon and organic phosphorus insecticides to freshwater fish, insect larvae, crustaceans, and tadpoles. Lüdemann and Kayser(73) determined the toxicity of herbicides to insect larvae and three microcrustaceans of value as fish food organisms.

Crayfish, which are considered as delicacies and form the basis for minor commercial fisheries whenever they are present in sufficient numbers, have been used as bioassay organisms by Hendrick et al.(74), Muncy and Oliver(75), and Hubschman(76). Hubschman's work is of considerable use to those interested in methodology, as his tests were of long duration, lasting up to 16 days, and were conducted in a continuous flow apparatus. His study(76) gives one a good idea of the standard of toxicological work now being maintained with aquatic organisms.

b. Bioassays with Mollusks

Freshwater mollusks are extremely sensitive to toxicants in water and are useful in evaluating heavy metal pollution(77). Although they are not especially attractive as laboratory animals in evaluating the toxicity of industrial wastes, there is considerable literature on their reaction to various toxicants because of their importance as vectors of parasitic diseases, principally schistosomiasis. Research is continuing on the development of selectively lethal molluscicides cheap enough to be used in vector control programs. Wurtz(77) is perhaps the only American to conduct bioassays with mollusks in regard to industrial waste problems. Harry and Aldrich(78) studied the reaction of the gastropod, *Taphius* sp. to seven heavy metals. The distress syndrome demonstrated by *Taphius* was useful in evaluating the effects of heavy metals. Morrill (79) observed the effects of cobaltous chloride on the morphological development of eggs of the common freshwater snail, *Limnea* sp.

c. Bioassays with Insects

There has been great concern among conservationists about the effect of insecticides upon resident fish species. In addition, others have been concerned with the effect of insecticides and industrial wastes on insects that are of value as fish food. Patterson and von Windeguth(80) determined the toxicity of the larvicide, Baytex, on five species of fish, an annelid, three aquatic crustaceans, and chironomid larvae, Concentrations effective in controlling the chironomid larvae did not affect any of the other organisms except *Daphnia*.

Surber and Thatcher(81) carried out a study to determine the effects of an ABS detergent upon bottom-dwelling larval insects. They used a constant flow system in tanks modified to simulate stream conditions. Paddle wheels were used to generate a current. Mayfly nymphs (*Stenonema* and *Isonychia*), as well as crayfish and other freshwater crustaceans, were reduced in number after exposure to 10 ppm ABS for 10–14 days. Gaufin and co-workers(83–85) and Carlson(82) have made extensive bioassay studies to evaluate the effects of insecticides upon aquatic insects and other invertebrates.

D. Bioassays with Vertebrates Other than Fish

Of the freshwater vertebrates, fish are, of course, the most commonly used as test animals, but some workers have used frog tadpoles or frog eggs to determine the toxicity of certain substances. Barbieri and Legnane (86) used the fertilized eggs of *Bufo arenarum* to observe the changes in embryological development caused by hydrogen peroxide. Fingal and Kaplan(87) and Kaplan and Yoh(88) studied the effect of copper sulfate on frogs (*Xenopus laevis* and *Rana pipiens*). Exposure to concentrations of copper ion greater than 10–15 ppm for more than a week resulted in significant mortalities. The toxicity of modern insecticides to *Bufo* tadpoles was determined by Lüdemann and Neumann(72), and to the tadpoles of the bullfrog, *Rana catesbiana*, by Mulla(89). The toxicity of copper to adult *R. pipiens* was determined by Kaplan and Overpeck (90). They found frogs to be considerably more tolerant than fish to insecticides.

E. Bioassays with Algae

Concern about toxicants discharged into our waters is not restricted to the effects on animals but extends also to aquatic plants. Patrick and

Strawbridge(*91*) have suggested the use of diatoms as indicators of the effects of water pollution. A standard procedure for the use of diatoms to determine toxicity has been adopted by the ASTM(*92*); unfortunately, the available literature from Patrick's group gives few reports on results obtained with diatoms in their toxicity bioassay applications. Kahn(*93*) also advocated the use of algae as biological reagents and suggested the further development of the algal bioassay. Matulova(*94*) used the microscopic algae *Chlamydomonas, Scenedesmus*, and *Chlorella* to evaluate the effects of four types of detergents — alkyl sulfonates, alkylaryl sulfonates, cation-active detergents, and neutral detergents. The cation-active detergents were found to inhibit *Chlamydomonas* at 0.1 ppm. Schlüter(*95*) tested the toxicity of two fungicides and three herbicides to the rooted alga *Chara*, two blue-green algae, two diatoms, and one green alga. With most of the substances tested, the rooted alga was more tolerant than the nonattached species. In static bioassays, Hicks and Neuhold(*96*) used ^{14}C to measure the negative effect of ABS detergents on the fixed algae *Vaucheria* and *Cladophora*. Vejvoda(*97*) determined the necessary concentrations of four herbicides to control the rooted alga *Anacharis canadensis*. At the same time, she determined the toxicity of the substances to perch and to carp fry. Algal control was possible at herbicide concentrations that would not kill these fish.

F. Bioassays with Marine Organisms

The effect of industrial wastes on the marine environment is a matter of relatively recent concern in the United States, but the Japanese have long been forced to take an interest in marine pollution. In the United States we have equated water pollution largely with freshwater streams and lakes, but in Japan water pollution problems have usually been confined to marine waters. This concern with marine pollution and its effects on aquatic resources has generated a large body of literature which is, unfortunately, mostly in Japanese. An important part of the Japanese research effort has been the development of methods for the determination of the toxicity of wastes discharged into the sea. Okubo(*98*) studied the reaction of the brine shrimp (*Artemia salina*) to toxicants in order to evaluate it as a possible bioassay organism. He felt that although *Artemia* was more tolerant than other organisms of economic importance, it could be utilized as a reference organism. In a later study, Okubo and Okubo (*99*) used the freshly fertilized eggs of two species of sea urchins and two bivalves to determine the toxicity of substances. They stated that the fertilized eggs were useful biological reagents because (1) the effects of pollutants were readily recognized by the disturbed developmental patterns, (2) all four species were remarkably similar in their tolerance, and (3) the larvae were far more sensitive than were other test organisms. It was hoped that a level of toxicity which would not affect the developing larvae might also be a level which would not affect fish.

Tomiyama and Kawabe(*100*) determined the 24- and 48-hr TLm of sodium pentachlorophenate (PCP) to two species of marine fish (*Nibea* and *Odontamblyopus*), a shrimp (*Leander japonicus*), and an eel (*Anguilla japonica*). The shrimp was the most tolerant. *Nibea* sp. was able to detect and avoid the herbicide at a concentration of 0.2–0.3 ppm in an avoidance apparatus.

The culture of the laver *Conchocelis*, an alga, is important in the Ariake Bay area of Japan. Tomiyama et al.(*101*) developed a bioassay procedure based upon changes in the appearance of the alga, the activity of the succinodehydrogenase enzyme system, and the rate of ^{32}P uptake. No change in these functions was observed in concentrations of PCP that were lethal to fish. In another paper in the series evaluating the effect of PCP in the marine environment, Tomiyama and co-workers(*102*) evaluated the effects of PCP that drained from the rice paddies on the mollusk *Venerupis philippinarium*. The toxic effect was measured by ^{32}P uptake and survival time. An appreciable effect on ^{32}P uptake was noted at a level of 0.1 ppm. Other Japanese workers especially M. Fujiya at Hisoshima, have showed remarkable ingenuity in developing procedures that help evaluate the effects of agricultural and industrial wastes upon marine organisms(*103*).

In the United States, Hidu(*104*) has conducted tests to determine the toxicity of synthetic surfactants to the larvae of the clam *Mercenaria mercenaria* and the oyster *Crassostrea virginica*. He determined the effect of eight synthetic surfactants on the development of fertilized eggs and on the survival and growth of veliger larvae. It was observed that oyster larvae were more sensitive than clam larvae. Dimick and Breese (*105*) proposed the common bay mussel, *Mytilus* sp., as a useful marine bioassay organism and presented experimental data with three pulping wastes, sodium pentachlorophenate, and the insecticide, sevin.

There has been a considerable amount of toxicity bioassay work with marine organisms associated with fouling, largely in an effort to develop substances that would inhibit the growth of barnacles and other attached marine organisms. Many of these data are applicable to marine water pollution problems. Typical of these studies is that of Christie and Crisp (*106*), who used the nauplius larva of the barnacle, *Elminius modestus*, to assess the toxicity to fouling organisms of some primary, secondary, and tertiary aliphatic amines and quarternary compounds.

Cook and Boyd(*107*) conducted a behavioral type of bioassay in which they determined the reaction of a marine amphipod to low dissolved oxygen. It was observed that these crustaceans actively avoided the anoxic conditions, and observations indicated the function of a chemoreceptory mechanism. Juvenile blue crabs, *Callinectes sapidus*, were reared in flowing seawater containing sublethal concentrations of DDT (*108*). The crabs fed, molted, and grew successfully in seawater containing 0.25 ppb DDT, but survived only a few days in water containing over 0.5 ppb.

G. Woelke's Oyster Larvae Bioassay

Oysters are among the most important of the marine biological resources. They are restricted to estuaries and are therefore frequently subjected to degradation of water quality. They are perhaps the only marine organism that is extensively cultivated in the United States, and oyster growers frequently come into conflict with municipalities and industries which discharge wastes that either are lethal to oysters or make the oysters unfit for the market. A typical water quality conflict, that between oyster growers and wood pulping interests in the state of Washington, is examined in detail by Gunter and McKee(*109*).

There have been numerous attempts to evaluate the effects of pulping wastes upon oysters. Bioassay tests are handicapped by the ability of the oyster to close its shell for several days when its environment becomes unsatisfactory. The short-term bioassay of 96 hr, which is suitable for fish, cannot be used. An unusually rigorous test is reported by McKernan et al.(*110*), who subjected oysters to concentrations of sulfite waste liquor for 575 days and obtained some useful information. Obviously, the collection of toxicity data in a 2-year experiment is impractically time-consuming, and costly.

The collection of toxicity information applicable to the water quality problems of the oyster industry has been greatly facilitated by the studies of C. E. Woelke of the Washington State Department of Fisheries. Woelke's procedures, which are outlined briefly by Katz and Woelke (*111*) and in more detail by Woelke [e.g., (*112*)], demonstrate that meaningful toxicity data can be collected within 48 hr. The applicability of the oyster larvae bioassay to the elucidation of a regulatory problem has been demonstrated by the Federal Water Pollution Control Administration in the Pugest Sound area of Washington(*113*) and by Woelke(*112*).

Woelke(*112*) developed a technique whereby he was able to induce oysters to mature and spawn whenever needed, by regulating water temperatures. The developing oyster larvae were used as the biological reagent, and excellent data regarding the toxicity of a particular waste sample could be obtained within 48 hr. In a field study, suspect water samples were collected with a float plane and were flown to the laboratory where freshly fertilized embryos were ready for use. Woelke found an excellent correlation between the concentration of pulping wastes and the percentage of deformed larvae in his bioassay tests.

Using Woelke's technique, the response of the oyster larvae to the waste is evaluated by the per cent of normal and abnormal larvae in the samples. The abnormal larvae can be readily distinguished from the normally developing larvae by technicians. The Woelke technique has been thoroughly evaluated and can be conducted by any intelligent and conscientious technician.

REFERENCES

1. C. Penny and C. Adams, *4th Rept., Roy. Comm. Pollution of Rivers in Scotland, Vol. 2, Evidence*, London, 1863, pp. 377–391; from J. R. E. Jones, *Fish and River Pollution*, Butterworth, Washington, D. C., 1964.
2. C. Weigelt, O. Saare, and L. Schwab, *Arch. Hyg.*, **3**, 39 (1885).
3. J. Kupzis, *Z. Fischerei*, **9**, 1 (1902).
4. H. W. Clark and G. O. Adams, *44th Annual Rept., Mass. State Board of Health*, 1913, p. 336; also, *Eng. News*, **69**, 300 (1913).
5. M. Dodero, *Ann. Univ. Grenoble, Sci.-Med.*, (n.s.) **1**, 159 (1924).
6. Ibid., (n.s.) **3**, 423 (1926).
7. L. Leger, *Ann. Univ. Grenoble*, **24**, 41 (1912).
8. M. C. Marsh, *U.S. Geol. Surv. Water Supply Irrigation Paper No. 192*, 1907, p. 337.
9. H. Reuss, *Rev. Bayer. Biol. Versuchssta.*, **2**, 89 (1909).
10. H. Reuss, *Z. Biol.*, **53** (n.s. 35), 555 (1910).
11. G. F. White and A. J. Thomas, *J. Biol. Chem.*, **11**, 381 (1912).
12. M. M. Wells, *J. Exptl. Zool.*, **19**, 248 (1915).
13. V. E. Shelford and W. C. Allee, *ibid.*, **14**, 207 (1913).
14. V. E. Shelford and E. B. Powers, *Biol. Bull.*, **28**, 315 (1915).
15. E. B. Powers, *Illinois Biol. Monographs*, **4**, 1 (1917).
16. D. L. Belding, *Trans. Am. Fisheries Soc.*, **57**, 100 (1927).
17. P. Steinmann, *Handbuch Binnenfischerei Mitteleuropas*, Vol. 6, No. 3, Schweizbart'sche Verlagsbuchhandlung (Erwin Nägele GmbH), Stuttgart, 1928, p. 288.
18. M. M. Ellis, *U. S. Bur. Fisheries Bull. No. 22*, **48**, 365 (1937).
18a. M. M. Ellis, B. A. Westfall, and M. D. Ellis, *U. S. Fish and Wildlife Serv. Res. Rept. 9*, 1946.
19. W. B. Hart, P. Doudoroff, and J. Greenbank, *Waste Control Lab.*, Atlantic Refining Co., Philadelphia, 1945.
20. P. Doudoroff and M. Katz, *Sewage Ind. Wastes*, **22**, 1432 (1950).
21. Ibid., **25**, 802 (1953).
22. P. Doudoroff and Committee, *Sewage Ind. Wastes*, **23**, 1380 (1951).
23. R. F. Weston, *ASTM Designation D-1345-59*, adopted 1959, copyrighted supplement to book of ASTM Standard, Part 10, American Society for Testing Materials, Philadelphia, 1959, p. 348.

24. *Standard Methods For The Examination Of Water And Wastewater.* Part VI, 11th ed., American Public Health Association, New York, 1960.

25. J. S. Alabaster and F. S. H. Abram, in: *Advan. Water Pollution Res., Proc. Intern. Conf., Tokyo, August 1964*, Vol. 1, Pergamon, London, 1965, p. 41.

26. V. C. Applegate and E. L. King, Jr., *Trans. Am. Fisheries Soc.*, **91**, 342 (1961).

26a. C. MacPhee, personal communication, 1968.

27. W. M. Van Horn and M. Katz, *Science*, **104**, 557 (1946).

28. W. M. Van Horn, J. B. Anderson, and M. Katz, *Trans. Am. Fisheries Soc.*, **79**, 55 (1949).

29. W. M. Van Horn, J. B. Anderson, and M. Katz, *Tappi*, **33**, 209 (1950).

30. Q. H. Pickering and C. Henderson, *Intern. J. Air Water Pollution*, **10**, 453 (1966).

31. Q. H. Pickering and C. Henderson, *Ohio J. Sci.*, **66**, 508 (1966).

32. M. Katz and G. C. Chadwick, *Trans. Am. Fisheries Soc.*, **91**, 394 (1961).

33. C. Henderson, Q. H. Pickering, and J. M. Cohen, *Sewage Ind. Wastes*, **31**, 295 (1959).

34. M. Katz, *Trans. Am. Fisheries Soc.*, **90**, 264 (1960).

35. K. B. Cumming, *Progressive Fish Culturist*, **25**, 92 (1966).

36. G. G. Chadwick and U. Kiigemagi, *J. Water Pollution Control Federation*, **40**, 76 (1968).

37. D. Mount and C. E. Stephan, *Trans. Am. Fisheries Soc.*, **96**, 185 (1967).

38. H. E. Johnson, Ph. D. Thesis, Univ. of Washington, 1967.

39. D. W. M. Herbert, D. H. M. Jordan, and R. Lloyd, *Inst. Sewage Purif. J. Proc.*, Part 6, 1965, p. 1.

40. R. Eisler, *Trans. Am. Fisheries Soc.*, **94**, 26 (1965).

40a. P. Doudoroff, personal communication, 1968.

41. R. Lloyd and D. H. M. Jordan, *Inst. Sewage Purif. J. Proc.*, Part 2, 1963, p. 167.

42. Y. Matida, *Bull. Freshwater Fisheries Res. Lab.*, **9**, 1 (1960).

43. F. S. H. Abram, in *Advan. Water Pollution Res., Proc. Intern. Conf., Munich, September 1966*, Vol. 1, Pergamon, London, 1967, p. 75.

44. J. R. E. Jones, *Fish and River Pollution*, Butterworth, Washington, D.C., 1964.

45. D. L. Mount and R. E. Warner, *Public Health Serv. Publ. No. 999-WP-23*, U.S. Dept. Health, Education, and Welfare, Cincinnati, 1965.

45a. W. D. Burke and D. E. Ferguson, *Trans. Am. Fisheries Soc.*, **97**, 498 (1968).

45b. J. M. Solon, J. L. Lincer, and J. H. Nair III, *ibid.*, **97**, 501 (1968).

46. D. L. Mount, *Water Res.*, **2**, 215 (1968).

47. V. E. Shelford, *Illinois State Lab. Nat. Hist. Bull.*, **11**, 379 (1917).

48. B. F. Jones, C. E. Warren, C. E. Bond, and P. Doudoroff, *Sewage Ind. Wastes*, **31**, 950 (1956).

49. C. M. Whitmore, C. E. Warren, and P. Doudoroff, *Trans. Am. Fisheries Soc.*, **89**, 17 (1960).

50. S. Ishio, in *Advan. Water Pollution Res., Proc. Intern. Conf., Tokyo, August 1964*, Vol. 1, Pergamon, London, 1965, p. 19.

51. J. B. Sprague, P. F. Elson, and R. L. Saunders, in *ibid.*, p. 61.

52. T. Tamura, formal discussion, Ref. (*51*), p. 73.

53. R. Sato, S. Murachi, O. Mita, and M. Fujimura, formal discussion, Ref. *51*, pp. 1–17.

54. R. E. Warner, K. K. Peterson, and L. Borgman, *J. Appl. Ecol.*, **3**, (Suppl.), 223 (1966).

55. R. Bainbridge, *J. Exptl. Biol.*, **37**, 129 (1960).

56. F. E. J. Fry, in *The Physiology of Fishes, Vol. 1, Metabolism* (M. E. Brown, ed.), Academic, New York, 1957, pp. 1–63.

57. M. Katz, A. Pritchard, and C. E. Warren, *Trans. Am. Fisheries Soc.*, **88**, (1959).
58. G. E. Davis, J. Foster, C. E. Warren, and P. Doudoroff, *ibid.*, **92**, 111 (1963).
59. D. F. Alderdice, *J. Fisheries Res. Board Can.*, **20**, 525 (1963).
60. D. F. Alderdice, in *Biological Problems in Water Pollution, Third Seminar, 1962*, Public Health Serv. Publ. No. 999-WP-25, 1965, p. 320.
61. J. Veger, *Vodn. Hospodarstvi*, **12**, 172 (1962); through *Chem. Abstr.*, **57**, 10947d (1962).
62. B. A. Adams, *Water Works Eng.*, **29**, 361 (1927).
63. B. G. Anderson, *Sewage Works J.*, **18**, 82 (1946).
64. Ibid., **16**, 1156 (1944).
65. B. G. Anderson, *Trans. Am. Fisheries Soc.*, **78**, 96 (1950).
66. I. Cabejsek and M. Stasiak, *Roczniki Panstwowego Zakladu Hig.*, **11**, 303 (1960); *Water Pollution Abstr.*, **35**, Abstr. No. 794 (1962).
67. D. M. Gillespie, *Proc. Mont. Acad. Sci.*, **24**, 11 (1965).
68. S. Godzik, *Acta Hydrobiol.*, **3**, 281 (1960).
69. N. S. Stroganov and L. V. Kolosova, *Zool. Zh.*, **41**, 24 (1962); *Water Pollution Abstr.*, **36**, Abstr. No. 1366 (1963).
70. C. B. Wurtz and C. H. Bridges, *Proc. Penna. Acad. Sci.*, **35**, 51 (1961).
71. A. V. Nebeker and A. R. Gaufin, *Proc. Utah Acad. Sci.*, **41**, 64 (1964).
72. D. Lüdemann and H. Neumann, *Schr. Reihe Ver. Wasser Boden Lufthyg.*, **19**, 131 (1961); *Water Pollution Abstr.*, **35**, Abstr. No 789 (1962).
72a. D. Lüdemann and H. Neumann, *Anz. Schaedlingskunde*, **35**, 5 (1962); through *Chem. Abstr.*, **57**, 7552g (1962).
73. D. Lüdemann and H. Kayser, *Gas-Wasserfach.*, **107**, 256 (1966); through *Chem. Abstr.*, **64**, 20542d (1966).
74. R. D. Hendrick, T. R. Everett, and H. R. Caffey, *J. Econ. Entomol.*, **59**, 188 (1966).
75. R. J. Muncy and A. D. Oliver, Jr., *Trans. Am. Fisheries Soc.*, **92**, 428 (1963).
76. J. H. Hubschman, *Crustaceana*, **12**, 33 (1967).
77. C. B. Wurtz, *Nautilus*, **76**, 52 (1962).
78. H. W. Harry and D. V. Aldrich, *Malacologia*, **1**, 283 (1963).
79. J. B. Morrill, *Biol. Bull.*, **125**, 508 (1963).
80. R. S. Patterson and D. L. von Windeguth, *Mosquito News*, **24**, 46 (1964).
81. E. G. Surber and T. O. Thatcher, *Trans. Am. Fisheries Soc.*, **92**, 152 (1963).
82. C. A. Carlson, *ibid.*, **95**, 1 (1966).
83. L. D. Jensen and A. R. Gaufin, *ibid.*, **93**, 27 (1964).
84. Ibid., **93**, 357 (1964).
85. A. R. Gaufin, L. D. Jensen, A. V. Nebeker, T. Nelson, and R. W. Teel, *Water Sewage Works*, **12**, 276 (1965).
86. F. D. Barbieri and C. R. Legnane, *Arch. Bioquim., Quim. Farm., Tucuman*, **10**, 59 (1962); through *Chem. Abstr.*, **60**, 14890h (1964).
87. W. Fingal and H. M. Kaplan, *Copeia*, 155 (1963).
88. H. M. Kaplan and L. Yoh, *Herpetologica*, **17**, 131 (1961).
89. M. S. Mulla, *Mosquito News*, 23, 299 (1963).
90. H. M. Kaplan and J. G. Overpeck, *Herpetologica*, **20**, 163 (1964).
91. R. Patrick and D. Strawbridge, *J. Water Pollution Control Federation*, **35**, 151 (1963).
92. R. Patrick, *ASTM Designation D 2037-64T*, American Society for Testing Materials, Philadelphia, 1964, p. 732.
93. K. R. Kahn, *Environ. Health*, **6**, 274 (1964).
94. D. Matulova, *Vodn. Hospodarstvi*, **14**, 377 (1964); through *Chem. Abstr.*, **62**, 10210 (1965).

95. M. Schlüter, *Z. Fischerei*, **13** (n.s.) 303 (1965).
96. C. E. Hicks and J. M. Neuhold, *Bull. Environ. Contam. Toxicol.*, **1**, 225 (1966).
97. M. Vejvoda, *Byul. Vodnany*, **2**, 8 (1966).
98. K. Okubo, *Bull. Tokai Reg. Fisheries Res. Lab.*, **18**, 31 (1957).
99. K. Okubo and T. Okubo, *ibid.*, **32**, 131 (1962).
100. T. Tomiyama and K. Kawabe, *Bull. Japan. Soc. Sci. Fisheries*, **28**, 379 (1962).
101. T. Tomiyama, K. Kobayashi, and K. Kawabe, *ibid.*, **28**, 383 (1962).
102. *Ibid.*, **29**, 417 (1963).
103. M. Katz, formal discussions in M. Fujiya, in *Advan. Water Pollution Res., Proc. Intern. Conf., Tokyo, Aug. 1964*, Vol. 3, Pergamon, N.Y. 1965, p. 315.
104. H. Hidu, *J. Water Pollution Control Federation*, **37**, 262 (1965).
105. R. E. Dimick and W. P. Breese, *Proc. 12th Pacific Northwest Ind. Waste Conf., 12th, Univ. of Washington, Seattle, 1965*, p. 165.
106. A. O. Christie and D. J. Crisp, *Comp. Biochem. Physiol.*, **18**, 59 (1966).
107. R. H. Cook and C. M. Boyd, *Can. J. Zool.*, **43**, 971 (1965).
108. J. I. Lowe, *Ecology*, **46**, 899 (1965).
109. G. Gunter and J. McKee, *On Oysters and Sulfite Waste Liquor, A Special Consultants Report*, Washington Pollution Control Commission, Olympia, Wash., 1960.
110. D. L. McKernan, V. Tartar, and R. Tollefson, *Washington State Dept. Fisheries, Biol. Bull. 49-A*, Olympia, Wash., 1949, p. 117.
111. M. Katz and C. E. Woelke, *Water Quality Criteria, STP 416*, American Society for Testing Materials, Philadelphia, 1966, p. 90.
112. C. E. Woelke, *ibid.*, p. 112.
113. *Pollutional Effects of Pulp and Paper Mill Wastes in Puget Sound*, Federal Water Pollution Control Admin., Portland, Ore., March, 1967.